Concept Practice

16. Chemistry is the study of matter and the changes that matter undergoes. Matter is the stuff material things are made of.

17. Chemistry is the study of matter and its changes for the sake of understanding them; chemical technology is the application of this knowledge to attain specific goals.

18. **a.** 4 **b.** 3 **c.** 1 **d.** 5 **e.** 2

19. **a.** 2 **b.** 5 **c.** 1 **d.** 6 **e.** 3 **f.** 4

20. Energy research could help produce cleaner energy more efficiently and reduce the amount of nonrenewable fossil fuels expended in producing it.

21. The ozone layer protects Earth from harmful ultraviolet rays.

22. Some plastics are stronger than steel and do not rust. Automobiles with many plastic components are lighter than automobiles made completely from steel and are, therefore, more fuel-efficient.

23. Experiments are used to test hypotheses.

24. Answers will vary but might include diagnosing what is wrong with a bicycle, a computer, or an electric appliance.

25. If you are certain that your experiment is not flawed, you must revise your hypothesis.

26. c.

27. A language uses its vocabulary to express thoughts about anything—food, politics, religion, and so forth. The vocabulary of the sciences is used to express concepts and facts about the workings of the material world.

28. b.

Concept Mastery

29. Students' diagrams should show one string that is threaded through both holes at A and C. The string at hole B is a separate thread from the string passing through holes A and C.

30. The doctor's hypothesis is that you have a strep throat. She tests the hypothesis with an experiment—a throat culture to learn whether your throat is infected with strep bacteria.

31. The experiment may be flawed; if not, the results are evidence that the theory may need to be revised.

32. In general, the more you know, the better off you are. The study of chemistry helps you think logically and analytically. This skill is useful in any career.

Critical Thinking

33. **a.** 1 **b.** 3 **c.** 1

34. A hypothesis is retained if it is supported by the results of experiments; otherwise, it is rejected.

35. No; for any discovery to take place, the discoverer must have the knowledge to recognize the significance of the observation or data.

36. A theory can never be proven. Although a theory may be strongly supported by existing experiments, there is always the possibility that a new kind of experiment will prove it false.

37. **a.** The textbook contains all of the major content and concepts covered in the course. The visuals, reading/studying guides, and practice/review features are essential elements in learning and understanding chemistry.

b. (false statement) Chemistry concepts are interwoven and are best understood as parts of a big picture. Seeing connections and building a framework imply understanding, not memorization.

c. Learning in small chunks is more effective. Studying on a regular basis helps build a big picture of chemistry into which individual facts can be placed. It assures understanding rather than memorization.

d. An exchange of ideas and perspectives is valuable.

e. Talking about chemistry aids understanding and retention.

Standardized Test Prep

1. (d)
2. (c)
3. (b)
4. (c)
5. (c)
6. Contact lenses increase the possibility of eye damage because chemicals can become trapped behind a lens. Safety glasses also protect the eyes from flying debris.
7. No food should be eaten in the laboratory because food may become contaminated with a toxic substance.
8. The teacher may modify the instructions to suit available equipment or chemicals. The teacher will stress any safety precautions. Accidents are more likely to happen when instructions or warnings are ignored.
9. (b)
10. (1) and (4)
11. (2) and (5)
12. (3)

The modified true-false format used in problems 13–17 may be unfamiliar to students. We have designed this first set with examples of all possible outcomes.

13. True, True, correct explanation
14. True, True
15. True, False
    Theories explain; laws summarize.
16. False, True
    The more specific the pesticide, the less the danger for untargeted species.
17. False, False
    If students think either statement is true, refer them to the Chemistry Serving feature on SE page 23.

Chemistry

ADDISON-WESLEY

Solutions Manual

For Chapter Reviews

Prentice Hall

Needham, Massachusetts
Upper Saddle River, New Jersey
Glenview, Illinois

Cover photographs: Clockwise from top left: Test tube with zinc in acid, Richard Megma, Fundamental Photographs; Molecular structure of "Bucky ball," Ken Eward, Photo Researchers; Bunsen burner flame, and flask containing precipitate of lead(II) iodide, Richard Megma, Fundamental Photographs; Scanning tunneling microscope image, Fran Heyl Associates.

Prentice Hall

ISBN 0-13-054857-X

3 4 5 6 7 8 9 10 05 04 03 02 01

CONTENTS

2 MATTER AND CHANGE

Concept Practice

24. solid, metallic luster, gray color, high melting point, malleable

25. **a.** solid **b.** liquid **c.** gas **d.** solid **e.** liquid **f.** liquid

26. **a.** solid **b.** gas **c.** liquid **d.** liquid **e.** solid **f.** gas

27. a vapor; The term "vapor" generally describes a substance in the gaseous state, but whose usual state at room temperature is either a liquid or a solid.

28. water, gasoline, acetone (fingernail polish remover), aromatic salves such as those used in vaporizers, butter

29. chlorine, mercury, bromine, and water; Chlorine condenses, and mercury, bromine and water all freeze when the temperature drops within the stated range.

30. **a.** heterogeneous **b.** heterogeneous **c.** homogeneous **d.** homogeneous **e.** homogeneous

31. one; A solution is a system with uniform composition and properties. Solutions are homogeneous mixtures, consisting of a single phase.

32. **a.** element **b.** mixture **c.** mixture **d.** element **e.** mixture **f.** mixture

33. **a.** nitrogen, hydrogen, chlorine
b. potassium, manganese, oxygen
c. carbon, hydrogen, oxygen
d. calcium, iodine

34. color change; energy absorbed or released; gas produced; odor change; product different from reactants

35. **a.** physical **b.** chemical **c.** chemical **d.** physical

36. The iron combines with oxygen in the air, and oxygen has mass.

37. As the wax burns, the chemical composition of the wax changes, producing the products water and carbon dioxide, which are released into the surrounding air.

Concept Mastery

38. Add sufficient water to dissolve all of the sugar. Separate the charcoal and sand from the sugar water by filtration. Large pieces of charcoal could be separated on the basis of color. Small pieces of charcoal could be burned.

39. **a.** mixtures
b. mixtures

40. **a.** color **b.** six **c.** sodium chloride **d.** sulfur

41. **a.** homogeneous mixture
b. homogeneous mixture
c. heterogeneous mixture
d. homogeneous mixture
e. heterogeneous mixture
f. compound
g. homogeneous mixture
h. heterogeneous mixture

42. **a.** physical **b.** physical **c.** physical **d.** physical **e.** chemical

43. **a.** color and odor change, irreversible
b. gas is produced
c. formation of a precipitate (solid), not easily reversed
d. color change, not easily reversed, new product different from reactants
e. energy change, irreversible, odor, gas is produced

Critical Thinking

44. **a.** 1
b. 3

45. The particles in a solid are close together and in fixed positions in relation to each other. The particles in a liquid are also close to each other, but their positions are not fixed in relation to each other. The particles in a gas are neither close to each other (except when they collide) nor in fixed positions.

46. The appearance of a substance will change during a change of state, which is a physical change.

Concept Challenge

47. a. Yes; because the graph is a straight line, the proportion of iron to oxygen is a constant, which is true for a compound.

b. No; plotting these values on the graph would not give a point on the line, indicating that the mass ratio of iron to oxygen is different from the other four samples.

48. a. Oxygen and calcium are abundant in both the human body and Earth's surface.

b. Silicon, aluminum, and iron are abundant in Earth's surface but not in the human body.

c. Different. The second most abundant element in Earth's crust, silicon, is not present in the human body, and the second most abundant element in the human body, carbon, is not among the most abundant elements of Earth's crust. If the elements found in the two places are different, then the compounds must be different too.

49. a. two, mercury and sulfur

b. Sulfur melts at 113 °C and boils at 445 °C. Between 113 °C and 445 °C, it exists as a liquid. Mercury melts at −39 °C, and boils at 357 °C. In between these temperatures, it exists as a liquid.

c. Possibilities include: alphabetically, by color, by boiling point, or by density.

50. Many answers are possible.

Standardized Test Prep

1. (a)

2. (a)

3. (b)

4. (d)

5. (c)

6. (c)

7. (D)

8. (A)

9. (C)

10. (B)

11. (a) 10.8 g − 6.5 g = 4.3 g
(b) 13.6 g + 9.0 g = 22.6 g
(c) 31.5 g − 12.5 g = 19.0 g

12.

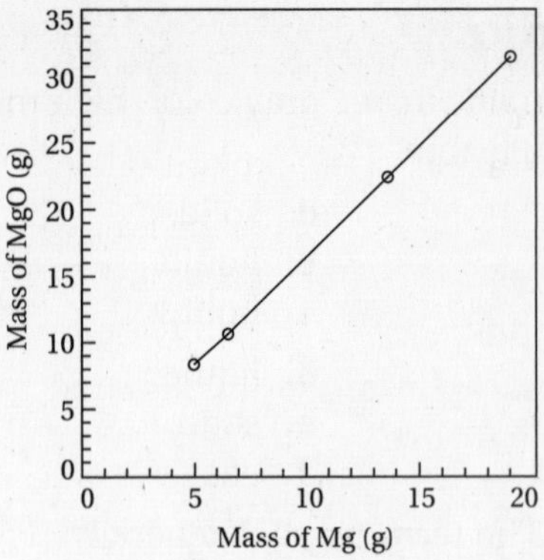

13. $8.0\,\cancel{\text{g Mg}} \times \dfrac{31.5\text{ g MgO}}{19.0\,\cancel{\text{g Mg}}} = 13.3\text{ g MgO}$

14. $20.0\,\cancel{\text{g MgO}} \times \dfrac{19.0\text{ g Mg}}{31.5\,\cancel{\text{g MgO}}} = 12.1\text{ g Mg}$

20.1 g MgO − 12.1 g Mg = 7.9 g oxygen

15. ethanol; Neon is a gas and water is a liquid at −30 °C.

16. neon; The other two colorless substances (ethanol and water) are liquids at 60 °C.

17. Sulfur is the only substance listed with a melting point higher than 7 °C.

3 SCIENTIFIC MEASUREMENT

Concept Practice

36. **a.** qualitative **b.** quantitative **c.** qualitative **d.** quantitative

37. **a.** precision **b.** accuracy **c.** precision **d.** precision **e.** accuracy **f.** accuracy

38. when using an improperly calibrated measuring device

39. Lissa: inaccurate and imprecise
Lamont: accurate and precise
Leigh Anne: inaccurate but precise

40. **a.** accurate and precise
b. inaccurate but precise
c. inaccurate and imprecise

41. **a.** infinite **b.** infinite **c.** infinite **d.** 4 **e.** infinite **f.** 3

42. **a.** 98.5 L **b.** 0.000 763 cg **c.** 57.0 m **d.** 12.2 °C **e.** 0.007 50 × 10^4 mm **f.** 1760 mL

43. **a.** 9.85×10^1 L **b.** 7.63×10^{-4} cg **c.** 5.70×10^1 m **d.** 1.22×10^1 °C **e.** 7.50×10^1 mm **f.** 1.76×10^3 mL

44. **a.** 43 g **b.** 7.3 cm^2 **c.** 225.8 L **d.** 92.0 kg **e.** 32.4 m^3 **f.** 104 m^3

45. **a.** 4.3×10^1 g **b.** 7.3×10^0 cm^2 **c.** 2.258×10^2 L **d.** 9.20×10^1 kg **e.** 3.24×10^1 m^3 **f.** 1.04×10^2 m^3

46. The error is the difference between the accepted and the experimental values. The percent error is the error divided by the accepted value multiplied by 100%.

47. The absolute value of the error is used.

48. $$\text{Percent error} = \frac{|208 - 200|}{208} \times 100\% = \frac{8}{208} \times 100\% = 4\%$$

49. Mass of stopper = 146.72 g − (35.4g + 87.432 g)
= 23.9 g

50. Possible answers are: Units are based on multiples of ten; prefixes have the same meaning when attached to different units of measure.

51. **a.** second, s **b.** meter, m **c.** kelvin, K **d.** kilogram, kg

52. picometer (10^{-12} m), nanometer (10^{-9} m), micrometer (10^{-6} m), millimeter (10^{-3} m), centimeter (10^{-2} m), decimeter (10^{-1} m), meter, kilometer (10^3 m)

53. **a.** 2.4 mm **b.** 17.6 cm **c.** 27.6 cm

54. Volume units are length units cubed.

55. Volume = $3.14 \times (3.0\ \text{cm})^2 \times 28$ cm
= 7.9×10^2 cm^3

56. **a.** (2) **b.** (3) **c.** (1) **d.** (4)

57. **a.** 0.01 g **b.** 0.000 001 g **c.** 1000 g **d.** 0.001 g

58. The mass of an object is constant. The weight of an object varies with location.

59. **a.** (1) **b.** (4) **c.** (2) **d.** (3)

60. Yes, neither mass nor volume changes with location.

61. No; the density of the metal bar is 12 g/cm^3, but the density of gold is 19 g/cm^3.

62. Specific gravity is a ratio of two density measurements, so the density units cancel.

63. **a.** 2.70 **b.** 13.6 **c.** 0.917

64. The carbon dioxide-filled balloon would sink. The neon- and hydrogen-filled balloons would rise, the hydrogen at a much faster rate.

65. germanium

Concept Mastery

66. improper calibration or improper use of the measuring device.

67. **e., d., c., f., a., b.**

68. Significant figures in the answer of an addition problem depend on the measurement with the least number of decimal places.

69. Set x = °C and y = °F
Let $(x_1, y_1) = (0, 32)$ and $(x_2, y_2) = (37, 98.6)$.

$$\text{slope} = m = \frac{y_1 - y_2}{x_1 - x_2} = \frac{32 - 98.6}{0 - 37} = 1.8$$

$$y - y_1 = m(x - x_1)$$
$$y - 32 = 1.8(x - 0)$$
$$= 1.8x + 32$$

°F = 1.8 °C + 32

70. **a.** cg **b.** L **c.** kcal **d.** cs **e.** mL **f.** 1 dm^3

71. The digit to the right of the last significant figure is dropped if it is less than five.

72. 0.69 – 0.789 g/cm^3

73. Yes; an object can charge position such that the force of gravity acting on it changes, causing its weight to change.

74. The egg is floating at the juncture of two liquids of different densities.

Critical Thinking

75. **a.** (2) **b.** (1)

76. It is not possible when measurements are being compared to only one true value. Accurate measurements would all come close to the true value; therefore, they would also be precise.

77. You do not change your estimate. The extra 15 ducks are negligible compared to 850 000 ducks.

78. Gasoline is a mixture and has a variable composition.

Cumulative Review

79. to understand the world around us

80. **a.** Na **b.** Al **c.** Cl **d.** Cu **e.** S **f.** Sr

81. **a.** chemical **b.** physical **c.** physical **d.** chemical **e.** chemical **f.** physical

82. Add water to dissolve the salt. Then decant or filter.

83. The components of a homogeneous mixture can be separated by physical means; a compound must be chemically broken apart into its components. A homogeneous mixture has a variable composition; a compound has a definite composition.

Concept Challenge

84. Answers will vary. Lakes would freeze solid from the bottom up; aquatic life would be killed; possible climate changes.

85. $$\text{Volume} = \frac{\text{mass}}{\text{density}} = \frac{355\text{ g Fe}}{\frac{7.87\text{ g Fe}}{1\text{ cm}^3}} = 45.2\text{ cm}^3$$

$$\text{Mass} = \text{density} \times \text{volume}$$

$$\text{Mass} = \frac{11.4\text{ g Pb}}{1\text{ cm}^3} \times 45.2\text{ cm}^3 = 515\text{ g Pb}$$

86. **a.** corn oil on top of water on top of mercury
b. The density of sugar is greater than the density of water and less than the density of mercury; it floats between the layers of mercury and water.
c. The sugar cube will dissolve in the water over time.

87.

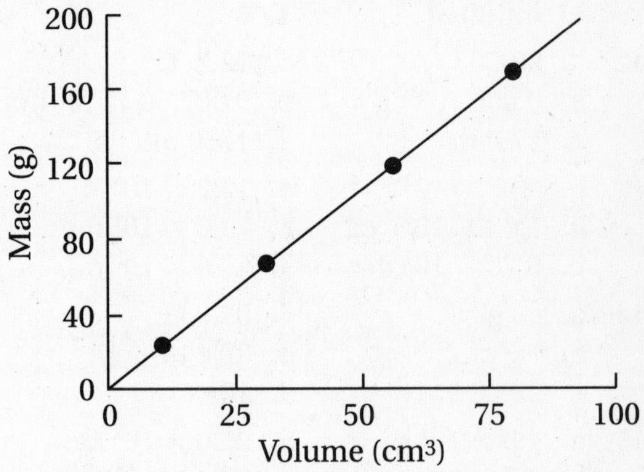

$$\text{Slope} = \frac{168\text{ g} - 115\text{ g}}{81.1\text{ cm}^3 - 55.5\text{ cm}^3} = 2.1\text{ g/cm}^3$$

Standardized Test Prep

1. (c)

2. (b)

$$\text{Density} = \frac{\text{mass}}{\text{volume}}$$

$$\frac{48.6\text{ g}}{51.3\text{ mL} - 44.2\text{ mL}} = \frac{48.6\text{ g}}{7.1\text{ mL}} = 6.8\text{ g/mL}$$

3. (b)

4. (d)

5. Nitrogen-filled balloons will rise; oxygen-filled balloons will sink.

6. Nitrogen because its density is much closer to that of air than is oxygen's density.

7. The higher the body density, the lower the percent body fat.

8.

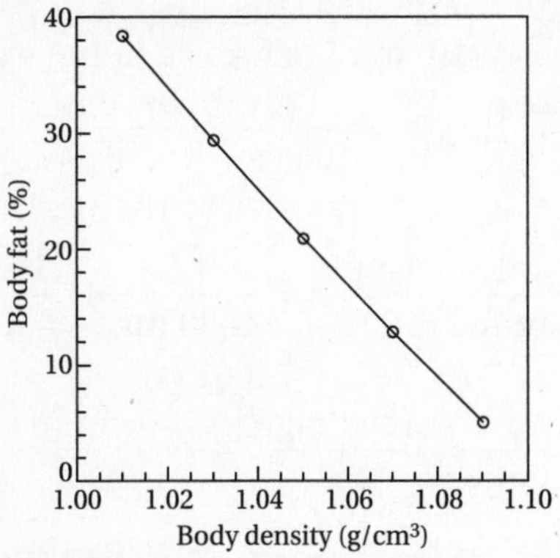

9. The variables are inversely related.

10. about 17%

11. (b), (c), (a)

12. The density in (a) is one-half the density in (b).

13. False, True
If volume decreases and mass remains constant, density must increase.

14. False, False
There are three significant figures. Zeros after a decimal point are significant only when they follow a nonzero digit.

15. False, False
A series of measurements can be reproducible and inaccurate if there are inherent flaws in the experimental design or consistent errors of technique.

16. True, True, correct explanation

4 PROBLEM SOLVING IN CHEMISTRY

Concept Practice

32. Developing a problem-solving strategy is part of step 1. ANALYZE.

33. mass of mercury = density × volume

$5.00\ \cancel{mL} \times 13.6\ g/\cancel{mL} = 68.0\ g$

mass of beaker + mass of mercury = total mass at STP

$87.3\ g + 68.0\ g = 155.3\ g$

34. conversion factor

35. $10\,000\ m^2 = 1$ hectare, therefore the ratio of

$$\frac{10^4\ m^2}{1\ \text{hectare}} = \frac{1\ \cancel{\text{hectare}}}{1\ \cancel{\text{hectare}}} = 1$$

36. $\frac{1\ g}{100\ cg}$; $\frac{100\ cg}{1\ g}$; $\frac{1\ g}{1000\ mg}$; $\frac{1000\ mg}{1\ g}$; $\frac{1000\ mg}{100\ cg}$; $\frac{100\ cg}{1000\ mg}$

37. For a ratio of two measurements to be a conversion factor, the measurements must equal one another.

38. $$\frac{26.0\ g\ \text{silver}}{(26.0 + 10.8 + 2.4 + 0.8)\ \cancel{g\ \text{amalgam}}} \times 25.0\ \cancel{g\ \text{amalgam}} = 16.3\ g\ \text{silver}$$

39. The unit of the conversion factor in the denominator must be identical to the unit in the given measurement.

40. $\text{density} = \frac{\text{mass}}{\text{volume}}$ $\quad \text{volume} = \frac{\text{mass}}{\text{density}}$

$$\text{volume} = \frac{5.00 \times 10^1\ \cancel{g}}{\frac{1.19 \times 10^{-3}\ \cancel{g}}{cm^3}} = 4.20 \times 10^4\ cm^3$$

41. Estimate an answer to see if your calculator answer makes sense and round the answer off to the correct number of significant figures.

42. $0.20\ \cancel{h} \times \frac{60\ \cancel{min}}{1\ \cancel{h}} \times \frac{60\ s}{1\ \cancel{min}} = 720\ s$

43. a. $157\ \cancel{cs} \times \frac{1\ s}{100\ \cancel{cs}} = 1.57\ s$

b. $42.7\ \cancel{L} \times \frac{1000\ mL}{1\ \cancel{L}} = 4.27 \times 10^4\ mL$

c. $261\ \cancel{nm} \times \frac{1\ \cancel{m}}{10^9\ \cancel{nm}} \times \frac{10^3\ mm}{1\ \cancel{m}} = 2.61 \times 10^{-4}\ mm$

d. $0.065\ \cancel{km} \times \frac{10^3\ \cancel{m}}{1\ \cancel{km}} \times \frac{10\ dm}{1\ \cancel{m}} = 6.5 \times 10^2\ dm$

e. $642\ \cancel{cg} \times \frac{1\ \cancel{g}}{10^2\ \cancel{cg}} \times \frac{1 kg}{10^3\ \cancel{g}} = 6.42 \times 10^{-3}\ kg$

f. $8.25 \times 10^2\ \cancel{cg} \times \frac{1\ \cancel{g}}{100\ \cancel{cg}} \times \frac{10^9\ ng}{1\ \cancel{g}} = 8.25 \times 10^9\ ng$

44. a. $0.44\ \frac{\cancel{mL}}{\cancel{min}} \times \frac{1\ \cancel{min}}{60\ s} \times \frac{1\ \cancel{L}}{1000\ \cancel{mL}} \times \frac{10^6\ \mu L}{1\ \cancel{L}} = 7.3\ \mu L/s$

b. $7.86\ \frac{\cancel{g}}{\cancel{cm^2}} \times \frac{1000\ mg}{1\ \cancel{g}} \times \left(\frac{100\ \cancel{cm}}{1\ \cancel{m}}\right)^2 \times \left(\frac{1\ \cancel{m}}{1000\ mm}\right)^2 = 78.6\ mg/mm^2$

c. $1.54\ \frac{\cancel{kg}}{\cancel{L}} \times \frac{1000\ g}{1\ \cancel{kg}} \times \frac{1\ \cancel{L}}{1000\ cm^3} = 1.54\ g/cm^3$

45. $1\ \cancel{m^3} \times \left(\frac{100\ \cancel{cm}}{1\ \cancel{m}}\right)^3 \times \frac{1\ mL}{1\ \cancel{cm^3}} = 10^6\ mL$

46. *See answer below.*

47. $112\ \frac{\cancel{km}}{\cancel{h}} \times \frac{10^3\ m}{1\ \cancel{km}} \times \frac{1\ \cancel{h}}{60\ \cancel{min}} \times \frac{1\ \cancel{min}}{60\ s} = 31\ m/s$

46.

$\frac{1}{1000}$ mg	$\frac{1}{g}$	$\frac{100}{cg}$	$\frac{1000}{kg}$
2.83×10^2	2.83×10^{-1}	28.3	2.83×10^{-4}
6.6×10^3	6.6 g	6.6×10^2	6.6×10^{-3}
2.8×10^{-1}	2.8×10^{-4}	2.8×10^{-2}	2.8×10^{-7}

48. The volume of a flask that holds 158 g of water is 158 cm^3.

$$\text{Density} = \frac{127\ \text{g}}{158\ \text{cm}^3} = 0.804\ \text{g/cm}^3$$

49. $$\frac{0.15\ \text{s}\ \cancel{\text{lost}}}{1\ \cancel{\text{min}}} \times \frac{1\ \text{min lost}}{60\ \text{s}\ \cancel{\text{lost}}} \times \frac{60\ \cancel{\text{min}}}{1\ \cancel{\text{h}}} \times \frac{24\ \cancel{\text{h}}}{1\ \text{day}} = 3.6\ \text{min lost/day}$$

50. $$\text{density} = \frac{\text{mass}}{\text{volume}}$$

$$\text{mass} = 1.38 \times 10^4\ \cancel{\text{g}} \times \frac{1\ \text{kg}}{10^3\ \cancel{\text{g}}} = 1.38 \times 10\ \text{kg}$$

$$\text{volume} = (2.86 \times 10^1\ \cancel{\text{cm}}) \times (7.30 \times 10^1\ \cancel{\text{mm}}) \times \frac{1\ \cancel{\text{cm}}}{10\ \cancel{\text{mm}}} \times (7.2 \times 10^{-1}\ \cancel{\text{m}}) \times \frac{10^2\ \cancel{\text{cm}}}{\cancel{\text{m}}} \times \frac{1\ \text{L}}{10^3\ \cancel{\text{cm}^3}} = 1.503 \times 10^1\ \text{L}$$

$$\text{density} = \frac{1.38 \times 10^1\ \text{kg}}{1.503 \times 10^1\ \text{L}} = 0.92\ \text{kg/L}$$

51. **a.** $C_2 = -90\ °C$, $C_4 = 0\ °C$, $C_6 = 70\ °C$, $C_8 = 125\ °C$
b. C_1 through C_4
c. three
d. Over the range C_1 through C_9, the increase is approximately 38 °C/additional carbon. Over the range C_3 through C_9, the increase is approximately 32 °C/additional carbon.

52. The number of kilometers light travels in 1 min is:

$$3.0 \times 10^8 \frac{\cancel{\text{m}}}{\cancel{\text{s}}} \times \frac{10^{-3}\ \text{km}}{1\ \cancel{\text{m}}} \times \frac{60\ \cancel{\text{s}}}{1\ \text{min}} = 1.8 \times 10^7\ \text{km/min}$$

To travel the 1.5×10^8 km from the sun to Earth will take:

$$1.5 \times 10^8\ \cancel{\text{km}} \times \frac{1\ \text{min}}{1.8 \times 10^7\ \cancel{\text{km}}} = 8.3\ \text{min}$$

53. $$\text{density} = \frac{\text{mass}}{\text{volume}}$$

mass = density × volume

$$= 2.7 \frac{\text{g}}{\cancel{\text{cm}^3}} \times (3.0\ \cancel{\text{cm}} \times 3.0\ \cancel{\text{cm}} \times 3.0\ \cancel{\text{cm}})$$

$$= 73\ \text{g}$$

54. $$5.52 \frac{\cancel{\text{g}}}{\cancel{\text{cm}^3}} \times \frac{1\ \text{kg}}{10^3\ \cancel{\text{g}}} \times \frac{10^3\ \cancel{\text{cm}^3}}{1\ \text{dm}^3} = 5.52 \frac{\text{kg}}{\text{dm}^3}$$

55. volume of aquarium 40.0 cm × 20.0 cm × 30.0 cm = 24 000 cm^3
For water at 4 °C
1 cm^3 = 1 mL = 1 g = 10^{-3} kg

$$\text{Therefore, } 24\ 000\ \cancel{\text{cm}^3} \times \frac{10^{-3}\ \text{kg}}{1\ \cancel{\text{cm}^3}} = 24.0\ \text{kg}$$

Critical Thinking

56. **a.** 2
b. 3

57. Answers will vary.

Cumulative Review

58. Using units properly assures the accurate translation of word problems into mathematical language. Units serve as guides to help solve problems. Without units, numerical values would be meaningless.

59. According to the law of conservation of mass, the mass of fuel plus the mass of oxygen must equal the mass of ash plus gaseous products. According to the law of conservation of energy, the chemical energy of the fuel equals the heat and light energy released.

60. **a.** The glass is solid, transparent, hard, colorless, and insoluble in water.
b. The soda is a liquid, a mixture, and colorless.
c. The ice is solid, less dense than the soda, cold, and colorless.
d. The bubbles are a clear, tasteless, odorless gas.

61. **a.** mixture
b. mixture
c. compound
d. element

62. kelvins = 962 + 273 = 1235 K

63. Convert all measurements to the same unit and compare.
a. cg = 10^{-2} g; mg = 10^{-3} g; centigram is larger
b. dL = 10^{-2} L; kL = 10^3 L; kiloliter is larger
c. ms = 10^{-3} s; μs = 10^{-6} s; ms is larger
d. $dm^3 = (10\ cm)^3 = 10^3\ cm^3$; mL = 1 cm^3; cubic decimeter is larger
e. μm = 10^{-6} m; nm = 10^{-9} m; micrometer is larger

64. Answers will vary.

65. **a.** 3
b. 4
c. 2
d. 4
e. 5
f. 4

66. **a.** 5.1 g
b. 3.5×10^6 kg
c. 7.8×10^{-5} dm^3
d. 4.5×10^{-2} mm
e. 9.9×10^2 K
f. 65 s

Concept Challenge

67. $$8.0 \times 10^{-1} \frac{\text{cg Sr}}{\text{kg seawater}} \times \frac{1\text{ kg}}{10^3\text{ g}} \times \frac{1\text{ g}}{10^2\text{ cg}}$$
$$\times 1.0 \frac{\text{g}}{\text{mL}} \times \frac{1\text{ mL}}{1\text{ cm}^3} \times \left(\frac{100\text{ cm}}{1\text{ m}}\right)^3 \times 1\text{ m}^3$$
$$= 8.0\text{ g}$$

68. Mass = 121 g + 400 g = 521 g

$$\text{Density} = \frac{521\text{ g}}{437\text{ mL}} = 1.19\text{ m/mL}$$

$$\text{Specific gravity} = \frac{\text{density of solution}}{\text{density of water}} = \frac{1.19\text{ g/mL}}{1.00\text{ g/mL}} = 1.19$$

69. Balsa wood specific gravity = 0.20; density = 0.20 g/cm^3

$$\text{density} = \frac{\text{mass}}{\text{volume}}$$

$$\text{volume} = \frac{\text{mass}}{\text{density}} = \frac{98.0\text{ g}}{0.20\frac{\text{g}}{\text{cm}^3}} = 490\text{ cm}^3$$

volume = height × width × depth

$$\text{height} = \frac{\text{volume}}{\text{width} \times \text{depth}} = \frac{490\text{ cm}^3}{4.4\text{ cm} \times 3.5\text{ cm}}$$
$$= 31.8\text{ cm}$$
= 32 cm (2 significant figures)

70. Volume of room:
$= 25.0\text{ m} \times 15.0\text{ m} \times 4.0\text{ m}$
$= 1500\text{ m}^3$
$1\text{ m}^3 = 10^3\text{ dm}^3$
$1\text{ dm}^3 = 1\text{ L}$

$$1500\text{ m}^3 \times \frac{10^3\text{ dm}^3}{1\text{ m}^3} \times \frac{1\text{ L}}{1\text{ dm}^3} = 1\,500\,000\text{ L}$$

volume of room = 1.50×10^6 L

$$\text{density} = \frac{\text{mass}}{\text{volume}}$$

mass = density × volume
$$= 1.20\frac{\text{g}}{\text{L}} \times 1.50 \times 10^6\text{ L}$$
$$= 1.80 \times 10^6\text{ g}$$
$$= 1.80 \times 10^3\text{ kg}$$

71.

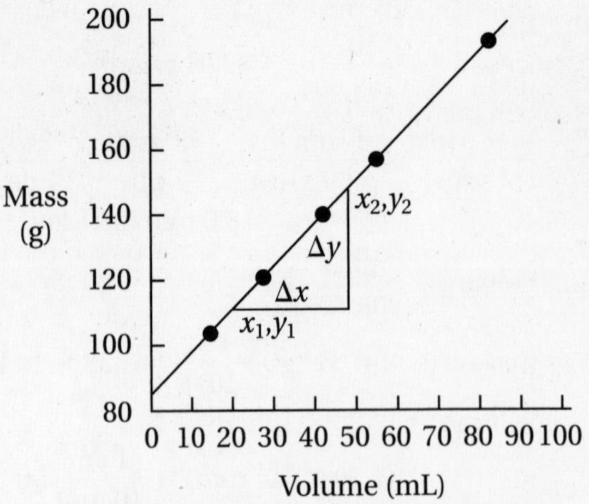

a. The mass of the flask is the y-intercept. This is the mass when the flask is empty (volume of liquid equals zero). The mass of the flask is 83.

b. The density is the slope of the line. This is the ratio of the change in mass to the change in volume. Using the points labeled on the graph, the slope is calculated as follows:

$$m = \frac{y_2 - y_1}{x_2 - x_1}$$
$$= \frac{150 - 110\text{ g}}{50 - 20\text{ mL}} = \frac{40\text{ g}}{30\text{ mL}} = 1.3\text{ g/mL}$$

Standardized Test Prep

1. (a)
2. (d)
$$325\ \cancel{\text{mg}} \times \frac{1\ \text{g}}{1000\ \cancel{\text{mg}}} = 0.325\ \text{g}$$
3. (a)
$$\text{Volume} = \frac{\text{mass}}{\text{density}}$$
$$\frac{15.6\ \text{g}}{9.394\ \text{g/cm}^3} = 1.66\ \text{cm}^3$$
4. (d)
$1\ \text{cm} \times 1\ \text{cm} \times 1\ \text{cm} = 1\ \text{cm}^3$
$10^4\ \mu\text{m} \times 10^4\ \mu\text{m} \times 10^4\ \mu\text{m} = 10^{12}\ \mu\text{m}$
5. (d)
$$\frac{95\ \cancel{\text{km}}}{\cancel{\text{h}}} \times \frac{103\ \text{m}}{\cancel{\text{km}}} \times \frac{1\ \cancel{\text{h}}}{60\ \cancel{\text{min}}} \times \frac{1\ \cancel{\text{min}}}{60\ \text{s}} = 26\ \text{m/s}$$
6. (b)
7. Known: volume in liters; unknown: volume in deciliters
8. Known: density of gold in g/cm^3 and mass of gold in grams; unknown: volume of gold in milliliters
9. Known: lost time in seconds
Unknown: lost time in minutes per day
10. Known: eggs per carton, cartons per box, and boxes per crate; unknown: crates per truck and number of eggs per 5 truckloads
11. To compare prices, students need to know what a gallon of gasoline costs at the pump marked in liters.
$1\ \cancel{\text{gal}} \times \frac{3.79\ \cancel{\text{L}}}{1\ \cancel{\text{gal}}} \times \frac{\$0.35}{1\ \cancel{\text{L}}} = \$1.33$, which is more than \$1.25/gal.
12. (D)
13. (B) and (C)
14. (B)
15. (A)
16. diameter of "helium atom" is 9.0 mm; diameter of "xenon atom" is 23.5 mm
17. He : Xe = 9.0 mm : 23.5 mm = 1 : 2.6
18. volume of He
$\frac{4}{3} \times 3.14 \times (4.5\ \text{mm})^3 = 382\ \text{mm}^3$
volume of Xe
$\frac{4}{3} \times 3.14 \times (11.75\ \text{mm})^3 = 6792\ \text{mm}^3$
He : Xe = $382\ \text{mm}^3 : 6796\ \text{mm}^3 = 1 : 17.8$

5 ATOMIC STRUCTURE AND THE PERIODIC TABLE

Concept Practice

33. Dalton would agree with all four statements because they all fit his atomic theory.

34. a. A beam of electrons (cathode rays) is deflected by an electric field toward the positively charged plate.

b. The cathode rays were always composed of electrons regardless of the metal used in the electrodes or the gas used in the cathode-ray tube.

35. Electrons should repel each other because all electrons have negative charges.

36. He did not expect any alpha particles to be deflected over a large angle.

37. Every atomic nucleus is positively charged.

38. Atoms have equal numbers of positively charged protons and negatively charged electrons.

39. The atomic number represents the number of protons in the nucleus of an atom.

40. a. 15 **b.** 42 **c.** 13 **d.** 48 **e.** 24 **f.** 82

41. The atomic number is the number of protons. The mass number is the sum of the number of protons and number of neutrons.

42.

Atomic number	Mass number	Number of protons	Number of neutrons	Number of electrons	Symbol of element
9	19	9	10	9	F
14	29	14	15	14	Si
22	47	22	25	22	Ti
25	55	25	30	25	Mn

43. mass number, number of neutrons, and atomic mass

44. Because elements have so many isotopes, there are more than 1000 kinds of atoms, but only about 100 kinds of elements.

45. The mass of each isotope and its percent composition are required to calculate an element's atomic mass.

46. The atomic mass of an element is the weighted average of the masses of all of its isotopes.

47. Answers will vary.

48. Moseley arranged the elements in order of increasing atomic number, not atomic mass.

49. a. C, Si **b.** La **c.** B, Ne, P, Br **d.** Hg, Br **e.** Bi, Sb

Concept Mastery

50. The volume of an atom is large relative to the volume of the nucleus. The density of the nucleus is high relative to the density of the atom.

51. There are five protons and six neutrons in the nucleus. There are five electrons outside the nucleus.

52. Scientists now know that, because of the existence of isotopes, all atoms of the same element are not identical. Scientists also know that the atom is not the smallest particle of matter but is itself composed of smaller particles.

53. Multiply the percent abundance by the atomic mass of each isotope and add the resulting products.

$204 \text{ amu} \times 0.0137 = 2.79 \text{ amu}$
$206 \text{ amu} \times 0.2626 = 54.10 \text{ amu}$
$207 \text{ amu} \times 0.2082 = 43.10 \text{ amu}$
$\underline{208 \text{ amu} \times 0.5155 = 107.22 \text{ amu}}$
207.21 amu

54. No; in general, Dalton proposed a valid theory in line with the experimental evidence he had available to him.

55. Atoms are the smallest particles of an element that retain the properties of the element.

56. a. $\frac{8\,289\,000}{8\,922\,261} \times 100\% = 92.90\%$

b. $\frac{8\,912\,140}{8\,922\,261} \times 100\% = 99.89\%$

c. $\frac{886}{8\,922\,261} \times 100\% = 0.00993\%$

Critical Thinking

57. a. 3 **b.** 1 **c.** 4

58. The number of alpha particles deflected by any nucleus would be proportional to the size of the nucleus. Thus relative sizes could be determined by counting the number of particles deflected for each nucleus.

59. The following are reasonable hypotheses: The space in an individual atom is large relative to the volume of the atom, but very small relative to an object the size of a hand. There are many layers of atoms in a wall or a desk. The space that exists is distributed evenly throughout the solid, similar to the distribution of air pockets in foam insulation.

60. The theory must be modified. Then the modified theory must be tested.

61. Answers will vary.

62. Using the law of conservation of mass,
$54\text{ g} - 6\text{ g} = 48\text{ g } O_2$.

63. **a.** 4 **b.** 3 **c.** 3 **d.** 4

64. In a chemical change, atoms are not created or destroyed; they are rearranged.

65. Change all the lengths to centimeters.
1.10 m = 110 cm
Volume = 55.0 cm × 110 cm × 80.0 cm
$= 484\ 000\text{ cm}^3$
$= 4.84 \times 10^5\text{ cm}^3$

66. mass = density × volume

$$\text{mass} = 5.42\ \cancel{\text{cm}^3} \times 22.5\frac{\text{g}}{\cancel{\text{cm}^3}} = 121.95\text{ g}$$

67. **a.** element **d.** mixture
b. mixture **e.** mixture
c. mixture **f.** mixture

Concept Challenge

68. Because diamond is more dense than graphite, pressure could be used to squeeze the carbon atoms closer together.

69. Set up two equations with two unknowns.
x = part that is lithium-6
y = part that is lithium-7
Then, $x + y = 1$. Also, the equation for the calculation of the atomic mass is:
$(x)(6.015) + (y)(7.016) = 6.941$
Substitute and solve.
$(1 - y)(6.015) + (y)(7.016) = 6.941$
$6.015 - 6.015y + 7.016y = 6.941$
$1.001y = 0.926$
$y = 0.925$ and $x = 0.075$
The percent of lithium-6 is 7.5%; the percent of lithium-7 is 92.5%.

70. Calculate the mass of a chlorine-35 atom from its subatomic composition.

$$\begin{array}{r} 17p \times 1.67 \times 10^{-24}\text{ g} = 2.84 \times 10^{-23}\text{ g} \\ 18n^\circ \times 1.67 \times 10^{-24}\text{ g} = 3.01 \times 10^{-23}\text{ g} \\ 17e^- \times 9.11 \times 10^{-28}\text{ g} = 1.55 \times 10^{-26}\text{ g} \\ \hline 5.85 \times 10^{-23}\text{ g} \end{array}$$

The mass defect is 0.04×10^{-23} g, or 4×10^{-25} g.

Standardized Test Prep

1. (c)

2. (a)

3. (b)

4. (e)

5. (b)

6. 9; Three ^{42}Ca atoms have an approximate mass of 3 × 42 = 126 amu; one ^{14}N atom has an approximate mass of 14 amu; 126/14 = 9 ^{14}N atoms with an approximate mass of 126 amu.

7. the nucleus of an atom

8. very small volume; almost all the mass of the atom; high density; positive charge

9. electron

10. False, True
The number 27 is the sum of the protons and neutrons in an atom of aluminum-27.

11. True, False
All atoms of a given element have the same number of protons. If the number of protons changes, the identity of the element changes.

12. True, True, correct explanation

13. False, True
Although hydrogen is placed above group 1A in the periodic table because it has one valence electron, it shares properties with both alkali metals and halogens.

6 CHEMICAL NAMES AND FORMULAS

Concept Practice

45. An ion is an atom, or group of atoms, with an electrical charge. An anion is formed when an atom gains one or more electrons. A cation is formed when an atom loses one or more electrons.

46. a. 1 gained
 b. 1 lost
 c. 3 gained
 d. 2 lost
 e. 1 lost
 f. 1 gained

47. a. bromide ion, anion
 b. sodium ion, cation
 c. arsenide ion, anion
 d. calcium ion, cation
 e. copper(I) ion, cation
 f. hydride ion, anion

48. Ionic compounds are electrically neutral; the net positive charge on the cations is exactly balanced by the net negative charge on the anions.

49. Ionic compounds are composed of a metal and a nonmetal. Molecular compounds are composed of two nonmetals.

50. a. Yes; the ratio of the mass of the colorless gas to the mass of the white powder is a constant.
 b. law of definite compositions
 c. 3.5 g colorless gas

51. a. carbon 6, hydrogen 8, oxygen 6
 b. carbon 5, hydrogen 8, oxygen 4, sodium 1
 c. carbon 12, hydrogen 22, oxygen 11
 d. carbon 7, hydrogen 5, nitrogen 3, oxygen 6
 e. nitrogen 2, hydrogen 4, oxygen 3

52. High melting points are characteristic of ionic compounds.

53. a. O^{2-}
 b. Pb^{2+}
 c. Li^{+}
 d. N^{3-}
 e. Cu^{2+}
 f. F^{-}

54. a. barium ion
 b. iodide ion
 c. silver ion
 d. mercury(II) ion
 e. phosphide ion
 f. tin(IV) ion

55. cyanide (CN^{-}) and hydroxide (OH^{-})

56. a. hydroxide
 b. lead(IV)
 c. sulfate
 d. oxide
 e. hydrogen phosphate
 f. dichromate
 g. aluminum
 h. chlorite

57. The net ionic charge is zero. Ionic compounds are electrically neutral and thus have no net ionic charge.

58. a. Na_2O
 b. SnS_2
 c. KCl
 d. Mg_3N_2

59. Knowing the number of each ion in the formula and the ionic charge of the anion, the charge of the cation must be such that the net ionic charge is zero.

60. Parentheses are used to indicate more than one of a polyatomic ion.

61. a. $CaCO_3$
 b. $Ba(HCO_3)_2$
 c. LiClO
 d. $Sn(Cr_2O_7)_2$

62. NH_4NO_3, ammonium nitrate
 $(NH_4)_2CO_3$, ammonium carbonate
 NH_4CN, ammonium cyanide
 $(NH_4)_3PO_4$, ammonium phosphate
 $Sn(NO_3)_4$, tin(IV) nitrate
 $Sn(CO_3)_2$, tin(IV) carbonate
 $Sn(CN)_4$, tin(IV) cyanide
 $Sn_3(PO_4)_4$, tin(IV) phosphate
 $Fe(NO_3)_3$, iron(III) nitrate
 $Fe_2(CO_3)_3$, iron(III) carbonate
 $Fe(CN)_3$, iron(III) cyanide
 $FePO_4$, iron(III) phosphate
 $Mg(NO_3)_2$, magnesium nitrate
 $MgCO_3$, magnesium carbonate
 $Mg(CN)_2$, magnesium cyanide
 $Mg_3(PO_4)_2$, magnesium phosphate

63. The components of a binary molecular compound are two nonmetals.

64. a. BCl_3
 b. N_2H_4
 c. dinitrogen pentoxide
 d. carbon tetrachloride

65. a. hydrochloric acid
 b. nitric acid
 c. H_2SO_4
 d. $HC_2H_3O_2$

66. a. tri-
 b. mono-
 c. di-
 d. hexa-
 e. penta-
 f. tetra-

Concept Mastery

67. a. sodium chlorate
 b. mercury(I) bromide
 c. potassium chromate

d. aluminum iodide
e. tin(IV) oxide
f. iron(III) acetate
g. potassium hydrogen sulfate
h. calcium hydride

68. a. $KMnO_4$ **e.** NaH_2PO_4
b. $Ca(HCO_3)_2$ **f.** PBr_5
c. Cl_2O_7 **g.** CCl_4
d. Si_3N_4

69. a. lithium perchlorate
b. dichlorine monoxide
c. mercury(II) fluoride
d. calcium oxide
e. barium phosphate
f. iodine
g. strontium sulfate
h. copper(I) acetate

70. a. MgS **e.** SO_3^{2-}
b. N_2 **f.** $CaCO_3$
c. $Ba(OH)_2$ **g.** NaBr
d. $Cu(NO_2)_2$ **h.** $Fe_2(SO_4)_3$

71. a. magnesium permanganate
b. beryllium nitrate
c. potassium carbonate
d. dinitrogen tetrahydride
e. lithium hydroxide
f. barium fluoride
g. phosphorus triiodide
h. zinc oxide

72. a. total chemical production
$= 165.4 \times 10^9$ kg;
lime production $= 16.3 \times 10^9$ kg
$$\text{percentage} = \frac{16.3 \times 10^9 \cancel{\text{kg}}}{165.4 \times 10^9 \cancel{\text{kg}}} \times 100\%$$
$= 9.85\%$

b. nitrogen, oxygen, and chlorine; 5.49×10^{10} kg

c. total chemical production
$= 165.4 \times 10^9$ kg;
acid production $= 57.4 \times 10^9$ kg
$$\text{percentage} = \frac{57.4 \times 10^9 \cancel{\text{kg}}}{165.4 \times 10^9 \cancel{\text{kg}}} \times 100\%$$
$= 34.7\%$

d. sulfuric acid, H_2SO_4, nitrogen, N_2; ammonia, NH_3; oxygen, O_2; lime is calcium oxide, CaO; sodium hydroxide, NaOH; chlorine, Cl_2; phosphoric acid, H_3PO_4; sodium carbonate, Na_2CO_3; nitric acid, HNO_3

73. a. $CaBr_2$ **e.** $Sn(CN)_4$
b. AgCl **f.** LiH
c. Al_4C_3 **g.** $Sr(C_2H_3O_2)_2$
d. NO_2 **h.** Na_2SiO_3

Critical Thinking

74. a. 1
b. 4
c. 2

75. A molecular formula shows the number of each kind of atom in a molecule of the compound. The formula unit shows the lowest whole number ratio of ions in a compound.

76. Elements in binary molecular compounds occur on the right side of the periodic table. Both elements in a binary molecular compound are nonmetals.

77. Using a common system, chemists can communicate with each other and be assured that they are both speaking of the same thing. The system of naming compounds that chemists use also conveys information about chemical composition, whereas common names do not.

78. The statement is true for the representative (Group A) metals; it is not true for the transition metals, which often have more than one ionic charge.

79. Possible answers include: cations always come before anions; when a cation has more than one ionic charge, the charge is indicated by a Roman numeral; monatomic anions use an *-ide* ending.

80. a. $$775 \cancel{\text{mL}} \times \frac{1 \cancel{\text{L}}}{10^3 \cancel{\text{mL}}} \times \frac{10^6\ \mu\text{L}}{1 \cancel{\text{L}}}$$
$= 7.75 \times 10^5\ \mu$L

b. K = °C + 273
K = −65 + 273 = 208

c. $$8.32 \cancel{\text{mg}} \text{ silver} \times \frac{1 \cancel{\text{g}}}{10^3 \cancel{\text{mg}}} \times \frac{10^2 \text{ cg}}{1 \cancel{\text{g}}}$$
= 0.832 cg silver

81. a. 12 protons, 10 electrons
b. 35 protons, 36 electrons
c. 38 protons, 36 electrons
d. 16 protons, 18 electrons

82. Answers will vary but may include color (physical), solid (physical), magnetic (physical), malleable (physical), conducts electricity (physical), burns (chemical).

83. $$\text{density} = \frac{\text{mass}}{\text{volume}} = \frac{6.62 \text{ g}}{12.3 \text{ cm}^3}$$
$= 0.538\ \text{g/cm}^3$

84.

Name	Formula	Crystalline form or color	Density (g/cm^3)	Melting point (°C)	Boiling point (°C)	Solubility (g/100 g)
ammonium chloride	NH_4Cl	colorless	1.527	sublimes 340	520	29.7 (0 °C)
barium	Ba	yellow-silver	3.51	725	1640	decomposes water
barium sulfate	$BaSO_4$	white	4.50	1580	—	2.22×10^{-4} (18 °C)
bromine	Br_2	dark red liquid	3.12	−7.2	58.78	4.17 (0 °C)
calcium carbonate	$CaCO_3$	colorless	2.71	—	898.6 decomposes	1.4×10^{-3} (0 °C)
chlorine	Cl_2	green-yellow gas	3.214 g/L (0 °C)	−100.98	−34.6	1.46 (0 °C)
copper(II) sulfate pentahydrate	$CuSO_4 \cdot 5H_2O$	blue	2.284	$-4H_2O$ (110 °C)	$-5H_2O$ (150 °C)	31.6 (0 °C)
iodine	I_2	violet-black metallic luster	4.93	113.5	184.35	2.9×10^{-2} (20 °C)
iron(II) sulfate pentahydrate	$FeSO_4 \cdot 5H_2O$	white	2.2	$-5H_2O$ (300 °C)	—	slightly soluble
mercury	Hg	silver-white metallic luster	13.59	−38.87	356.58	insoluble
potassium carbonate	K_2CO_3	colorless	2.428	891	decomposes	112 (20 °C)
sulfur (α)	S	yellow	2.07	112.8	444.6	insoluble

85. **a.** Potassium carbonate has a much greater water solubility than $CaCO_3$.
b. The copper compound is blue; the iron compound is white.
c. Because of differences in solubilities, water could be added to dissolve the NH_4Cl. The resulting solution could be filtered leaving the insoluble $BaSO_4$.
d. chlorine (nonmetal), sulfur (nonmetal), bromine (nonmetal), barium (metal), iodine (nonmetal), mercury (metal)
e. barium sulfate, calcium carbonate, potassium carbonate, copper(II) sulfate pentahydrate, iron(II) sulfate pentahydrate, ammonium chloride
f. mass = density × volume

$$\text{mass} = 47.0\ \cancel{\text{cm}^3}\ \text{Hg} \times 13.59\ \frac{\text{g}}{\cancel{\text{cm}^3}} = 639\ \text{g Hg}$$

g. $$\text{Volume} = \frac{\text{mass}}{\text{density}} = \frac{16.6\ \text{g}}{2.07\ \text{g/cm}^3} = 8.02\ \text{cm}^3$$

h. Color, density, melting point, and boiling point could all be used to distinguish among the halogens.

Standardized Test Prep

1. (d)
2. (d)
3. (a)

$$3.56\ \text{g O} \times \frac{4.20\ \text{g}\ \cancel{\text{C}}}{6.00\ \text{g}\ \cancel{\text{C}}} = 2.49\ \text{g O}$$

4. (b)
5. (a)
6. (c)

Students can use the crisscross method to solve problems 7–11.

7. (D)
Al^{3+} and S^{2-} form Al_2S_3
8. (C)
K^+ and O^{2-} form K_2O
9. (A)
Li^+ and Cl^- form LiCl
10. (B)
Sr^{2+} and Br^- form $SrBr_2$
11. (C)
Na^+ and S^{2-} form Na_2S

Students can reverse the crisscross method to solve problem 12.

12. cations: M^{2+}, N^+, P^{3+};
anions: A^-, B^{2-}, C^{3-}, D^{2-}
$MA_2 = M^{2+}$ and A^-
$N_2B = N^+$ and B^{2-}
$P_2D_3 = P^{3+}$ and D^{2-}
C is C^{3-} because one C ion combines with one P ion, which has a 3+ charge.
13. (1) MB, (2) M_3C_2, (3) NA, (4) N_3C, (5) N_2D, (6) P_2B_3
14. C and D are substances; A and B are mixtures.
15. A contains elements and compounds; B and C contain only elements; D contains only a compound.

7 CHEMICAL QUANTITIES

Concept Practice

44. Matter may be measured by number or count, mass, or volume. Examples will vary.

45. **a.** molecule **b.** formula unit **c.** molecule **d.** atom

46. **a.** 3 **b.** 2 **c.** 9 **d.** 10

47. Because each compound consists of one mole, all contain 6.02×10^{23} molecules.

48. Each mole consists of the same number of representative particles. A representative particle of H_2O_2 contains 4 atoms. A representative particle of C_2H_6 contains 8 atoms. A representative particle of CO contains 2 atoms. Therefore 1 mol of C_2H_6 contains the most atoms.

49. **a.** $3.00 \text{ mol Sn} \times \frac{6.02 \times 10^{23} \text{ atoms Sn}}{1 \text{ mol Sn}} = 1.81 \times 10^{24} \text{ atoms Sn}$

b. $0.400 \text{ mol KCl} \times \frac{6.02 \times 10^{23} \text{ formula units KCl}}{1 \text{ mol KCl}} = 2.41 \times 10^{23} \text{ formula units KCl}$

c. $7.5 \text{ mol } SO_2 \times \frac{6.02 \times 10^{23} \text{ molecules } SO_2}{1 \text{ mol } SO_2} = 4.52 \times 10^{24} \text{ molecules } SO_2$

d. $4.80 \times 10^{-3} \text{ mol NaI} \times \frac{6.02 \times 10^{23} \text{ formula units NaI}}{1 \text{ mol NaI}} = 2.89 \times 10^{21} \text{ formula units NaI}$

50. **a.** $3 \times 1 \text{ g} + 1 \times 30.9 \text{ g} + 4 \times 16 \text{ g} = 97.9 \text{ g}$
b. $2 \times 14 \text{ g} + 3 \times 16 \text{ g} = 76 \text{ g}$
c. $1 \times 40.1 \text{ g} + 1 \times 12 \text{ g} + 3 \times 16 \text{ g} = 100.1 \text{ g}$
d. $2 \times 14 \text{ g} + 8 \times 1 \text{ g} + 1 \times 32.1 \text{ g} + 4 \times 16 \text{ g} = 132.1 \text{ g}$
e. $4 \times 12 \text{ g} + 9 \times 1 \text{ g} + 2 \times 16 \text{ g} = 89.0 \text{ g}$
f. $2 \times 79.8 \text{ g} = 159.8 \text{ g}$

51. **a.** $1 \times 28.1 \text{ g} + 2 \times 16 \text{ g} = 60.1 \text{ g}$
b. $2 \times 14 \text{ g} = 28 \text{ g}$
c. $1 \times 55.8 \text{ g} + 3 \times 16 \text{ g} + 3 \times 1 \text{ g} = 106.8 \text{ g}$
d. $1 \times 63.5 \text{ g} = 63.5 \text{ g}$

52. Answers will vary but should include:
(1) Determine the number of moles of each atom from the formula.
(2) Look up the atomic mass of each element.
(3) Multiply the number of moles of each atom by its molar mass.
(4) Sum these products.

53. $\text{gmm of } Cl_2 = 2 \text{ mol Cl} \times \frac{35.5 \text{ g}}{1 \text{ mol Cl}} = 71.0 \text{ g}$

54. Answers will vary.

55. **a.** $15.5 \text{ g } SiO_2 \times \frac{1 \text{ mol } SiO_2}{60 \text{ g } SiO_2} = 0.258 \text{ mol } SiO_2$

b. $6.88 \times 10^{-2} \text{ g AgCl} \times \frac{1 \text{ mol AgCl}}{143.3 \text{ g AgCl}} = 4.8 \times 10^{-4} \text{ mol AgCl}$

c. $79.3 \text{ g } Cl_2 \times \frac{1 \text{ mol } Cl_2}{71.0 \text{ g } Cl_2} = 1.12 \text{ mol } Cl_2$

d. $5.96 \text{ g KOH} \times \frac{1 \text{ mol KOH}}{56.1 \text{ g KOH}} = 1.06 \times 10^{-1} \text{ mol KOH}$

e. $937 \text{ g } Ca(C_2H_2O_2)_2 \times \frac{1 \text{ mol } Ca(C_2H_3O_2)_2}{158.1 \text{ g } Ca(C_2H_3O_2)_2} = 5.93 \text{ mol } Ca(C_2H_3O_2)_2$

f. $0.800 \text{ g Ca} \times \frac{1 \text{ mol Ca}}{40.1 \text{ g Ca}} = 2.00 \times 10^{-2} \text{ mol Ca}$

56. **a.** $1.5 \text{ mol } C_5H_{12} \times \frac{72 \text{ g } C_5H_{12}}{1 \text{ mol } C_5H_{12}} = 108 \text{ g } C_5H_{12}$

b. $14.4 \text{ mol } F_2 \times \frac{38.0 \text{ g } F_2}{1 \text{ mol } F_2} = 547 \text{ g } F_2$

c. $0.780 \text{ mol } Ca(CN)_2 \times \frac{92.1 \text{ g } Ca(CN)_2}{1 \text{ mol } Ca(CN)_2} = 71.8 \text{ g } Ca(CN)_2$

d. $7.00 \text{ mol } H_2O_2 \times \frac{34.0 \text{ g } H_2O_2}{1 \text{ mol } H_2O_2} = 238 \text{ g } H_2O_2$

e. $5.60 \text{ mol NaOH} \times \frac{40.0 \text{ g NaOH}}{1 \text{ mol NaOH}} = 224 \text{ g NaOH}$

f. $3.21 \times 10^{-2}\ \text{mol Ni} \times \dfrac{58.7\ \text{g Ni}}{1\ \text{mol Ni}}$

$= 1.88\ \text{g Ni}$

57. At STP, one mole of any gas occupies a volume of 22.4 L.

a. $7.6\ \text{mol Ar} \times \dfrac{22.4\ \text{L Ar}}{1\ \text{mol Ar}} = 170\ \text{L Ar}$

b. $0.44\ \text{mol } C_2H_6 \times \dfrac{22.4\ \text{L } C_2H_6}{1\ \text{mol } C_2H_6}$

$= 9.9\ \text{L } C_2H_6$

c. $1.2\ \text{mol } O_2 \times \dfrac{22.4\ \text{L } O_2}{1\ \text{mol } O_2} = 26.9\ \text{L } O_2$

58. At STP, one mole of any gas occupies a volume of 22.4 L.

$\text{Density} = \dfrac{\text{mass}}{\text{volume}}$

a. $\dfrac{44.0\ \text{g } C_3H_8}{22.4\ \text{L } C_3H_8} = 1.96\ \text{g/L}$

b. $\dfrac{20.1\ \text{g Ne}}{22.4\ \text{L Ne}} = 0.897\ \text{g/L}$

c. $\dfrac{46.0\ \text{g } NO_2}{22.4\ \text{L } NO_2} = 2.05\ \text{g/L}$

59. a. $835\ \text{g } SO_3 \times \dfrac{1\ \text{mol } SO_3}{80.1\ \text{g } SO_3} \times \dfrac{22.4\ \text{L } SO_3}{1\ \text{mol } SO_3}$

$= 234\ \text{L } SO_3$

b. $1\ \text{molecule } C_9H_8O_4$

$\times \dfrac{1\ \text{mol } C_9H_8O_4}{6.02 \times 10^{23}\ \text{molecules } C_9H_8O_4}$

$\times \dfrac{180.0\ \text{g } C_9H_8O_4}{1\ \text{mol } C_9H_8O_4}$

$= 2.99 \times 10^{-22}\ \text{g } C_9H_8O_4$

c. $5.78\ \text{mol } NH_4NO_3$

$\times \dfrac{6.02 \times 10^{23}\ \text{formula units}}{1\ \text{mol } NH_4NO_3}$

$\times \dfrac{9\ \text{atoms}}{1\ \text{formula unit}} = 3.13 \times 10^{25}\ \text{atoms}$

60. For each compound, the ratio of the mass of the element to the mass of the compound gives the percent of that element.

a. $\dfrac{2.0\ \text{g H}}{34.1\ \text{g } H_2S} \times 100\% = 5.9\%\ \text{H}$

$\dfrac{32.1\ \text{g S}}{34.1\ \text{g } H_2S} \times 100\% = 94.1\%\ \text{S}$

b. $\dfrac{28.0\ \text{g N}}{124.0\ \text{g } (NH_4)_2C_2O_4} \times 100\% = 22.6\%\ \text{N}$

$\dfrac{8.0\ \text{g H}}{124.0\ \text{g } (NH_4)_2C_2O_4} \times 100\% = 6.5\%\ \text{H}$

$\dfrac{24.0\ \text{g C}}{124.0\ \text{g } (NH_4)_2C_2O_4} \times 100\% = 19.4\%\ \text{C}$

$\dfrac{64.0\ \text{g O}}{124.0\ \text{g} (NH_4)_2C_2O_2} \times 100\% = 51.6\%\ \text{O}$

c. $\dfrac{24.3\ \text{g Mg}}{58.3\ \text{g Mg(OH)}_2} \times 100\% = 41.7\%\ \text{Mg}$

$\dfrac{32.0\ \text{g O}}{58.3\ \text{g Mg(OH)}_2} \times 100\% = 54.9\%\ \text{O}$

$\dfrac{2.0\ \text{g H}}{58.3\ \text{g Mg(OH)}_2} \times 100\% = 3.4\%\ \text{H}$

d. $\dfrac{69.0\ \text{g Na}}{164.0\ \text{g } Na_3PO_4} \times 100\% = 42.1\%\ \text{Na}$

$\dfrac{31.0\ \text{g P}}{164.0\ \text{g } Na_3PO_4} \times 100\% = 18.9\%\ \text{P}$

$\dfrac{64.0\ \text{g O}}{164.0\ \text{g } Na_3PO_4} \times 100\% = 39.0\%\ \text{O}$

61. a. $3.54\ \text{g } H_2S \times \dfrac{94.1\ \text{g S}}{100\ \text{g } H_2S} = 3.33\ \text{g S}$

b. $25.0\ \text{g } (NH_4)_2C_2O_4 \times \dfrac{22.6\ \text{g N}}{100\ \text{g } (NH_4)_2C_2O_4}$

$= 5.65\ \text{g N}$

c. $97.4\ \text{g Mg(OH)}_2 \times \dfrac{41.7\ \text{g Mg}}{100\ \text{g Mg(OH)}_2}$

$= 40.6\ \text{g Mg}$

d. $804\ \text{g } Na_3PO_4 \times \dfrac{18.9\ \text{g P}}{100\ \text{g } Na_3PO_4} = 152\ \text{g P}$

62. Calculate the percent of iron in each compound.

a. $\dfrac{55.8\ \text{g Fe}}{126.6\ \text{g } FeCl_2} \times 100\% = 44.1\%\ \text{Fe}$

b. $\dfrac{55.8\ \text{g Fe}}{232.8\ \text{g Fe}(C_2H_3O_2)_3} \times 100\% = 24.0\%\ \text{Fe}$

c. $\dfrac{55.8\ \text{g Fe}}{89.8\ \text{Fe(OH)}_2} \times 100\% = 62.1\%\ \text{Fe}$

d. $\dfrac{55.8\ \text{g Fe}}{71.8\ \text{g FeO}} \times 100\% = 77.7\%\ \text{Fe}$

The compound with the highest iron content is **d.** FeO

63. *See answer below.*

64. a. molecular **d.** molecular
b. molecular **e.** empirical
c. empirical **f.** empirical

65. Divide the gram formula mass of the compound by the mass of the empirical formula.

a. $\frac{90\ \cancel{g/mol}}{30\ \cancel{g/mol}} = 3$, $C_3H_6O_3$

b. $\frac{472.2\ \cancel{g/mol}}{236.1\ \cancel{g/mol}} = 2$, Hg_2Cl_2

c. $\frac{146\ \cancel{g/mol}}{73\ \cancel{g/mol}} = 2$, $C_6H_{10}O_4$

66. First find the empirical formula. Then use the empirical formula mass and the gram formula mass to determine the molecular formula.

a. $94.1\ \cancel{g\,O} \times \frac{1\ mol\ O}{16.0\ \cancel{g\,O}} = 5.88\ mol\ O$

$5.9\ \cancel{g\,H} \times \frac{1\ mol\ H}{1.0\ \cancel{g\,H}} = 5.9\ mol\ H$

Divide by 5.88. The empirical formula is HO.

$\frac{gfm}{efm} = \frac{34\ \cancel{g}}{17\ \cancel{g}} = 2$

The molecular formula is H_2O_2.

b. $40.0\ \cancel{g\,C} \times \frac{1\ mol\ C}{12.0\ \cancel{g\,C}} = 3.33\ mol\ C$

$53.4\ \cancel{g\,O} \times \frac{1\ mol\ O}{16.0\ \cancel{g\,O}} = 3.34\ mol\ O$

$6.6\ \cancel{g\,H} \times \frac{1\ mol\ H}{1.0\ \cancel{g\,H}} = 6.6\ mol\ H$

Divide by 3.33. The empirical formula is CH_2O.

$\frac{gfm}{efm} = \frac{120\ \cancel{g}}{30\ \cancel{g}} = 4$

The molecular formula is $C_4H_8O_4$.

Concept Mastery

67. You can measure the mass of 22.4 L of the compound at STP; this is the molar volume of the gas. The mass of the molar volume is the molar mass.

68. a. *See answer below.*

b. $\text{slope} = \frac{\Delta y}{\Delta x} = \frac{\Delta\ \text{molar mass}}{\Delta\ \text{mass of C}}$

$= \frac{150.0 - 60.0}{60.0 - 24.0} = \frac{2.5}{1}$

The slope is the same as the ratio of the empirical formula mass to the mass of carbon in the compound, 30.0 g/12.0 g = 2.5/1.

c. The two other data points occur when molar mass/efm = 3 and 4. These data points correspond to compounds with molecular formulas $C_3H_6O_3$ and $C_4H_8O_4$ respectively. Thus, the (x, y) = (mass of C, molar mass) values are (36, 90) and (48, 120).

69. a. One mole of any substance contains the same number of representative particles, not only atoms. It may be atoms, molecules, or formula units.

b. The gram atomic mass of an element, not a compound, is the atomic mass expressed in grams.

c. A mole of CO_2 has three times Avogadro's number of atoms.

63.

empirical formula	efm	$\frac{\text{molar mass}}{\text{efm}}$	molecular formula
HO	17.0	34.0/17.0 = 2	H_2O_2

68. a.

	empirical formula	efm	$\frac{\text{molar mass}}{\text{efm}}$	molecular formula
Compound A	CH_2O	30.0	60.0/30.0 = 2	$C_2H_4O_2$
Compound D	CH_2O	30.0	150.0/30.0 = 5	$C_5H_{10}O_5$
Compound E	CH_2O	30.0	180.0/30.0 = 6	$C_6H_{12}O_6$

70. Calculate the number of atoms in each substance.

a. $$82.0\ \text{g Kr} \times \frac{1\ \text{mol Kr}}{83.8\ \text{g Kr}} \times \frac{6.02 \times 10^{23}\ \text{atoms Kr}}{1\ \text{mol Kr}} = 5.89 \times 10^{23}\ \text{atoms Kr}$$

b. $$0.842\ \text{mol } C_2H_4 \times \frac{6.02 \times 10^{23}\ \text{molecules } C_2H_4}{1\ \text{mol } C_2H_4} \times \frac{6\ \text{atoms of C, H}}{1\ \text{molecule } C_2H_4} = 3.04 \times 10^{24}\ \text{atoms of C, H}$$

c. $$36.0\ \text{g } N_2 \times \frac{1\ \text{mol } N_2}{28.0\ \text{g } N_2} \times \frac{6.02 \times 10^{23}\ \text{molecules } N_2}{1\ \text{mol } N_2} \times \frac{2\ \text{atoms N}}{1\ \text{molecule } N_2} = 1.548 \times 10^{24}\ \text{atoms N}$$

The 0.842 mol of C_2H_4 contains the largest number of atoms.

71. Find the mass of each component of the mixture, then add.

$$3.5 \times 10^{22}\ \text{formula units } Na_2SO_4 \times \frac{1\ \text{mol } Na_2SO_4}{6.02 \times 10^{23}\ \text{formula units } Na_2SO_4} \times \frac{142.1\ \text{g } Na_2SO_4}{1\ \text{mol } Na_2SO_4} = 8.26\ \text{g } Na_2SO_4$$

$$0.500\ \text{mol } H_2O \times \frac{18.0\ \text{g } H_2O}{1\ \text{mol } H_2O} = 9.00\ \text{g } H_2O$$

Mass total = 8.26 g Na_2SO_4 + 9.00 g H_2O + 7.23 g AgCl = 24.49 g

72. a. In 100.0 g of the compound there are 42.9 g C and 57.1 g O.
Change mass ratio to mole ratio.

$$42.9\ \text{g C} \times \frac{1\ \text{mol C}}{12.0\ \text{g C}} = 3.58\ \text{mol C}$$

$$57.1\ \text{g O} \times \frac{1\ \text{mol O}}{16.0\ \text{g O}} = 3.57\ \text{mol O}$$

Divide by the smallest number of moles.

$$\frac{3.58\ \text{mol C}}{3.57} = 1\ \text{mol C}$$

$$\frac{3.57\ \text{mol O}}{3.57} = 1\ \text{mol O}$$

The empirical formula is CO.

b. In 100.0 g of the compound there are 32.00 g C, 42.66 g O, 18.67 g N, and 6.67 g H. Change mass ratio to mole ratio.

$$32.00\ \text{g C} \times \frac{1\ \text{mol C}}{12.00\ \text{g C}} = 2.67\ \text{mol C}$$

$$42.66\ \text{g O} \times \frac{1\ \text{mol O}}{16.00\ \text{g O}} = 2.67\ \text{mol O}$$

$$18.67\ \text{g N} \times \frac{1\ \text{mol N}}{14.00\ \text{g N}} = 1.33\ \text{mol N}$$

$$6.67\ \text{g N} \times \frac{1\ \text{mol H}}{1.00\ \text{g H}} = 6.67\ \text{mol H}$$

Divide by smallest number of moles.

$$\frac{2.67\ \text{mol C}}{1.33} = 2\ \text{mol C}$$

$$\frac{2.67\ \text{mol O}}{1.33} = 2\ \text{mol O}$$

$$\frac{1.33\ \text{mol N}}{1.33} = 1\ \text{mol N}$$

$$\frac{6.67\ \text{mol H}}{1.33} = 5\ \text{mol H}$$

The empirical formula is $C_2O_2NH_5$.

c. In 100.0 g of the compound there are 71.82 g Cl, 16.16 g O, and 12.12 g C. Change mass ratio to mole ratio.

$$71.72\ \text{g Cl} \times \frac{1\ \text{mol Cl}}{35.5\ \text{g Cl}} = 2.02\ \text{mol Cl}$$

$$16.16\ \text{g O} \times \frac{1\ \text{mol O}}{16.00\ \text{g O}} = 1.01\ \text{mol O}$$

$$12.12\ \text{g C} \times \frac{1\ \text{mol C}}{12.00\ \text{g C}} = 1.01\ \text{mol C}$$

Divide by smallest number of moles.

$$\frac{2.02\ \text{mol Cl}}{1.01} = 2\ \text{mol Cl}$$

$$\frac{1.01\ \text{mol O}}{1.01} = 1\ \text{mol O}$$

$$\frac{1.01\ \text{mol C}}{1.01} = 1\ \text{mol C}$$

The empirical formula is Cl_2OC.

73. a. The mass of 15 boron atoms is 162 amu (10.8 amu × 15 atoms). Therefore the mass of the six atoms of element E is 162 amu. The mass of one atom of element E is 27 amu (162 amu ÷ 6 = 27 amu).

b. Element E is aluminum, which has an atomic mass of 27.0 amu.

74. $$6.02 \times 10^{23}\ \text{particles} \times \frac{5 \times 10^{-6}\ \text{cm}}{1\ \text{particle}} \times \frac{1\ \text{m}}{10^2\ \text{cm}} \times \frac{1\ \text{km}}{10^3\ \text{m}} = 3.01 \times 10^{13}\ \text{km}$$

75. a. formula is $Cu_{0.4\ \text{mol}}Br_{0.8\ \text{mol}}$; simplify the formula by dividing each component by 0.40 mol; empirical formula is $CuBr_2$

b. molecular formula is C_4H_{12}; simplify the formula by dividing each component by 4; empirical formula is CH_3

Critical Thinking

76. a. 1

b. 4

c. 4

77. A molecular formula is a whole number multiple of its empirical formula.

78. Sulfur atoms have a greater atomic mass. Most sulfur atoms have 16 protons, 16 electrons, and 16 neutrons; carbon is composed of 6 protons, 6 electrons, and 6 neutrons. Therefore, 6.02×10^{23} sulfur atoms will have a greater mass than the same number of carbon atoms.

79. Gas molecules are separated by so much empty space, their own volumes are insignificant when considering how much space a certain quantity of gas occupies.

Cumulative Review

80. a. 40, 40, 50
b. 46, 46, 62
c. 35, 35, 46
d. 51, 51, 72

81. $\text{density} = \dfrac{\text{mass}}{\text{volume}}$

$\text{mass} = \text{density} \times \text{volume}$

$= \dfrac{21.45\ \text{g}}{\cancel{\text{cm}^3}} \times 14.5\ \cancel{\text{cm}^3} = 311\ \text{g Pt}$

Conversion factor: 1 mol Pt has a mass of 195 g.

$311\ \cancel{\text{g Pt}} \times \dfrac{1\ \text{mol Pt}}{195\ \cancel{\text{g Pt}}} = 1.59\ \text{mol Pt}$

82. A molecule is composed of two or more atoms chemically joined together.

83. a. $4.72\ \cancel{\text{g}} \times \dfrac{10^3\ \text{mg}}{\cancel{\text{g}}} = 4.72 \times 10^3\ \text{mg}$

b. $\dfrac{2.7 \times 10^3\ \cancel{\text{cm}}}{\cancel{\text{s}}} \times \dfrac{\cancel{\text{m}}}{10^2\ \cancel{\text{cm}}} \times \dfrac{\text{km}}{10^3\ \cancel{\text{m}}} \times \dfrac{60\ \cancel{\text{s}}}{\cancel{\text{min}}} \times \dfrac{60\ \cancel{\text{min}}}{\text{h}} = 97\ \text{km/h}$

c. $4.4\ \cancel{\text{mm}} \times \dfrac{\cancel{\text{m}}}{10^3\ \cancel{\text{mm}}} \times \dfrac{\text{dm}}{10^{-1}\ \cancel{\text{m}}} = 4.4 \times 10^{-2}\ \text{dm}$

84. a. iron(III) hydroxide
b. ammonium iodide
c. sodium carbonate
d. carbon tetrachloride

85. a. KNO_3
b. CuO
c. Mg_3N_2
d. AgF

Concept Challenge

86. From the statements the ratio of atoms is $C_{0.6}H_1O_{1.8}N_{0.6}$. Multiplying by five gives the empirical formula, $C_3H_5O_9N_3$. The molar mass of this compound is:

$\dfrac{1.00\ \text{g}}{0.00441\ \text{mol}} = 227\ \dfrac{\text{g}}{\text{mol}}$

carbon = 3 × 12 amu = 36 amu
hydrogen = 5 × 1 amu = 5 amu
oxygen = 9 × 16 amu = 144 amu
nitrogen = 3 × 14 amu = 42 amu
total = 227 amu

Because this is the mass of the empirical formula, the molecular formula is $C_3H_5O_9N_3$.

87. $2.00 \times 10^{24}\ \text{atoms Ni} \times \dfrac{1\ \text{mol Ni}}{6.02 \times 10^{23}\ \text{atoms Ni}} \times \dfrac{57.8\ \text{g Ni}}{1\ \text{mol Ni}} = 1.95 \times 10^2\ \text{g Ni}$

$\text{Volume of Ni} = \dfrac{1.95 \times 10^2\ \text{g Ni}}{8.91\ \text{g/cm}^3} = 21.9\ \text{cm}^3$

88. $75.0\ \cancel{\text{g air}} \times \dfrac{1\ \cancel{\text{L air}}}{1.19\ \cancel{\text{g air}}} \times \dfrac{20.95\ \cancel{\text{L O}_2}}{100\ \cancel{\text{L air}}} \times \dfrac{1\ \cancel{\text{mol}}}{22.4\ \cancel{\text{L O}_2}} \times \dfrac{6.02 \times 10^{23}\ \text{molecules O}_2}{1\ \cancel{\text{mol}}}$

$= 3.54 \times 10^{23}\ \text{molecules O}_2$

89. a.

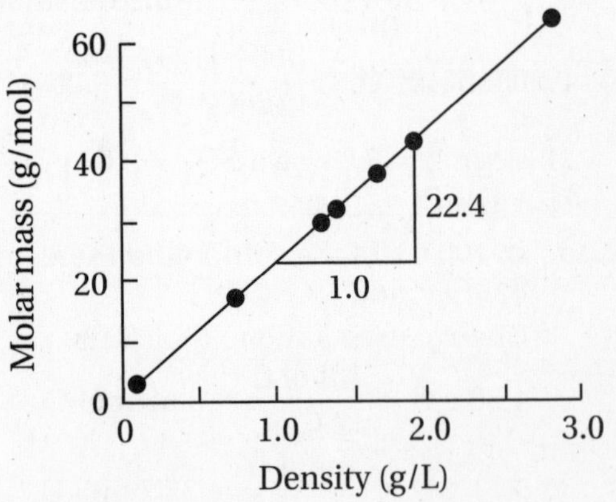

b. The slope is the molar volume, 22.4 L/mol.

c. molar mass = density × molar volume
$= 1.10\ \text{g}/\cancel{\text{L}} \times 22.4\ \cancel{\text{L}}/\text{mol}$
$= 24.6\ \text{g/mol}$

d. 2.5 g/L

90. First find the kilograms of gold in the ocean.

$$4 \times 10^{20}\ \cancel{kg}\ \text{seawater} \times \frac{10^3\ \cancel{g}}{1\ \cancel{kg}} \times \frac{1\ \cancel{cm^3}}{1\ \cancel{g}} \times \frac{1\ \cancel{m^3}}{(10^2\ \cancel{cm})^3} \times \frac{6 \times 10^{-6}\ \cancel{g}\ \text{Au}}{1\ \cancel{m^3}\ \text{seawater}} \times \frac{1\ \text{kg}}{10^3\ \cancel{g}}$$
$$= 2.4 \times 10^9\ \text{kg Au}$$

Now calculate the liters of water needed to yield 1 kg of gold.

$$1\ \cancel{\text{kg Au}} \times \frac{10^3\ \cancel{g}}{1\ \cancel{kg}} \times \frac{1\ \cancel{m^3}\ \text{seawater}}{1 \times 10^{-6}\ \cancel{\text{g Au}}} \times \frac{10^6\ \cancel{cm^3}}{1\ \cancel{m^3}} \times \frac{1\ \text{L}}{10^3\ \cancel{cm^3}} = 2 \times 10^{11}\ \text{L seawater}$$

The recovery operation is not feasible.

91. The gram formula mass of sodium chloride is 58.44 g/mol. Calculate the volume of a mole of NaCl.

$$58.44\ \frac{\cancel{g}}{\text{mol}} \times \frac{1\ \text{cm}^3}{2.165\ \cancel{g}} = 26.99\ \text{cm}^3/\text{mol}$$

Find the length of a side.

$$\sqrt[3]{26.99\ \text{cm}^3} = 2.999\ \text{cm}$$

Find the number of ions per side.

$$2.999\ \cancel{cm} \times \frac{1\ \text{ion}}{2.819 \times 10^{-8}\ \cancel{cm}} = 1.064 \times 10^8\ \text{ions}$$

Calculate the total number of ions.

$(1.064 \times 10^8\ \text{ions})^3 = 1.205 \times 10^{24}$ ions.

Divide by two to get the number of formula units per mole.

$$1.205 \times 10^{24}\ \text{ions} \times \frac{1\ \text{formula unit}}{2\ \text{ions}} = 6.025 \times 10^{23}\ \text{formula units}$$

Standardized Test Prep

1. (a)

$$3\ \cancel{\text{mol N}} \times \frac{14.0\ \text{g N}}{1\ \cancel{\text{mol N}}} = 42.0\ \text{g N}$$
$$12\ \cancel{\text{mol H}} \times \frac{1.0\ \text{g H}}{1\ \cancel{\text{mol H}}} = 12.0\ \text{g H}$$
$$1\ \cancel{\text{mol P}} \times \frac{31.0\ \text{g P}}{1\ \cancel{\text{mol P}}} = 31.0\ \text{g P}$$
$$4\ \cancel{\text{mol O}} \times \frac{16.0\ \text{g O}}{1\ \cancel{\text{mol O}}} = 64.0\ \text{g O}$$

molar mass of $(NH_4)_3PO_4$ = 149.0 g

2. (a)
If students are confused about the difference between a molecular formula and an empirical formula, they may choose alternative (b).

3. (b)
There are 6 hydrogen atoms per molecule and 36 hydrogen atoms in 6 molecules.

4. (c)
Students who choose alternative (e) probably have not considered that the nitrogen molecule is diatomic.

5. (a)
Students should consider the ratio of nitrogen atoms to oxygen atoms in each compound: (a) 2 : 1; (b) 1 : 1; (c) 1 : 2; (d) 1 : 1.5; (e) 1 : 1. The ratios show that N_2O has the highest percent of nitrogen.

6. (c)
The number of carbon atoms must be multiplied by the ratio of hydrogen atoms to carbon atoms, 1.66.

7. (E)

8. (A)

9. (B)

10. (D)

11. (C)

12. C_3H_8O, 60.0 g/mol

$$3\ \cancel{\text{mol C}} \times \frac{12.0\ \text{g C}}{1\ \cancel{\text{mol C}}} = 36.0\ \text{g C}$$
$$8\ \cancel{\text{mol H}} \times \frac{1.0\ \text{g H}}{1\ \cancel{\text{mol H}}} = 8.0\ \text{g H}$$
$$1\ \cancel{\text{mol O}} \times \frac{16.0\ \text{g O}}{1\ \cancel{\text{mol O}}} = 16.0\ \text{g O}$$

molar mass of C_3H_8O = 60.0 g

13. $C_2H_5NO_2$, 75.0 g/mol

$$2\ \cancel{\text{mol C}} \times \frac{12.0\ \text{g C}}{1\ \cancel{\text{mol C}}} = 24.0\ \text{g C}$$
$$5\ \cancel{\text{mol H}} \times \frac{1.0\ \text{g H}}{1\ \cancel{\text{mol H}}} = 5.0\ \text{g H}$$
$$1\ \cancel{\text{mol N}} \times \frac{14.0\ \text{g N}}{1\ \cancel{\text{mol N}}} = 14.0\ \text{g N}$$
$$2\ \cancel{\text{mol O}} \times \frac{16.0\ \text{g O}}{1\ \cancel{\text{mol O}}} = 32.0\ \text{g O}$$

molar mass of $C_2H_5NO_2$ = 75.0 g

14. $C_3H_6O_2$, 74.0 g/mol

$$3\ \cancel{\text{mol C}} \times \frac{12.0\ \text{g C}}{1\ \cancel{\text{mol C}}} = 36.0\ \text{g C}$$
$$6\ \cancel{\text{mol H}} \times \frac{1.0\ \text{g H}}{1\ \cancel{\text{mol H}}} = 6.0\ \text{g H}$$
$$2\ \cancel{\text{mol O}} \times \frac{16.0\ \text{g O}}{1\ \cancel{\text{mol O}}} = 32.0\ \text{g O}$$

molar mass of $C_3H_6O_2$ = 74.0 g

8 CHEMICAL REACTIONS

Concept Practice

32. a. reactants: sodium and water; products: hydrogen and sodium hydroxide
    b. reactants: carbon dioxide and water; products: oxygen and glucose
33. Dalton said that the atoms of reactants are rearranged to form new substances as products.
34. The arrow separates the reactants from the products and indicates a reaction that progresses in a forward direction. A plus sign separates individual reactants and individual products from one another.
35. a. Gaseous ammonia and oxygen react in the presence of platinum to produce nitrogen monoxide gas and water vapor.
    b. Aqueous solutions of sulfuric acid and barium chloride are mixed to produce a precipitate of barium sulfate and aqueous hydrochloric acid.
    c. The gas dinitrogen trioxide reacts with water to produce an aqueous solution of nitrous acid.
36. A catalyst speeds up a chemical reaction. It is not used up in a reaction.
37. a. $C + 2F + 2G \rightarrow CF_2G_2$
    b. $F + 3W + S + 2P \rightarrow FW_3SP_2$
38. It is incorrect because a formula is a unique identifier of a substance. A different formula would indicate a different substance, not the one that is taking part in the reaction you are trying to balance.
39. a. $2PbO_2 \rightarrow 2PbO + O_2$
    b. $2Fe(OH)_3 \rightarrow Fe_2O_3 + 3H_2O$
    c. $(NH_4)_2CO_3 \rightarrow 2NH_3 + H_2O + CO_2$
    d. $2NaCl + H_2SO_4 \rightarrow Na_2SO_4 + 2HCl$
    e. $4H_2 + Fe_3O_4 \rightarrow 3Fe + 4H_2O$
    f. $2Al + 3CuSO_4 \rightarrow Al_2(SO_4)_3 + 3Cu$
40. It helps in predicting products of reactions.
41. Use ionic charges to write an electrically neutral formula.
42. Every combination reaction has a single product.
43. a. $2Mg + O_2 \rightarrow 2MgO$
    b. $4P + 5O_2 \rightarrow 2P_2O_5$
    c. $Ca + S \rightarrow CaS$
    d. $2Fe + O_2 \rightarrow 2FeO$
    e. $N_2O_5 + H_2O \rightarrow 2HNO_3$
44. a. $2Ag_2O \xrightarrow{\Delta} 4Ag + O_2$
    b. $NiCO_3 \xrightarrow{\Delta} NiO + CO_2$
    c. $NH_4NO_3 \xrightarrow{\Delta} N_2O + 2H_2O$
45. Every decomposition reaction has a single reactant.
46. a. sodium displaces iron
    b. copper displaces silver
    c. zinc displaces hydrogen
47. a. no reaction
    b. $Zn + 2AgNO_3 \rightarrow Zn(NO_3)_2 + 2Ag$
    c. $2Al + 3H_2SO_4 \rightarrow Al_2(SO_4)_3 + 3H_2$
    d. no reaction
    e. $2Al + 3CuSO_4 \rightarrow Al_2(SO_4)_3 + 3Cu$
48. a. $2HCl + Ca(OH)_2 \rightarrow CaCl_2 + 2H_2O$
    b. $3Ag_2SO_4 + 2AlCl_3 \rightarrow 6AgCl + Al_2(SO_4)_3$
    c. $H_2C_2O_4 + 2KOH \rightarrow K_2C_2O_4 + 2H_2O$
    d. $CdBr_2 + Na_2S \rightarrow CdS + 2NaBr$
49. All combustion reactions require oxygen.
50. a. $C_4H_8 + 6O_2 \rightarrow 4CO_2 + 4H_2O$
    b. $2C_8H_{18} + 25O_2 \rightarrow 16CO_2 + 18H_2O$
    c. $2C_3H_8O_3 + 7O_2 \rightarrow 6CO_2 + 8H_2O$
    d. $C_3H_6O + 4O_2 \rightarrow 3CO_2 + 3H_2O$
51. a. $3Hf + 2N_2 \rightarrow Hf_3N_4$; combination
    b. $Mg + H_2SO_4 \rightarrow MgSO_4 + H_2$; single-replacement
    c. $2C_2H_6 + 7O_2 \rightarrow 4CO_2 + 6H_2O$; combustion
    d. $Pb(NO_3)_2 + 2NaI \rightarrow PbI_2 + 2NaNO_3$; double-replacement
    e. $3Fe + 2O_2 \rightarrow Fe_3O_4$; combination
    f. $2Pb(NO_3)_2 \rightarrow 2PbO + 4NO_2 + O_2$; decomposition
    g. $Hg(NO_3)_2 + 2NH_4SCN \rightarrow Hg(SCN)_2 + 2NH_4NO_3$; double-replacement
    h. $(NH_4)_2SO_4 + 2NaOH \rightarrow 2NH_3 + 2H_2O + Na_2SO_4$; double-replacement then decomposition
52. a. $2Al(s) + 6H^+(aq) \rightarrow 2Al^{3+}(aq) + 3H_2(g)$
    b. $H^+(aq) + OH^-(aq) \rightarrow H_2O(l)$
    c. no reaction
53. A spectator ion is an ion that does not directly participate in a reaction.

Concept Mastery

54. a. $Cl_2 + 2NaI \rightarrow 2NaCl + I_2$
    b. $2NH_3 \rightarrow N_2 + 3H_2$
    c. $4Na + O_2 \rightarrow 2Na_2O$
    d. $Mg + H_2SO_4 \rightarrow MgSO_4 + H_2$
    e. $MgCl_2 + Ca(OH)_2 \rightarrow Mg(OH)_2 + CaCl_2$

f. $H_2 + Cl_2 \rightarrow 2HCl$

55. a. $Cl_2(g) + 2KI(aq) \rightarrow I_2(s) + 2KCl(aq)$
b. $2Fe(s) + 6HCl(aq) \rightarrow 2FeCl_3(aq) + 3H_2(g)$
c. $P_4O_{10}(s) + 6H_2O(l) \rightarrow 4H_3PO_4(aq)$
d. $2Ag_2O(s) \xrightarrow{\Delta} 4Ag(s) + O_2(g)$
e. $I_2(s) + 3Cl_2(g) \rightarrow 2ICl_3(s)$
f. $4HgS(s) + 4CaO(s) \xrightarrow{\Delta} 4Hg(l) + 3CaS(s) + CaSO_4(s)$

56. a. $ZnS(aq) + H_2SO_4(aq) \rightarrow H_2S(g) + ZnSO_4(aq)$
b. $NaOH(aq) + HNO_3(aq) \rightarrow H_2O(l) + NaNO_3(aq)$
c. $2KF(aq) + Ca(NO_3)_2(aq) \rightarrow CaF_2(s) + 2KNO_3(aq)$

57. a. $Na_2O(s) + H_2O(l) \rightarrow 2NaOH(aq)$
b. $H_2(g) + Br_2(g) \rightarrow 2HBr(g)$
c. $Cl_2O_7(l) + H_2O(l) \rightarrow 2HClO_4(aq)$

58. a. $Fe(s) + H_2SO_4(aq) \rightarrow FeSO_4(aq) + H_2(g)$
b. no reaction
c. $Br_2(l) + BaI_2(aq) \rightarrow BaBr_2(aq) + I_2(s)$

59. a. Tube B contains the sodium metal. Sodium will displace hydrogen from water; magnesium will not.
b. $2Na(s) + 2H_2O(l) \rightarrow 2NaOH(aq) + H_2(g)$
A single replacement reaction is occurring in tube A.

60. a. $2C_8H_{18} + 25O_2 \rightarrow 16CO_2 + 18H_2O$
b. $C_6H_{12}O_6 + 6O_2 \rightarrow 6CO_2 + 6H_2O$
c. $HC_2H_3O_2 + 2O_2 \rightarrow 2CO_2 + 2H_2O$

61. a. $2Al_2O_3 \xrightarrow{\text{energy}} 4Al + 3O_2$
b. $Sn(OH)_4 \xrightarrow{\Delta} SnO_2 + 2H_2O$
c. $Ag_2CO_3 \xrightarrow{\Delta} Ag_2O + CO_2$

62. a. $H^+(aq) + OH^-(aq) \rightarrow H_2O(l)$
b. $Cd^{2+}(aq) + S^{2-}(aq) \rightarrow CdS(s)$
c. $3OH^-(aq) + Fe^{3+}(aq) \rightarrow Fe(OH)_3(s)$

Critical Thinking

63. a. 4
b. 2
c. 1

64. Smoking is not permitted near an oxygen source because a fire will burn faster in an area of high oxygen concentration. However, if a match were struck in a room full of oxygen and isolated from combustible material, it would only burn more vigorously.

65. a. $C_5H_{12} + 8O_2 \rightarrow 5CO_2 + 6H_2O$
$C_9H_{20} + 14O_2 \rightarrow 9CO_2 + 10H_2O$
b. $2C_{12}H_{26} + 37O_2 \rightarrow 24CO_2 + 26H_2O$
$C_{17}H_{36} + 26O_2 \rightarrow 17CO_2 + 18H_2O$
c. $n = CO_2$; $(n + 1) = H_2O$

Cumulative Review

66. a. $54.0\ \cancel{L\ NO_2} \times \dfrac{1\ mol\ NO_2}{22.4\ \cancel{L\ NO_2}} = 2.41\ mol\ NO_2$

b. $1.68\ \cancel{g\ Mg^{2+}} \times \dfrac{1\ mol\ Mg^{2+}}{24.3\ \cancel{g\ Mg^{2+}}}$
$= 6.91 \times 10^{-2}\ mol\ Mg^{2+}$

c. $69.6\ \cancel{g\ NaOCl} \times \dfrac{1\ mol\ NaOCl}{74.5\ \cancel{g\ NaOCl}}$
$= 0.934\ mol\ NaOCl$

d. $4.27 \times 10^{24}\ \cancel{molecules\ CO} \times \dfrac{1\ mol\ CO}{6.02 \times 10^{23}\ \cancel{molecules\ CO}}$
$= 7.09\ mol\ CO$

67. $2.20\ \cancel{mol\ Al} \times \dfrac{27.0\ \cancel{g\ Al}}{1\ \cancel{mol\ Al}} \times \dfrac{1\ cm^3\ Al}{2.70\ \cancel{g\ Al}}$
$= 22.0\ cm^3\ Al$
The volume occupied by both aluminum and gold is the same.

$22.0\ \cancel{cm^3\ Au} \times \dfrac{19.3\ g\ Au}{1\ \cancel{cm^3\ Au}} = 425\ g\ Au$

68. Find the empirical formula.

$49.5\ \cancel{g\ C} \times \dfrac{1\ mol\ C}{12.0\ \cancel{g\ C}} = 4.13\ mol\ C$

$5.20\ \cancel{g\ H} \times \dfrac{1\ mol\ H}{1.01\ \cancel{g\ H}} = 5.15\ mol\ H$

$16.5\ \cancel{g\ O} \times \dfrac{1\ mol\ O}{16.0\ \cancel{g\ O}} = 1.03\ mol\ O$

$28.9\ \cancel{g\ N} \times \dfrac{1\ mol\ N}{14.0\ \cancel{g\ N}} = 2.06\ mol\ N$

Divided by 1.03. Empirical formula $= C_4H_5ON_2$. The mass of the empirical formula is 97 g.

$\dfrac{gfm}{efm} = \dfrac{194.1\ \cancel{g}}{97\ \cancel{g}} = 2$

The molecular formula is $C_8H_{10}O_2N_4$.

69. a.

$CaCl_2$ (g)	$CaCl_2$ (mol)	H_2O (g)	H_2O (mol)
17.3	0.156	5.62	0.312
48.8	0.439	15.8	0.878
124	1.12	40.3	2.24
337	3.03	109	6.06

b.

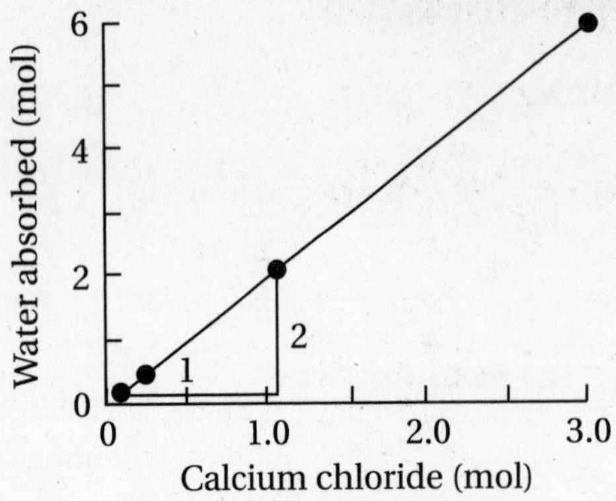

$$\text{slope} = \frac{\Delta \text{ water absorbed (mol)}}{\Delta \text{ calcium chloride (mol)}} = \frac{2 \text{ mol } H_2O}{1 \text{ mol } CaCl_2}$$

c. The slope of the line is 2 mol H_2O/1 mol $CaCl_2$. Two molecules of water are absorbed by each formula unit of $CaCl_2$.

Concept Challenge

70. a. $3NaI + H_3PO_4 \rightarrow 3HI + Na_3PO_4$; double-replacement

b. $K_2O + H_2O \rightarrow 2KOH$; combination

c. $2H_2SO_4 \xrightarrow{\Delta} 2H_2O + O_2 + 2SO_2$; decomposition

d. $2Al + 3H_2SO_4 \rightarrow 3H_2 + Al_2(SO_4)_3$; single-replacement

e. $C_5H_{12} + 8O_2 \rightarrow 5CO_2 + 6H_2O$; combustion

71. a. Calculate the mass of a mole of protons.

$$\frac{6.02 \times 10^{23} \text{ protons}}{1 \text{ mol protons}} \times \frac{1.67 \times 10^{-24} \text{ g}}{1 \text{ proton}} = \frac{1.01 \text{ g}}{\text{mol protons}}$$

Calculate the mass of a mole of electrons.

$$\frac{6.02 \times 10^{23} \text{ electrons}}{1 \text{ mol electrons}} \times \frac{9.11 \times 10^{-28} \text{ g}}{1 \text{ electron}} = \frac{5.48 \times 10^{-4} \text{ g}}{\text{mol electrons}}$$

b. Calculate the ratio.

$$\frac{1.67 \times 10^{-24} \text{ g/proton}}{9.11 \times 10^{-28} \text{ g/electron}} = 1.83 \times 10^{3} \text{ electrons/proton}$$

Standardized Test Prep

1. (b)
2. (e)
3. (c)
4. (d)
5. (b)
6. Students need to identify substance Q, which reacts with P to form a precipitate and R to form a gas. Q is potassium carbonate, P is calcium nitrate, and R is hydrochloric acid.
7. $Ca^{2+}(aq) + CO_3^{2-}(aq) \rightarrow CaCO_3(s)$
8. $2K^+(aq) + CO_3^{2-}(aq) + 2H^+(aq) + 2Cl^-(aq) \rightarrow 2K^+(aq) + 2Cl^-(aq) + H_2O(l) + CO_2(g)$
9. (c) represents the reactants; (b) represents the products
10. decomposition reaction
11. NH_3, CO_2, and H_2O
12. $(NH_4)_2CO_3(s) \rightarrow 2NH_3(g) + CO_2(g) + H_2O(g)$
13. to react with and identify the carbon dioxide

9 STOICHIOMETRY

Concept Practice

33. a. Two formula units $KClO_3$ decompose to form 2 formula units KCl and 3 molecules O_2.

b. Four molecules NH_3 react with 6 molecules NO to form 5 molecules N_2 and 6 molecules H_2O.

c. Four atoms K react with 1 molecule O_2 to form 2 formula units K_2O.

34. a. Two mol $KClO_3$ decompose to form 2 mol KCl and 3 mol O_2.

b. Four mol NH_3 react with 6 mol NO to form 5 mol N_2 and 6 mol H_2O.

c. Four mol K react with 1 mol O_2 to form 2 mol K_2O.

35. a. $2\text{ mol }KClO_3 \rightarrow 2\text{ mol KCl} + 3\text{ mol }O_2$

$2 \times 122.6\text{ g} = (2 \times 74.6\text{ g}) + (3 \times 32.0\text{ g})$

$245.2\text{ g} = 245.2\text{ g}$

b. $4\text{ mol }NH_3 + 6\text{ mol NO} \rightarrow 5\text{ mol }N_2 + 6\text{ mol }H_2O$

$(4 \times 17.0\text{ g}) + (6 \times 30.0\text{ g}) = (5 \times 28.0\text{ g}) + (6 \times 18.0\text{ g})$

$68.0\text{ g} + 180.0\text{ g} = 140.0\text{ g} + 108\text{ g}$

$248.0\text{ g} = 248.0\text{ g}$

c. $4\text{ mol K} + 1\text{ mol }O_2 \rightarrow 2\text{ mol }K_2O$

$(4 \times 39.1\text{ g}) + (1 \times 32.0\text{ g}) = 2 \times 94.2\text{ g}$

$156.4\text{ g} + 32.0\text{ g} = 188.4\text{ g}$

$188.4\text{ g} = 188.4\text{ g}$

All the reactions obey the law of conservation of mass.

36. Answers will vary but should include the idea of writing a ratio using the coefficients of two substances from a balanced equation as the number of moles of each substance reacting or being formed.

37. a. $2.7\,\cancel{\text{mol C}} \times \frac{1\text{ mol }CS_2}{5\,\cancel{\text{mol C}}} = 0.54\text{ mol }CS_2$

b. $5.44\,\cancel{\text{mol }SO_2} \times \frac{5\text{ mol C}}{2\,\cancel{\text{mol }SO_2}} = 13.6\text{ mol C}$

c. $0.246\,\cancel{\text{mol }CS_2} \times \frac{4\text{ mol CO}}{1\,\cancel{\text{mol }CS_2}} = 0.984\text{ mol CO}$

d. $118\,\cancel{\text{mol }CS_2} \times \frac{2\text{ mol }SO_2}{1\,\cancel{\text{mol }CS_2}} = 236\text{ mol }SO_2$

38. a. $360\,\cancel{\text{g }CH_3OH} \times \frac{1\,\cancel{\text{mol }CH_3OH}}{32.0\,\cancel{\text{g }CH_3OH}} \times \frac{1\text{ mol CO}}{1\,\cancel{\text{mol }CH_3OH}} = 11.3\text{ mol CO}$

$360\,\cancel{\text{g }CH_3OH} \times \frac{1\text{ mol }CH_3OH}{32.0\,\cancel{\text{g }CH_3OH}} \times \frac{2\text{ mol }H_2}{1\,\cancel{\text{mol }CH_3OH}} = 22.5\text{ mol }H_2$

b. $4.0\,\cancel{\text{mol }CH_3OH} \times \frac{1\,\cancel{\text{mol CO}}}{1\,\cancel{\text{mol }CH_3OH}} \times \frac{28.0\text{ g CO}}{1\,\cancel{\text{mol CO}}} = 112.0\text{ g CO}$

$4.0\,\cancel{\text{mol }CH_3OH} \times \frac{2\,\cancel{\text{mol }H_2}}{1\,\cancel{\text{mol }CH_3OH}} \times \frac{2.0\text{ g }H_2}{1\,\cancel{\text{mol }H_2}} = 16.0\text{ g }H_2$

c. $2.85\,\cancel{\text{mol CO}} \times \frac{2\,\cancel{\text{mol }H_2}}{1\,\cancel{\text{mol CO}}} \times \frac{2.0\text{ g }H_2}{1\,\cancel{\text{mol }H_2}} = 11.4\text{ g }H_2$

39. a. $66.6\,\cancel{\text{g }NH_3} \times \frac{1\,\cancel{\text{mol }NH_3}}{17.0\,\cancel{\text{g }NH_3}} \times \frac{5\,\cancel{\text{mol }F_2}}{2\,\cancel{\text{mol }NH_3}} \times \frac{38.0\text{ g }F_2}{1\,\cancel{\text{mol }F_2}} = 372\text{ g }F_2$

b. $4.65\,\cancel{\text{g HF}} \times \frac{1\,\cancel{\text{mol HF}}}{20.0\,\cancel{\text{g HF}}} \times \frac{2\,\cancel{\text{mol }NH_3}}{6\,\cancel{\text{mol HF}}} \times \frac{17.0\text{ g }NH_3}{1\,\cancel{\text{mol }NH_3}} = 1.32\text{ g }NH_3$

c. $225\,\cancel{\text{g }F_2} \times \frac{1\,\cancel{\text{mol }F_2}}{38.0\,\cancel{\text{g }F_2}} \times \frac{1\,\cancel{\text{mol }N_2F_4}}{5\,\cancel{\text{mol }F_2}} \times \frac{104.0\text{ g }N_2F_4}{1\,\cancel{\text{mol }N_2F_4}} = 123\text{ g }N_2F_4$

40. The coefficients indicate the relative number of moles (or particles) of reactants and products.

41. a. $32.9\,\cancel{\text{g }Li_3N} \times \frac{1\,\cancel{\text{mol }Li_3N}}{34.7\,\cancel{\text{g }Li_3N}} \times \frac{3\,\cancel{\text{mol }H_2O}}{1\,\cancel{\text{mol }Li_3N}} \times \frac{18.0\text{ g }H_2O}{1\,\cancel{\text{mol }H_2O}} = 51.2\text{ g }H_2O$

b. $32.9\,\cancel{\text{g }Li_3N} \times \frac{1\,\cancel{\text{mol }Li_3N}}{34.7\,\cancel{\text{g }Li_3N}} \times \frac{1\,\cancel{\text{mol }NH_3}}{1\,\cancel{\text{mol }Li_3N}} \times \frac{6.02 \times 10^{23}\text{ molecules }NH_3}{1\,\cancel{\text{mol }NH_3}} = 5.71 \times 10^{23}\text{ molecules }NH_3$

c. $15.0\ \text{L NH}_3 \times \frac{1\ \text{mol NH}_3}{22.4\ \text{L NH}_3} \times \frac{1\ \text{mol Li}_3\text{N}}{1\ \text{mol NH}_3} \times \frac{34.7\ \text{g Li}_3\text{N}}{1\ \text{mol Li}_3\text{N}} = 23.2\ \text{g Li}_3\text{N}$

42. The amount of the limiting reagent determines the maximum amount of product that can be formed. The excess reagent is only partially consumed in the reaction.

43. To identify the limiting reagent, express quantities of reactants as moles; compare to the mole ratios from the balanced equation.

44. Compare the given number of moles of the second reactant with the number of moles of that reactant required.

a. $3.6\ \text{mol Al} \times \frac{3\ \text{mol Cl}_2}{2\ \text{mol Al}} = 5.4\ \text{mol Cl}_2$ (needed)

Cl_2 is the limiting reagent.

b. $6.4\ \text{mol H}_2 \times \frac{1\ \text{mol O}_2}{2\ \text{mol H}_2} = 3.2\ \text{mol O}_2$ (needed)

H_2 is the limiting reagent.

c. $1.52\ \text{mol H}_2\text{O} \times \frac{2\ \text{mol P}_2\text{O}_5}{6\ \text{mol H}_2\text{O}} = 0.507\ \text{mol P}_2\text{O}_5$ (needed)

P_2O_5 is the limiting reagent.

d. $14.5\ \text{mol P} \times \frac{5\ \text{mol O}_2}{4\ \text{mol P}} = 18.1\ \text{mol O}_2$ (needed)

O_2 is the limiting reagent.

45. a. $5.3\ \text{mol Cl}_2 \times \frac{2\ \text{mol AlCl}_3}{3\ \text{mol Cl}_2} = 3.5\ \text{mol AlCl}_3$

b. $6.4\ \text{mol H}_2 \times \frac{2\ \text{mol H}_2\text{O}}{2\ \text{mol H}_2} = 6.4\ \text{mol H}_2\text{O}$

c. $0.48\ \text{mol P}_2\text{O}_5 \times \frac{4\ \text{mol H}_3\text{PO}_4}{2\ \text{mol P}_2\text{O}_5} = 0.96\ \text{mol H}_3\text{PO}_4$

d. $18.0\ \text{mol O}_2 \times \frac{2\ \text{mol P}_2\text{O}_5}{5\ \text{mol O}_2} = 7.20\ \text{mol P}_2\text{O}_5$

46. a. $5.3\ \text{mol Cl}_2 \times \frac{2\ \text{mol Al}}{3\ \text{mol Cl}_2} = 3.5\ \text{mol Al}$ used

moles excess $= 3.6\ \text{mol Al} - 3.5\ \text{mol Al} = 0.1\ \text{mol Al}$

b. moles excess $= 3.4\ \text{mol O}_2 - 3.2\ \text{mol O}_2 = 0.2\ \text{mol O}_2$

c. $0.48\ \text{mol P}_2\text{O}_5 \times \frac{6\ \text{mol H}_2\text{O}}{2\ \text{mol P}_2\text{O}_5} = 1.44\ \text{mol H}_2\text{O}$ used

moles excess $= 1.52\ \text{mol P}_4\text{O}_{10} - 1.44\ \text{mol P}_4\text{O}_{10} = 0.08\ \text{mol H}_2\text{O}$

d. $18.0\ \text{mol O}_2 \times \frac{4\ \text{mol P}}{5\ \text{mol O}_2} = 14.4\ \text{mol P}$ used

moles excess $= 14.5\ \text{mol P} - 14.4\ \text{mol P} = 0.1\ \text{mol P}$

47. $15.0\ \text{g Sb}_2\text{S}_3 \times \frac{1\ \text{mol Sb}_2\text{S}_3}{339.9\ \text{g Sb}_2\text{S}_3} \times \frac{2\ \text{mol Sb}}{1\ \text{mol Sb}_2\text{S}_3} \times \frac{121.8\ \text{g Sb}}{1\ \text{mol Sb}} = 10.8\ \text{g Sb}$

percent yield $= \frac{9.84\ \text{g}}{10.8\ \text{g}} \times 100 = 91.1\%$

48. a. Initially, the amount of NaCl formed increases as the amount of Na used increases. For this part of the curve sodium is the limiting reagent. Beyond a mass of about 2.5 g of Na, the amount of product formed remains constant because chlorine is now the limiting reagent.

b. Chlorine becomes the limiting reagent when the mass of sodium exceeds 2.5 g. This corresponds to a mass of:

$2.5\ \text{g Na} \times \frac{1\ \text{mol Na}}{23.0\ \text{g Na}} \times \frac{1\ \text{mol Cl}_2}{2\ \text{mol Na}} \times \frac{70.9\ \text{g Cl}_2}{1\ \text{mol Cl}_2} = 3.9\ \text{g Cl}_2$

$0.773\ \text{g H}_2\text{O} \times \frac{1\ \text{mol H}_2\text{O}}{18.0\ \text{g H}_2\text{O}} \times \frac{3\ \text{mol CO}_2}{3\ \text{mol H}_2\text{O}} \times \frac{44.0\ \text{g CO}_2}{1\ \text{mol CO}_2} = 1.89\ \text{g CO}_2$

49. Percent yield is a measure of the "efficiency" of a reaction; a ratio of the actual yield over the theoretical yield expressed as a percent.

50. 50.0% yield; 0.500 mol; 0.0500 mol; 20.0% yield

Concept Mastery

51. $3.74\ \text{g Ca}_3(\text{PO}_4)_2 \times \frac{1\ \text{mol Ca}_3(\text{PO}_4)_2}{310.3\ \text{g Ca}_3(\text{PO}_4)_2} \times \frac{2\ \text{mol H}_3\text{PO}_4}{1\ \text{mol Ca}_3(\text{PO}_4)_2} \times \frac{98.0\ \text{g H}_3\text{PO}_4}{1\ \text{mol H}_3\text{PO}_4} = 2.36\ \text{g H}_3\text{PO}_4$

52. **a.** $$1.49\ \cancel{g\ HNO_3} \times \frac{1\ \cancel{mol\ HNO_3}}{63.0\ \cancel{g\ HNO_3}} \times \frac{4\ \cancel{mol\ Zn}}{10\ \cancel{mol\ HNO_3}} \times \frac{6.02 \times 10^{23}\ \text{atoms Zn}}{1\ \cancel{mol\ Zn}} = 5.70 \times 10^{21}\ \text{atoms Zn}$$

b. $$29.1\ \cancel{g\ NH_4NO_3} \times \frac{1\ \cancel{mol\ NH_4NO_3}}{80.0\ \cancel{g\ NH_4NO_3}} \times \frac{4\ \cancel{mol\ Zn}}{1\ \cancel{mol\ NH_4NO_3}} \times \frac{65.4\ \text{g Zn}}{1\ \cancel{mol\ Zn}} = 95.2\ \text{g Zn}$$

53. **a.** Find the number of moles of each reactant.

$$1.0\ \cancel{kg\ N_2H_4} \times \frac{10^3\ \cancel{g\ N_2H_4}}{1\ \cancel{kg\ N_2H_4}} \times \frac{1\ \text{mol}\ N_2H_4}{32.0\ \cancel{g\ N_2H_4}} = 31\ \text{mol}\ N_2H_4$$

$$1.0\ \cancel{kg\ O_2} \times \frac{10^3\ \cancel{g\ O_2}}{1\ \cancel{kg\ O_2}} \times \frac{1\ \text{mol}\ O_2}{32.0\ \cancel{g\ O_2}} = 31\ \text{mol}\ O_2$$

Reactants are in the correct mole ratio. Either can be used to find the liters of N_2.

$$31\ \cancel{mol\ N_2H_4} \times \frac{1\ \cancel{mol\ N_2}}{1\ \cancel{mol\ N_2H_4}} \times \frac{22.4\ \text{L}\ N_2}{1\ \cancel{mol\ N_2}} = 6.9 \times 10^2\ \text{L}\ N_2$$

b. Because the reactants are in the correct mole ratio, there is no reagent in excess. Both reactants are completely used up in the reaction.

54. **a.** $$50.0\ \cancel{g\ SiO_2} \times \frac{1\ \cancel{mol\ SiO_2}}{60.08\ \cancel{g\ SiO_2}} \times \frac{1\ \cancel{mol\ SiC}}{1\ \cancel{mol\ SiO_2}} \times \frac{40.1\ \text{g SiC}}{1\ \cancel{mol\ SiC}} = 33.4\ \text{g SiC}$$

$$\text{Percent Yield} = \frac{32.2\ \text{g}}{33.4\ \text{g}} \times 100 = 96.4\%$$

b. $$32.2\ \cancel{g\ SiC} \times \frac{1\ \cancel{mol\ SiC}}{40.1\ \cancel{g\ SiC}} \times \frac{2\ \cancel{mol\ CO}}{1\ \cancel{mol\ SiC}} \times \frac{28.0\ \text{g CO}}{1\ \cancel{mol\ CO}} = 45.0\ \text{g CO}$$

55. Assuming 100% yield, calculate the theoretical yield.

$$5.24\ \cancel{kg\ SO_2} \times \frac{10^3\ \cancel{g\ SO_2}}{1\ \cancel{kg\ SO_2}} \times \frac{1\ \cancel{mol\ SO_2}}{64.1\ \cancel{g\ SO_2}} \times \frac{2\ \cancel{mol\ CaSO_4}}{2\ \cancel{mol\ SO_2}} \times \frac{136.2\ \cancel{g\ CaSO_4}}{1\ \cancel{mol\ CaSO_4}} \times \frac{1\ \text{kg}\ CaSO_4}{10^3\ \cancel{g\ CaSO_4}} = 11.1\ \text{kg}\ CaSO_4$$

$$\text{Actual yield} = 96.8\% \times 11.1\ \text{kg}\ CaSO_4 = 10.7\ \text{kg}\ CaSO_4$$

56. $$228\ \cancel{g\ NH_4NO_3} \times \frac{1\ \cancel{mol\ NH_4NO_3}}{80.0\ \cancel{g\ NH_4NO_3}} \times \frac{7\ \cancel{mol\ \text{“gas”}}}{2\ \cancel{mol\ NH_4NO_3}} \times \frac{22.4\ \text{L “gas”}}{1\ \cancel{mol\ \text{“gas”}}} = 223\ \text{L “gas”}$$

Critical Thinking

57. **a.** 2 **b.** 4

58. The percent yield is 115%; such a yield could be attributed to experimenter error, to unreacted starting material, or to outside materials contaminating the product.

59. Yes; a net ionic equation is balanced and thus obeys the law of conservation of mass.

60. **a.** $$29\cancel{EW_2P_6S_3} \times \frac{1\ F}{1\ \cancel{EW_2P_6S_3}} = 29\ \text{F (frames)}$$

b. $$29\cancel{EW_2P_6S_3} \times \frac{2\ W}{1\ \cancel{EW_2P_6S_3}} = 58\ \text{W (wheels)}$$

c. $$29\cancel{EW_2P_6S_3} \times \frac{6\ P}{1\ \cancel{EW_2P_6S_3}} = 174\ \text{P (pedals)}$$

d. $$29\cancel{EW_2P_6S_3} \times \frac{3\ S}{1\ \cancel{EW_3P_6S_3}} = 87\ \text{S (seats)}$$

Cumulative Review

61. **a.** $2Pb(NO_3)_2 \xrightarrow{\Delta} 2PbO + 4NO_2 + O_2$
b. $2C_3H_7OH + 9O_2 \rightarrow 6CO_2 + 8H_2O$
c. $2Al + 3FeO \rightarrow 3Fe + Al_2O_3$

62. 3 mol Be = 3 × 9.0 g = 27.0 g
2 mol Al = 2 × 27.0 g = 54.0 g
6 mol Si = 6 × 28.1 g = 168.6 g
18 mol O = 18 × 16.0 g = 288.0 g

537.6 g = 1 mol

$$147\ \cancel{g\ Be_3Al_2Si_6O_{18}} \times \frac{27.0\ \text{g Be}}{537.6\ \cancel{g\ Be_3Al_2Si_6O_{18}}} = 7.38\ \text{g Be}$$

63. **a.** $Ba(NO_3)_2(aq) + Na_2SO_4(aq) \rightarrow BaSO_4(s) + 2NaNO_3(aq)$
b. $AlCl_3(aq) + 3AqNO_3(aq) \rightarrow 3\ AgCl(s) + 3Al(NO_3)_3(aq)$
c. $H_2SO_4(aq) + Mg(OH)_2(aq) \rightarrow MgSO_4(aq) + 2H_2O(l)$

64. **a.** $Ba^{2+}(aq) + SO_4^{\ 2-} \rightarrow BaSO_4(s)$
b. $Ag^+(aq) + Cl^-(aq) \rightarrow AgCl(s)$
c. $H^+(aq) + OH^-(aq) \rightarrow H_2O(l)$

65. **a.** sodium ion and nitrate ion
b. aluminum ion and nitrate ion
c. magnesium ion and sulfate ion

66. **a.** 22, 22, 25 **b.** 50, 50, 70 **c.** 8, 8, 10 **d.** 12, 12, 14

67. $$1 \text{ molecule } C_6H_6 \times \frac{1 \text{ mol } C_6H_6}{6.02 \times 10^{23} \text{ molecules } C_6H_6} \times \frac{78.0 \text{ g } C_6H_6}{1 \text{ mol } C_6H_6} = 1.30 \times 10^{-22} \text{ g } C_6H_6$$

68. **a.** $Al_2(CO_3)_3$ **b.** SiO_2 **c.** K_2S **d.** $MnCrO_4$ **e.** NaBr

69. Find the empirical formula.

$$71.1 \text{ g O} \times \frac{1 \text{ mol O}}{16.0 \text{ g O}} = 4.44 \text{ mol O}$$

$$26.7 \text{ g C} \times \frac{1 \text{ mol C}}{12.0 \text{ g C}} = 2.23 \text{ mol C}$$

$$2.22 \text{ g H} \times \frac{1 \text{ mol H}}{1.00 \text{ g H}} = 2.22 \text{ mol H}$$

Divide by 2.22. Empirical formula is CHO_2. The mass of the empirical formula is 45 g. The gram molecular mass is 90 g; therefore, the molecular formula is $C_2H_2O_4$.

Concept Challenge

70. Write a balanced equation.
$2C_8H_{18} + 25O_2 \rightarrow 16CO_2 + 18H_2O$

$$1250 \text{ km} \times \frac{1 \text{ L gasoline}}{9.2 \text{ km}} \times \frac{10^3 \text{ mL gasoline}}{1 \text{ L gasoline}}$$

$$\times \frac{0.69 \text{ g gasoline}}{1 \text{ mL gasoline}} \times \frac{1 \text{ g } C_8H_{18}}{1 \text{ g gasoline}}$$

$$\times \frac{1 \text{ mol } C_8H_{18}}{114 \text{ g } C_8H_{18}} \times \frac{25 \text{ mol } O_2}{2 \text{ mol } C_8H_{18}}$$

$$\times \frac{22.4 \text{ L } O_2}{1 \text{ mol } O_2} \times \frac{1 \text{ L air}}{0.21 \text{ L } O_2} = 1.1 \times 10^6 \text{ L air}$$

71. Write a balanced equation.
$C_6H_{12}O_6 \rightarrow 2C_2H_5OH + 2CO_2$

$$\times 1.0 \times 10^3 \text{ kg } C_6H_{12}O_6 \times \frac{10^3 \text{ g } C_6H_{12}O_6}{1 \text{ kg } C_6H_{12}O_6}$$

$$\times \frac{1 \text{ mol } C_6H_{12}O_6}{180.0 \text{ g } C_6H_{12}O_6} \times \frac{2 \text{ mol } C_2H_5OH}{1 \text{ mol } C_6H_{12}O_6}$$

$$\times \frac{46.0 \text{ g } C_2H_5OH}{1 \text{ mol } C_2H_5OH} \times \frac{1 \text{ kg } C_2H_5OH}{10^3 \text{ g } C_2H_5OH}$$

$$\times \frac{5 \text{ h}}{8 \text{ kg } C_2H_5OH} \times \frac{1 \text{ day}}{24 \text{ h}} = 13 \text{ days}$$

72. $$225 \text{ L } CO_2 \times \frac{1 \text{ mol } CO_2}{22.4 \text{ L } CO_2} \times \frac{44.0 \text{ g } CO_2}{1 \text{ mol } CO_2} = 442 \text{ g } CO_2$$

$$\text{density} = \frac{442 \text{ g}}{225 \text{ L}} = 1.96 \text{ g/L}$$

73. Calculate the amount of $CaCO_3$ needed to produce 81.8 g of $CaCl_2$.

$$81.8 \text{ g } CaCl_2 \times \frac{1 \text{ mol } CaCl_2}{111.0 \text{ g } CaCl_2} \times \frac{1 \text{ mol } CaCO_3}{1 \text{ mol } CaCl_2} \times \frac{100.1 \text{ g } CaCO_3}{1 \text{ mol } CaCO_3} = 73.8 \text{ g } CaCO_3$$

Calculate the percent of $CaCO_3$ in the limestone.

$$\frac{73.8 \text{ g } CaCO_3}{84.4 \text{ g limestone}} \times 100\% = 87.4\% \ CaCO_3$$

Standardized Test Prep

1. (a)

$$8.4 \text{ mol } NO_2 \times \frac{1 \text{ mol } H_2O}{3 \text{ mol } NO_2} = 2.8 \text{ mol } H_2O$$

2. (c)

$$6.2 \text{ g } P_4 \times \frac{1 \text{ mol } P_4}{124 \text{ g } P_4} \times \frac{1 \text{ mol } F_2}{6 \text{ mol } P_4} \times \frac{38 \text{ g } F_2}{1 \text{ mol } F_2} = 11.4 \text{ g } F_2$$

3. (c)

4. (c)

5. (a)

6. $3P_2 + Q_2 \rightarrow 2P_3Q$

7. P_2 is the limiting reagent

8. True, True, correct explanation

9. False, True
Reactions that proceed to completion can have a yield of 100%.

10. True, True, correct explanation

11. False, True
Coefficients represent particles and moles.

12. False, False
A conversion factor is written so that the unit in the denominator can cancel the unit being multiplied.

10 STATES OF MATTER

Concept Practice

20. An elastic collision transfers energy from one particle to another. There is no change in the total kinetic energy.

21. pascal (Pa), millimeter of mercury (mm Hg), atmosphere (atm); Pa is the SI unit.

22. $1656 \not{kPa} \times \dfrac{1 \text{ atm}}{101.3 \not{kPa}} = 16.35 \text{ atm}$

23. **a.** $190 \text{ \sout{mm Hg}} \times \dfrac{101.3 \text{ kPa}}{760 \text{ \sout{mm Hg}}} = 25 \text{ kPa}$

b. $190 \text{ \sout{mm Hg}} \times \dfrac{1 \text{ atm}}{760 \text{ \sout{mm Hg}}} = 0.25 \text{ atm}$

24. $3.1 \not{atm} \times \dfrac{760 \text{ mm Hg}}{1 \not{atm}} = 2.4 \times 10^3 \text{ mm Hg}$

25. Kinetic energy is directly proportional to the absolute temperature.

26. Because there is no temperature change, the average kinetic energy stays the same.

27. STP stands for standard temperature and pressure, and is defined as 0 °C and 101.3 kPa respectively.

28. Temperature = 0 °C + 273 = 273 K
Pressure = 101.3 kPa = 760 mm Hg

29. Average kinetic energy of particles is zero.

30. The average kinetic energy triples.

31. Its volume is minimally affected by an increase in pressure.

32. **a.** Because of attractive forces between particles, liquids are denser than gases.
b. The molecules of liquids are in close contact and cannot be squeezed together. The molecules of gases are far apart and, thus, compressible.

33. In both cases, particles with sufficient kinetic energy move from the liquid to the vapor phase. In a container, a dynamic equilibrium is set up between the liquid and its vapor.

34. Vapor pressure results from collisions of vapor particles with the container's walls. A dynamic equilibrium exists when the rate of evaporation of the liquid equals the rate of condensation of the vapor.

35. More molecules have enough energy to escape attractions within the liquid.

36. No; vapor continuously leaves the surface of the liquid preventing a dynamic equilibrium from being established.

37. It increases the kinetic energy, which increases the vapor pressure.

38. The boiling point is the temperature at which the vapor pressure equals the external pressure. At the normal boiling point, external pressure is 1 atm.

39. **a.** ~55 mm Hg
b. ~93 °C
c. 760 mm Hg is standard pressure.

40. ~82 °C

41. about 150 mm Hg

42. Escaping molecules have more kinetic energy than remaining molecules, which lowers the average kinetic energy.

43. Ionic compounds have crystalline structures with relatively high melting points.

44. Its molecules gain sufficient kinetic energy to overcome attractive forces.

45. The forces between the molecules of molecular solids are weaker.

46. Moisture in the food has sublimed and then resolidified on the container lid.

47. Molecules use the added heat to escape the liquid; average kinetic energy remains the same.

Concept Mastery

48. Evaporation is the conversion of a liquid to a vapor at temperatures below the boiling point. Vapor pressure is the force per unit area exerted by the vapor particles on the container walls. Boiling point is the temperature at which vapor pressure equals external pressure.

49. The atmospheric pressure on Mt. McKinley is $330 \text{ \sout{mm Hg}} \times \dfrac{101.3 \text{ kPa}}{760 \text{ \sout{mm Hg}}} = 44.0 \text{ kPa}$

Water would boil at about 75 °C.

50. Atmospheric pressure is caused by the mass of the air pressing on the air molecules below the mass. Atmospheric pressure is lower on top of a mountain than at sea level because the mass of air above the mountain is less than the mass of air above sea level.

51. A *dynamic equilibrium* involves a continual exchange of particles even though net amounts stay constant. Molecules from the liquid escape to the vapor when they obtain sufficient energy. Molecules from the vapor fall back into the liquid if a collision sends them in that direction.

52. At −196 °C, the kinetic energy of the air particles decreases drastically as does the pressure the particles exert, thus reducing the balloon's flexible volume. The kinetic energy of the air particles increases as the balloon warms back to room temperature.

53. The average kinetic energy of the water molecules in your body increases when you get a fever because your body temperature increases.

54. The temperature, in kelvins, is directly proportional to the average kinetic energy. The new temperature is $3 \times 273\text{ K} = 819\text{ K}$.

55. At the *melting point*, a substance has sufficient average kinetic energy in its molecules to disrupt the forces holding the solid crystal together. The molecules start to flow and the solid becomes a liquid. During melting the temperature remains constant because the energy is used to separate molecules and does not increase their kinetic energy.

Critical Thinking

56. **a.** 2
b. 1

57. Possible answers include: odors travel through a room; ink will move throughout a beaker of water.

58. They are the same because the temperature is the same.

59. No; collisions between non-atomic objects involve the conversion of kinetic energy into heat.

60. The energy needed to evaporate perspiration comes from skin cells, which helps lower body temperature.

61. Some compounds have stronger intermolecular forces than others.

Cumulative Review

62. **a.** $V_2O_5 + 2H_2 \rightarrow V_2O_3 + 2H_2O$
b. $(NH_4)_2Cr_2O_7 \rightarrow Cr_2O_3 + N_2 + 4H_2O$
c. $4NH_3 + 5O_2 \rightarrow 4NO + 6H_2O$
d. $2C_6H_{14} + 13O_2 \rightarrow 12CO + 14H_2O$

63. At STP, one mole of gas has a volume of 22.4 L, or 22 400 mL.

$$1\ \cancel{\text{mol Kr}} \times \frac{83.8\text{ g Kr}}{1\ \cancel{\text{mol Kr}}} = 83.8\text{ g Kr}$$

$$\text{Density} = \frac{\text{mass}}{\text{volume}} = \frac{83.8\text{ g Kr}}{22\,400\text{ mL}}$$

$$= 0.00374\text{ g/mL Kr} = 0.00374\text{ g/cm}^3\text{ Kr}$$

64. Compare the molar ratios of the two reactants.

$$40.0\ \cancel{\text{g } C_2H_4} \times \frac{1\text{ mol } C_2H_4}{28.0\ \cancel{\text{g } C_2H_4}} = 1.43\text{ mol } C_2H_4$$

$$3.0\ \cancel{\text{g } H_2} \times \frac{1\text{ mol } H_2}{2.0\ \cancel{\text{g } H_2}} = 1.50\text{ mol } H_2$$

$$\text{The ratio is } \frac{1.43\text{ mol } C_2H_4}{1.50\text{ mol } H_2}$$

The limiting reagent is C_2H_4 because the theoretical ratio is 1:1.

65. **a.** $888\ \cancel{\text{g } SO_2} \times \frac{1\text{ mol } SO_2}{64.1\ \cancel{\text{g } SO_2}} = 13.9\text{ mol } SO_2$

b. $2.84 \times 10^{22}\ \cancel{\text{molecules } NH_3} \times \frac{1\text{ mol } NH_3}{6.02 \times 10^{23}\ \cancel{\text{molecules } NH_3}} = 0.0472\text{ mol } NH_3$

c. $0.47\ \cancel{\text{L}} \times \frac{1\text{ mol } CO_2}{22.4\ \cancel{\text{L}}} = 0.021\text{ mol } CO_2$

66. **a.** $Cl_2O_7 + H_2O \rightarrow 2HClO_4$

$$56.2\ \cancel{\text{g } HClO_4} \times \frac{1\text{ mol } HClO_4}{100.5\ \cancel{\text{g } HClO_4}} = 0.559\text{ mol } HClO_4$$

$$0.559\ \cancel{\text{mol } HClO_4} \times \frac{1\text{ mol } Cl_2O_7}{2\ \cancel{\text{mol } HClO_4}} = 0.280\text{ mol } Cl_2O_7$$

$$0.280\ \cancel{\text{mol } Cl_2O_7} \times \frac{183\text{ g } Cl_2O_7}{1\ \cancel{\text{mol } Cl_2O_7}} = 51.2\text{ g } Cl_2O_7$$

b. $3.40\ \cancel{\text{mol } HClO_4} \times \frac{1\text{ mol } H_2O}{2\ \cancel{\text{mol } HClO_4}} = 1.70\text{ mol } H_2O$

$$1.70\ \cancel{\text{mol } H_2O} \times \frac{18.0\text{ g } H_2O}{1\ \cancel{\text{mol } H_2O}} = 30.6\text{ g } H_2O$$

$$\text{volume} = \frac{\text{mass}}{\text{density}} = \frac{30.6\ \cancel{\text{g } H_2O}}{1.00\ \cancel{\text{g } H_2O}/\text{mL}} = 30.6\text{ mL } H_2O$$

Concept Challenge

67. Vapor pressure depends only on the kinetic energy of the escaping molecules.

68. Drawing should show alternating rows of sodium and chloride ions similar to the following diagram.

$Na^+Cl^-Na^+Cl^-$
$Cl^-Na^+Cl^-Na^+$
$Na^+Cl^-Na^+Cl^-$
$Cl^-Na^+Cl^-Na^+$

69. **a.** orthorhombic
b. rhombohedral
c. tetragonal
d. triclinic
e. cubic

Standardized Test Prep

1. (b)
If students forget to convert temperatures from °C to K, they are likely to choose alternative (d). (27 °C + 273 = 300 K)

2. (d)

3. (c)

4. Vapor pressure is lower in flask (b) because the level of mercury in the left arm of (b) is higher, which indicates less pressure on the mercury.

5. Temperature is higher in flask (a) because vapor pressure increases with temperature.

6. by measuring the difference in heights between the two arms

7. ≈78 °C

8. no

9. ≈82 °C

10. False, False
In an open container, the rate of condensation does not equal the rate of vaporization because the vapor can escape from the system.

11. True,True, correct explanation

12. False, True
The temperature does not increase as heat is added to a system during a phase change.

13. True, False
Particles in a solid vibrate around fixed locations.

14. True, True, correct explanation

11 THERMOCHEMISTRY—HEAT AND CHEMICAL CHANGE

Concept Practice

36. Answers will vary, but should include the idea that energy is conserved in every physical and chemical process.

37. Heat flows from the object at the higher temperature to the object at the lower temperature.

38. Potential energy is energy stored in a substance because of its chemical composition.

39. The chemical composition of the substance and its mass.

40. 1 Cal = 1000 cal = 1 kcal

41. **a.** $850 \not{cal} \times \frac{1 \text{ Cal}}{10^3 \not{cal}} = 0.85 \text{ Cal}$

b. $444 \not{cal} \times \frac{4.18 \text{ J}}{1 \not{cal}} = 1.86 \times 10^3 \text{ J}$

c. $1.8 \not{kJ} = \frac{10^3 \text{ J}}{1 \not{kJ}} = 1.8 \times 10^3 \text{ J}$

d. $0.45 \not{kJ} \times \frac{10^3 \not{J}}{1 \not{kJ}} \times \frac{1 \text{ cal}}{4.18 \not{J}} = 1.1 \times 10^2 \text{ cal}$

42. Thermochemistry measures heat flow across the boundary between the system and the surroundings.

43. A negative sign is given to heat flow from the system to the surroundings. A positive sign is given to heat flow to the system from the surroundings.

44. **a.** exothermic

b. The immediate surroundings are the glass beaker and the air. If one or more of the substances is an aqueous solution, the water is also considered part of the surroundings.

45. **a.** exothermic

b. endothermic

c. exothermic

d. endothermic

46. Heat changes for reactions carried out at constant pressure are the same as changes in enthalpy, symbolized as ΔH.

47. A calorimeter is an instrument used to measure heat changes in physical or chemical processes.

48. The foam cup will absorb heat. Some heat will be lost to the air. If the reactants are not completely mixed, temperature measurements will be inaccurate.

49. A bomb calorimeter is used to measure heat changes at constant volume.

50. Heats of combustion are reported as the enthalpy changes when the reactions are carried out at 101.3 kPa of pressure and the reactants and products are in their physical states at 25 °C.

51. A thermochemical equation gives the heat released or absorbed in a chemical change at constant pressure.

52. Heat is converting solid ice into liquid water.

53. **a.** $3.50 \not{mol\ H_2O} \times \frac{6.01 \text{ kJ}}{1 \not{mol\ H_2O}}$

$= 21.0$ kJ of heat lost

b. $0.44 \not{mol\ H_2O} \times \frac{40.7 \text{ kJ}}{1 \not{mol\ H_2O}}$

$= 18$ kJ of heat lost

c. $1.25 \not{mol\ NaOH} \times \frac{-445.1 \text{ kJ}}{1 \not{mol\ NaOH}}$

$= -556$ kJ

d. $0.15 \not{mol\ C_2H_5OH} = \frac{43.5}{1 \not{mol\ C_2H_5OH}}$

$= 6.5$ kJ

54. The temperature of the water will increase because the process is exothermic.

55. It allows the calculation of the enthalpy of a reaction from the known enthalpies of two or more other reactions.

56. **a.** The decomposition of 2 mol Al_2O_3 requires +3352 kJ. The formation of 1 mol Al_2O_3 from its elements would involve half this amount. $\Delta H = +1676$ kJ

b. Endothermic

57. Reverse the second equation and change the sign of ΔH. Then add the equations and the values of ΔH.

$$Pb(s) + 2Cl_2 \rightarrow PbCl_4(l) \quad \Delta H = -329.2 \text{ kJ}$$
$$PbCl_2(s) \rightarrow Pb(s) + Cl_2(g) \quad \Delta H = +359.4 \text{ kJ}$$
$$PbCl_2(s) \rightarrow + Cl_2(g) + PbCl_4(l) \quad \Delta H = 30.2 \text{ kJ}$$

58. Reverse the first equation and change the sign of ΔH and then add the equations and the values of ΔH.

$$\begin{array}{ll} NO(g) \rightarrow \frac{1}{2}N_2(g) + \frac{1}{2}O_2(g) & \Delta H = -90.4\ kJ \\ \frac{1}{2}N_2(s) + O_2(g) \rightarrow NO_2(s) & \Delta H = +33.6\ kJ \\ \hline NO(g) + \frac{1}{2}O_2(g) \rightarrow NO_2(s) & \Delta H = -56.8\ kJ \end{array}$$

59. Add the two equations and the values of ΔH.

$$\begin{array}{rl} CuO(s) \rightarrow Cu(s) + Cu_2O(s) & \Delta H = -11.3\ kJ \\ Cu_2O(s) + \frac{1}{2}O_2(g) \rightarrow 2CuO(s) & \Delta H = -114.6\ kJ \\ \hline Cu(s) + \frac{1}{2}O_2(g) \rightarrow CuO_2(s) & \Delta H = -125.9\ kJ \end{array}$$

60. The standard heat of formation (ΔH_f^0) of a free element in its standard state is arbitrarily set at zero.

61. This statement is true, because stability implies lower energy. The greater the release of heat, the more stable is the compound relative to its elements (all of which have $\Delta H_f^0 = 0$).

62. **a.** $\Delta H_f^0\ (H_2O) = 2\ \cancel{mol\ H_2O(l)}$

$$\times \frac{-285.8\ kJ}{1\ \cancel{mol\ H_2O\ (l)}} = -571.6\ kJ$$

$$\Delta H_f^0\ (products) = \Delta H_f^0(O_2) + \Delta H_f^0\ (H_2O)$$
$$= (-393.5\ kJ) + (-571.6\ kJ)$$
$$= -965.1\ kJ$$

$$\Delta H^0 = \Delta H_f^0\ (products) - \Delta H_f^0\ (reactants)$$
$$= (-965.1\ kJ) - (-74.86\ kJ)$$
$$= -890.2\ kJ$$

b. $\Delta H_f^0\ (product) = 2\ \cancel{mol\ CO_2(g)}$

$$\times \frac{-393.5\ kJ}{1\ \cancel{mol\ CO_2(g)}} = -787.0\ kJ$$

$$\Delta H_f^0\ (reactant) = 2\ \cancel{mol\ CO}(g)$$

$$= \frac{-110.5\ kJ}{1\ \cancel{mol\ CO}\ (g)} = -221.0\ kJ$$

$$\Delta H^0 = \Delta H_f^0(product) - \Delta H_f^0(reactants)$$
$$= (-787.0\ kJ) - (-221.0\ kJ)$$
$$= -566.0\ kJ$$

Concept Mastery

63. The standard heat of formation, ΔH_f^0, is the change in enthalpy that accompanies the formation of a mole of a compound from its elements.

64. Substance B has the higher specific heat. For equal masses absorbing equal amounts of heat, the substance with the higher heat capacity undergoes the smaller temperature change.

65. Calculate the grams of ice that melt when 3.20 kcal is absorbed.

$$3.20\ \cancel{kcal} \times \frac{4.18\ \cancel{kJ}}{1\ \cancel{kcal}} \times \frac{1\ \cancel{mol\ H_2O}}{6.01\ \cancel{kJ}} \times \frac{18.0\ g\ H_2O}{1\ \cancel{mol\ H_2O}}$$
$$= 40.1\ g\ ice\ melts$$

The amount of ice remaining is:

$1000\ g - 40.1\ g = 960\ g\ ice$

$= 9.6 \times 10^2\ g\ ice$

66.

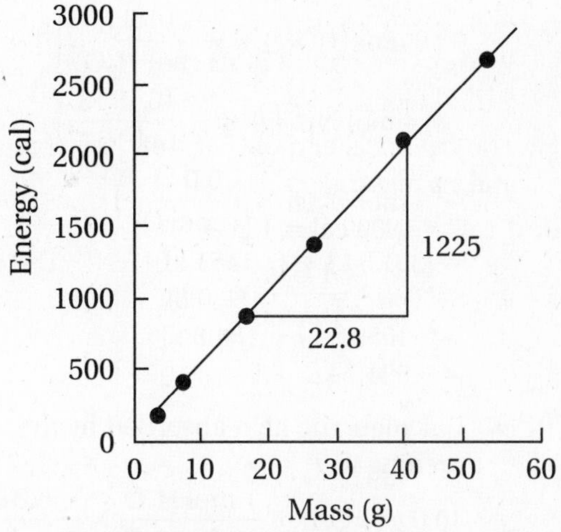

a. The graph will be a straight line with a positive slope.

b. about 54 cal/g

c. The two values are essentially the same.

67.

$$45.2\ \cancel{g\ steam} \times \frac{1\ \cancel{mol\ steam}}{18.0\ \cancel{g\ steam}} \times \frac{40.7\ \cancel{kJ}}{1\ \cancel{mol\ steam}} \times \frac{10^3\ J}{1\ \cancel{kJ}} = 1.02 \times 10^5\ J$$

$$1.02 \times 10^5\ \cancel{J} \times \frac{1\ cal}{4.18\ \cancel{J}} = 2.44 \times 10^4\ cal$$

68. Multiply the first equation by 2, reverse it, and change the sign of ΔH.

$$\begin{array}{l} 2PCl_3(g) + 2Cl_2(g) \rightarrow 2PCl_5(s) \\ 2P(s) + 3Cl_2(g) \rightarrow 2PCl_3(g) \\ \hline 2P(s) + 5Cl_2(g) \rightarrow 2PCl_5(s) \end{array}$$

$$\begin{array}{l} \Delta H = (2)(-87.9\ kJ) \\ \Delta H = -574\ kJ \\ \hline \Delta H = -750\ kJ \end{array}$$

69. $\Delta H^0 = \Delta H_f^0\ (products) - \Delta H_f^0\ (reactants)$

a.
$$\Delta H^0 = \left(2\ \cancel{mol\ CO(g)} \times \frac{-110.5\ kJ}{1\ \cancel{mol\ CO}}\right)$$
$$-\left[\left(2\ \cancel{mol\ C(s)} \times \frac{0.0\ kJ}{1\ \cancel{mol\ C}}\right) + \left(1\ \cancel{mol\ O_2(g)} \times \frac{0.0\ kJ}{1\ \cancel{mol\ O_2}}\right)\right]$$
$$= -221.0\ kJ - 0.0 + 0.0$$
$$= -221.0\ kJ$$

b. $\Delta H^0 = \left[\left(2\ \cancel{\text{mol } H_2O(l)} \times \frac{-285.8\ \text{kJ}}{1\ \cancel{\text{mol } H_2O}}\right)\right.$

$\left.+\left(1\ \cancel{\text{mol } O_2}(g) \times \frac{0.0\ \text{kJ}}{1\ \cancel{\text{mol } O_2}}\right)\right]$

$-\left(2\ \cancel{\text{mol } H_2O_2}(l) \times \frac{-187.8\ \text{kJ}}{1\ \cancel{\text{mol } H_2O_2}}\right)$

$= (-571.6\ \text{kJ} + 0) - (-375.6\ \text{kJ})$

$-196.0\ \text{kJ}$

c. $\Delta H^0 = \left[\left(4\ \cancel{\text{mol NO}}(g) \times \frac{90.37\ \text{kJ}}{1\ \cancel{\text{mol NO}}}\right)\right.$

$\left.+\left(6\ \cancel{\text{mol } H_2O}(g) \times \frac{-241.8\ \text{kJ}}{1\ \cancel{\text{mol } H_2O}}\right)\right]$

$-\left[\left(4\ \cancel{\text{mol } NH_3}(g) \times \frac{-46.19\ \text{kJ}}{1\ \cancel{\text{mol } NH_3}}\right)\right.$

$\left.+\left(5\ \cancel{\text{mol } O_2}(g) \times \frac{0.0\ \text{kJ}}{1\ \cancel{\text{mol } O_2}}\right)\right]$

$= [361.5\ \text{kJ} + (-1451\ \text{kJ})] - [(-184.8\ \text{kJ}) + 0.0]$

$= -1089.5\ \text{kJ} + 184.8\ \text{kJ}$

$= -904.7\ \text{kJ}$

70. a. Calculate the heat absorbed by the melting ice:

$40.0\ \text{g}\ \cancel{H_2O(l)} \times \frac{1\ \cancel{\text{mol } H_2O}}{18.0\ \cancel{\text{g } H_2O}} \times \frac{6.01\ \cancel{\text{kJ}}}{1\ \cancel{\text{mol } H_2O}} \times \frac{10^3\ \text{J}}{1\ \cancel{\text{kJ}}} = 1.34 \times 10^4\ \text{J}$

Change to calories:

$1.34 \times 10^4\ \cancel{\text{J}} \times \frac{1\ \text{cal}}{4.18\ \cancel{\text{J}}} = 3.21 \times 10^3\ \text{cal}$

Change to kilocalories:

$3.21 \times 10^3\ \cancel{\text{cal}} \times \frac{1\ \text{kcal}}{10^3\ \cancel{\text{cal}}} = 3.21\ \text{kcal}$

b. The mass of water undergoing a temperature change of 25 °C (25 °C − 0 °C) when energy change is 1.34×10^4 J is:

$\text{mass} = \frac{1.34 \times 10^4\ \cancel{\text{J}}}{(25\ \cancel{°\text{C}})\left(4.18\ \frac{\cancel{\text{J}}}{\text{g} \times \cancel{°\text{C}}}\right)}$

$= 1.3 \times 10^2\ \text{g}\ H_2O$

71. $25.0\ \cancel{\text{g}}\ C_2H_5OH \times \frac{1\ \cancel{\text{mol}}}{46.0\ \cancel{\text{g}}} \times \frac{43.5\ \text{kJ}}{1\ \cancel{\text{mol}}} = 23.6\ \text{kJ}$

72. The temperature change is 75 °C. Change to kJ to J.

$445\ \cancel{\text{kJ}} \times \frac{10^3\ \text{J}}{1\ \cancel{\text{kJ}}} = 4.45 \times 10^5\ \text{J}$

$\text{mass} = \frac{4.45 \times 10^5\ \cancel{\text{J}}}{(75\ \cancel{°\text{C}})\left(4.18\ \frac{\cancel{\text{J}}}{\text{g} \times \cancel{°\text{C}}}\right)}$

73. $4.79\ \cancel{\text{g } C_2H_4} \times \frac{1\ \cancel{\text{mol } C_2H_4}}{28.0\ \cancel{\text{g } C_2H_4}} \times \frac{1.39 \times 10^3\ \text{kJ}}{1\ \cancel{\text{mol } C_2H_4}}$

$= 2.38 \times 10^2\ \text{kJ}$

74. Reverse the first equation, changing the sign of the ΔH, and add.

$2N_2(g) + 6H_2O(l) \rightarrow 4NH_3(g) + 3O_2(g)$ $\quad \Delta H = +1530\ \text{kJ}$

$4NH_3(g) + 5O_2(g) \rightarrow 4NO(g) + 6H_2O(l)$ $\quad \Delta H = -1170\ \text{kJ}$

$2N_2(g) + 2O_2(g) \rightarrow 4NO(g)$ $\quad \Delta H = 360\ \text{kJ}$

Divide by 2.

$N_2(g) + O_2(g) \rightarrow 2NO(g)$

75. $45.0\ \cancel{\text{g}} \times \frac{1\ \cancel{\text{mol}}}{128.0\ \cancel{\text{g}}} \times \frac{191.2\ \text{kJ}}{1\ \cancel{\text{mol}}} = 67.2\ \text{kJ}$

Critical Thinking

76. a. 2

b. 3

c. 4

77. The region denoted by ΔH_{fus} represents the coexistence of solid and liquid. The region denoted by Δh_{vap} represents the coexistence of liquid and vapor.

Cumulative Review

78. The average kinetic energy is proportional to the absolute temperature.

$\frac{40\ \text{K}}{100\ \text{K}} = 0.4$

79. At STP 1 mol H_2 = 22.4 L H_2 = 6.02×10^{23} molecules H_2

$44.8\ \cancel{\text{L } H_2} \times \frac{1\ \cancel{\text{mol } H_2}}{22.4\ \cancel{\text{L } H_2}} \times \frac{6.02 \times 10^{23}\ \text{molecules}}{1\ \cancel{\text{mol } H_2}}$

$= 1.20 \times 10^{24}$ molecules H_2

80. $NaCl(aq) + AgC_2H_3O_2(aq) \rightarrow NaC_2H_3O_2(aq) + AgCl(s)$

$Na^+(aq) + Cl^-(aq) + Ag^+(aq) + C_2H_3O_2^-(aq) \rightarrow AgCl(s) + Na^+(aq) + C_2H_3O_2^-(aq)$

$Ag^+(aq) + Cl^-(aq) \rightarrow AgCl(s)$

81. $1.18 \times 10^1\ \text{g}\ O_2$

Concept Challenge

82. a. heat lost from the skin = heat gained by 2-proponal

Calculate the heat gained by 2-proponal as it evaporates.

$$175\ \text{g}\ C_3H_8O \times \frac{1\ \text{mol}\ C_3H_8O}{60.0\ \text{g}\ C_3H_8O} \times \frac{11.1\ \text{kcal}}{1\ \text{mol}\ C_3H_8O} = 32.4\ \text{kcal}$$

$$32.4 \times 10^3\ \text{cal} \times \frac{4.184\ \text{J}}{1\ \text{cal}} \times \frac{1\ \text{kJ}}{10^3\ \text{J}} = 1.36 \times 10^2\ \text{kJ}$$

b. $\Delta T = 4\ °C$

$$\text{mass} = \frac{1.36 \times 10^5\ \text{J}}{(4\ °C)\left(4.18\ \frac{\text{J}}{\text{g} \times °C}\right)} = 8.13 \times 10^3\ \text{g} = 8.13\ \text{kg}$$

83. Divide the first and third equations by 2; reverse the third equation, then add the three equations.

$H_2(g) + \frac{1}{2}O_2(g) \rightarrow H_2O(l)$	$\Delta H = +1530\ \text{kJ}$
$C_2H_4(g) + 3O_2(g) \rightarrow 2H_2O(l) + 2CO_2(g)$	$\Delta H = -1170\ \text{kJ}$
$3H_2O(l) + 2CO_2(g) \rightarrow C_2H_6(g) + \frac{7}{2}O_2(g)$	$\Delta H = +1550\ \text{kJ}$
$C_2H_4(g) + H_2(g) \rightarrow C_2H_6(g)$	$\Delta H = -137\ \text{kJ}$

84. Heat "lost" = heat "gained"

Calculate the heat "lost" as the water cooled from 45.0 °C to 19.5 °C (ΔT = 25.5 °C)

$$\text{heat "lost" (J)} = (30.0\ \text{g})(25.5\ °C)\left(4.18\ \frac{\text{J}}{\text{g} \times °C}\right) = 3.20 \times 10^3\ \text{J}$$

The heat gained is two terms; one for the melting of the ice, the other for the warming of the liquid water from 0.0 °C to 19.5 °C (ΔT = 19.5 °C).

First calculate the heat of fusion of ice in J/g.

$$\frac{6.01\ \text{kJ}}{\text{mol}} \times \frac{10^3\ \text{J}}{1\ \text{kJ}} \times \frac{1\ \text{mol}}{18.0\ \text{g}} = 334\ \frac{\text{J}}{\text{g}}$$

Let z = grams of ice

heat "lost" = heat "gained"

$$3.20 \times 10^3\ \text{J} = (z\ \text{g})\left(334\ \frac{\text{J}}{\text{g}}\right) + (z\ \text{g})(19.5\ °C)\left(4.18\ \frac{\text{J}}{\text{g} \times °C}\right)$$

$$3.20 \times 10^3\ \text{J} = 334\ \text{J} \times z + 82\ \text{J} \times z$$

$$3.20 \times 10^3\ \text{J} = 416\ \text{J} \times z$$

$$z = 7.69\ \text{g ice}$$

85. The heat "lost" as the glass cools will equal the heat "gained" by the water.

$(\text{mass}_{glass})(\Delta H_{glass})(\text{sp. ht.}_{glass})$ = heat lost_{glass} = heat gained_{water} = $(\text{mass}_{H_2O})(\Delta H_{H_2O})$ (sp. ht._{H_2O})

Substitute in the equation and solve for the final temperature, T_f.

$$(41.0\ \text{g})(95\ °C - T_f)\left(2.1\ \frac{\text{cal}}{\text{g} \times °C}\right) = (175\ \text{g})(T_f - 21\ °C)\left(1.0\ \frac{\text{cal}}{\text{g} \times °C}\right)$$

$$8179\ °C - 86.1\ T_f = 175\ T_f - 3675\ °C$$

$$11854\ °C = 261.1\ T_f$$

$$T_f = 45.4\ °C$$

86. ΔH_{vap} for water at 70 °C is approximately 42 kJ/mol. 1 L of water (1000 mL) has a mass of 1000 g and contains 55.6 mol water. Therefore, the amount of heat required is 42 kJ/mole × 55.6 mol = 2.34×10^3 kJ.

Standardized Test Prep

1. (a)
Students must calculate the molar mass of ethanol, convert grams to moles, and then multiply by the heat of fusion.
molar mass of ethanol = 46.0 g

$$24.5\ \cancel{g} \times \frac{1\ \cancel{mol}}{46.0\ \cancel{g}} \times \frac{4.60\ kJ}{\cancel{mol}} = 2.45\ kJ$$

2. (c)
Students need to know the specific heat of water, which is 4.18 J/(g × °C).
$175\ \cancel{g} \times 5.0\ \cancel{°C} \times 4.18\ \cancel{J}/(\cancel{g} \times \cancel{°C}) \times 1\ kJ/1000\ \cancel{J} = 3.7\ kJ$

3. (a)

4. (b)
Heat absorbed when HgO decomposes must be released when HgO is formed from its elements. The amount of heat must be divided by 2 to reflect the change in the equation.

5. (c)
Because alcohol absorbs 10 times as much heat for each degree change in temperature than silver releases per degree, the temperature of alcohol rises one-tenth of 45 °C, or 4.5 °C.

6. (D)

7. (E)

8. (A)

9. (C)

10.

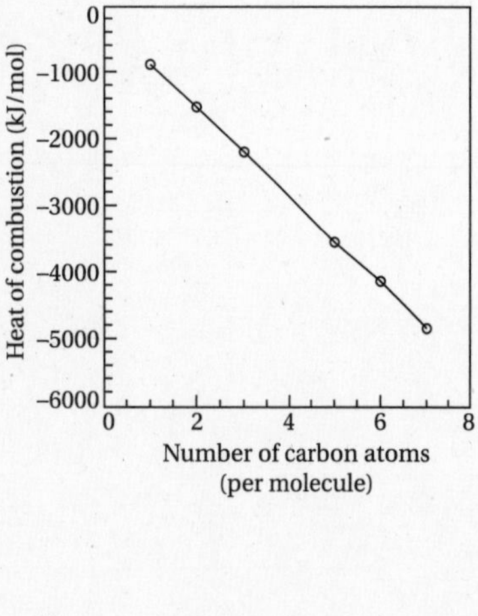

11. Heat of combustion of butane is about −3000 kJ/mol from the graph. The accepted value is −2877 kJ/mol.

12. Extrapolation gives a heat of combustion for octane of about −5400 kJ/mol. The accepted value is −5471 kJ/mol.

13. 0.33 kJ

14. 30.8 kJ

15. region B = 422 kJ
ΔT is 337.2 °C − 175.5 °C = 161.7 °C
$32.0\ \cancel{g} \times 161.7\ \cancel{°C} \times 81.6\ J/\cancel{g} \times \cancel{°C} \times 1\ kJ/1000\ \cancel{J} = 422\ kJ$
region C = 35.3 kJ

16. region A = 5.65 kJ
region B = 26.5 kJ
ΔT is 239.7 °C − 195.3 °C = 44.4 °C
$17.0\ \cancel{g} \times 44.4\ \cancel{°C} \times 35.1\ \cancel{J}/\cancel{g} \times \cancel{°C} \times 1\ kJ/1000\ \cancel{J} = 26.5\ kJ$
region C = 23.4 kJ

12 THE BEHAVIOR OF GASES

Concept Practice

45. Heating a contained gas at constant volume increases the kinetic energy of its molecules. This increases the force of intermolecular collisions. Since pressure = force/area and surface area remains constant at constant volume, the pressure increases.

46. The gas particles become closer together.

47. The pressure doubles if 1 mole of gas is added.

48. The pressure quadruples.

49. Temperatures measured on the Kelvin scale are always positive and directly proportional to the average kinetic energy of the gaseous particles.

50. The volume decreases. The molecules have less kinetic energy, which causes less pressure on the inside of the balloon.

51. Since the temperature decreases to one-third of its value, the pressure decreases from 300 kPa to 100 kPa.

52. $V_2 = \dfrac{P_1 \times V_1}{P_2} = \dfrac{(1.2 \times 10^2\ \cancel{\text{kPa}}) \times (1.50\ \text{L})}{(1.00 \times 10^2\ \cancel{\text{kPa}})}$
$= 1.80\ \text{L}$

53. $V_2 = \dfrac{P_1 \times V_1}{P_2} = \dfrac{90\ \cancel{\text{kPa}} \times 4.0\ \text{L}}{20\ \cancel{\text{kPa}}} = 18\ \text{L}$

54. $T_2 = \dfrac{V_2 \times T_1}{V_1} = \dfrac{600\ \cancel{\text{ml}} \times (150 + 273)\ \text{K}}{300\ \cancel{\text{ml}}}$
$= 846\ \text{K}\ (573\ °\text{C})$

55. High temperatures can sufficiently increase the pressure of the gas remaining in the container to cause it to explode.

56. $\dfrac{P_1 \times V_1}{T_1} = \dfrac{P_2 \times V_2}{T_2}$

57. $P_2 = \dfrac{P_1 \times T_2}{T_1} = \dfrac{1000\ \text{kPa} \times (50 \times 273)\ \cancel{\text{K}}}{(20 + 273)\ \cancel{\text{K}}}$
$= 1.10 \times 10^3\ \text{kPa}$

58. $\dfrac{P_1 \times V_1}{T_1} = \dfrac{P_2 \times V_2}{T_2}$

When the pressure is constant, $P_1 = P_2$, so the pressure terms cancel, leaving the equation for Charles's law:

$\dfrac{V_1}{T_1} = \dfrac{V_2}{T_2}$

59. Gas particles have a finite volume and are attracted to one another, especially at low temperatures.

60. The particles of ideal gas have no volume, no forces between them, and undergo elastic collisions. An ideal gas follows the gas laws at all temperatures and pressures.

61. At low temperatures, gas particles are attracted to one another; the finite volume of gas particles is significant at high pressures.

62. *See answer below.*

63. **a.** $V = 2.5\ \cancel{\text{mol N}_2} \times \dfrac{22.4\ \text{L N}_2}{1\ \cancel{\text{mol N}_2}} = 56\ \text{L N}_2$

b. $V = 0.600\ \cancel{\text{g H}_2} = \dfrac{1\ \cancel{\text{mol H}_2}}{2.0\ \cancel{\text{g H}_2}} \times \dfrac{22.4\ \text{L H}_2}{1\ \cancel{\text{mol H}_2}}$
$= 6.7\ \text{L H}_2$

c. $V = 0.350\ \cancel{\text{mol O}_2} \times \dfrac{22.4\ \text{L O}_2}{1\ \cancel{\text{mol O}_2}} = 7.84\ \text{L O}_2$

---

62. $P = \dfrac{n \times R \times T}{V}$

$$= \frac{4.50\ \cancel{\text{g CH}_4} \times \dfrac{1\ \cancel{\text{mol}}}{16.0\ \cancel{\text{g CH}_4}} \times \dfrac{8.31\ \cancel{\text{L}} \times \text{kPa}}{\cancel{\text{K}} \times \cancel{\text{mol}}} \times (35 + 273)\ \cancel{\text{K}}}{2.00\ \text{L}} = 36\ \text{kPa} = 3.6 \times 10^2\ \text{kPa}$$

---

64. Equal volumes of gases at the same pressure should contain equal numbers of particles.

65. $$\frac{\text{Rate}_{H_2}}{\text{Rate}_{Cl_2}} = \frac{\sqrt{\text{Molar mass}_{Cl_2}}}{\sqrt{\text{molar mass}_{H_2}}} = \frac{\sqrt{70.91}}{\sqrt{2.00}} \cong 6$$

At any temperature, hydrogen gas effuses faster than chlorine gas by an approximate factor of six.

66. The molar mass of oxygen is less than the molar mass of argon; therefore, oxygen should effuse faster than argon.

67. $$\frac{\text{Rate}_{He}}{\text{Rate}_{Ne}} = \frac{\sqrt{\text{formula mass}_{Ne}}}{\sqrt{\text{formula mass}_{He}}} = \frac{\sqrt{20.28}}{\sqrt{4.00}} = 2.25$$

68. $$\frac{\text{Rate}_{He}}{\text{Rate}_{F_2}} = \frac{\sqrt{\text{formula mass}_{F_2}}}{\sqrt{\text{formula mass}_{He}}} = \frac{\sqrt{38.00}}{\sqrt{4.00}} = 3.08$$

Concept Mastery

69. The variables are directly proportional.

70. $$\text{Mol. mass}_{gas} = \frac{\text{mol. mass}_{O_2} \times (\text{rate}_{O_2})^2}{(\text{rate}_{gas})^2} = \frac{32.00\text{ g} \times (\cancel{\text{rate}_{O_2}})^2}{(4 \times \cancel{\text{rate}_{O_2}})^2} = 2\text{ g}$$

71. $$T_2 = \frac{P_2 \times V_2 \times T_1}{P_1 \times V_1} = \frac{56.7\ \cancel{\text{kPa}} \times 8.00\ \cancel{\text{L}} \times (20 + 273)\text{ K}}{86.7\ \cancel{\text{kPa}} \times 3.5\ \cancel{\text{L}}} = 438\text{ K}$$

$(438 - 273)\ °C = 165$ K

72. $$\text{Mol mass}_{gas} = \frac{\text{mol mass}_{O_2} \times (\text{rate}_{O_2})^2}{(\text{rate}_{gas})^2} = \frac{32.00\text{ g} \times \left[\frac{\cancel{(\text{moles of gas})}}{30\ \cancel{s}}\right]^2}{\left[\frac{\cancel{(\text{moles of gas})}}{75\ \cancel{s}}\right]^2} = 200\text{ g}$$

Critical Thinking

73. **a.** 4
b. 1
c. 1
d. 3
e. 2

74. The gases that make up the atmosphere, just like any other form of matter, are held near Earth by the force of gravity.

75. A vacuum contains no matter to allow the transfer of kinetic energy between molecules.

76. Helium gas; It is composed of small, monatomic atoms with little attraction for each other.

Cumulative Review

77. The gfm is the sum of atomic masses.
a. $[40.1 + (4 + 12.0) + (6 \times 1.0) + (4 \times 16.0)]\text{ g} = 158.1\text{ g } Ca(C_2H_3O_2)_2$
b. $[(3 \times 1.0) + 31.0 + (4 \times 16.0)]\text{ g} = 98.0\text{ g } H_3PO_4$
c. $[(12 \times 12.0) + (22 \times 1.0) + (11 \times 16.0)]\text{ g} = 342.0\text{ g } C_{12}H_{22}O_{11}$
d. $[207.2 + (2 \times 14.0) + (6 \times 16.0)]\text{ g} = 331.2\text{ g } Pb(NO_3)_2$

78. **a.** tin(II) bromide
b. barium sulfate
c. magnesium hydroxide
d. iodine pentafluoride

79. **a.** $17.16 \times 12.0\text{ amu} = 206\text{ amu}$
b. 82 protons, 82 electrons, 124 neutrons

80. Energy = mass × specific heat × ΔT + mass × heat of ...

$$= \left\{40.\cancel{g} \times \frac{2.1\text{ J}}{\cancel{g}\ \cancel{°C}} \times [0 - (-12)]\cancel{°C}\right\} + \left\{40.0\ \cancel{g} \times \frac{334\text{ J}}{1\ \cancel{g}}\right\} + \left\{40.0\ \cancel{g} \times \frac{4.18\text{ J}}{\cancel{g}\ \cancel{°C}} \times (100 - 0)\cancel{°C}\right\} + \left\{40.0\ \cancel{g} \times \frac{2260\text{ J}}{1\ \cancel{g}}\right\} + \left\{40.0\ \cancel{g} \times \frac{1.7\text{ J}}{\cancel{g}\ \cancel{°C}} \times \left\{(130 - 100)\cancel{°C}\right\}\right\}$$

$= 124\ 000$ J
$= 124$ kJ

$$124\ \cancel{\text{kJ}} \times \frac{1\text{ Kcal}}{4.184\ \cancel{\text{kJ}}} = 29.6\text{ kcal}$$

81. **a.** $Ca + 2H_2O \rightarrow Ca(OH)_2 + H_2$
b. $P_4O_{10} + 6H_2O \rightarrow 4H_3PO_4$
c. $2HgO \xrightarrow{\Delta} 2Hg + O_2$
d. $Al_2S_3 + 6H_2O \rightarrow 2Al(OH)_3 + 3H_2S$

82. **a.** single-replacement
b. combination
c. decomposition
d. double-replacement

83. a. For C_2H_4O, gmm = $(2 \times 12.0) + (4 \times 1.0) + 16.0 = 44.0$ g/mol. Because the gmm is 88 g/mol, the molecular formula is $C_4H_8O_2$.

b. For CH, gmm = $12.0 + 1.0 = 13.0$ g/mol. Because the gmm is 104 g/mol, the molecular formula is C_8H_8.

c.
$$\frac{26.7\ \cancel{g\ C}}{12.0\ \cancel{g\ C}/\text{mol C}} = 2.23\ \text{mol C}$$
$$\frac{2.2\ \cancel{g\ H}}{1.0\ \cancel{g\ H}/\text{mol H}} = 2.2\ \text{mol H}$$
$$\text{ratio} = \frac{2.23\ \text{mol C}}{2.20\ \text{mol H}} = 1:1$$
$$\frac{71.1\ \cancel{g\ O}}{16.0\ \cancel{g\ O}/\text{mol O}} = 4.44\ \text{mol O}$$
$$\text{ratio} = \frac{4.44\ \text{mol O}}{2.20\ \text{mol H}} = 2:1$$

For CHO_2, gmm = $12.0 + 1.0 + (2 \times 16.0) = 45.0$ g/mol. Because the gmm is 90 g/mol, the molecular formula is $C_2H_2O_4$.

84. Density = mass/volume
$$= \frac{9.92\ \text{g}}{4.5\ \text{cm} \times 1.3\ \text{cm} \times 1.6\ \cancel{\text{mm}} \times \dfrac{1\ \text{cm}}{10\ \cancel{\text{mm}}}}$$
$$= 11\ \text{g/cm}^3$$

85.
$$\text{Percent} = \frac{\text{gram atomic mass}}{\text{gram molecular mass}} \times 100\%$$
gram molecular mass C_3H_7OH = $(3 \times 12.0\ \text{g}) + (8 \times 1.0\ \text{g}) + (1 \times 16.0\ \text{g}) = 60.0$ g
$$\frac{36.0\ \cancel{g}\ C}{60.0\ \cancel{g}} \times 100 = 60.0\%\ C$$
$$\frac{8.0\ \cancel{g}\ H}{60.0\ \cancel{g}} \times 100 = 13.3\%\ H$$
$$\frac{16.0\ \cancel{g}\ O}{60.0\ \cancel{g}} \times 100 = 26.\%\ O$$

86. a. $4Al + 3O_2 \rightarrow 2Al_2O_3$

b.
$$583\ \cancel{g\ Al_2O_3} \times \frac{1\ \cancel{mol\ Al_2O_3}}{102\ \cancel{g\ Al_2O_3}} \times \frac{4\ \cancel{mol\ Al}}{2\ \cancel{mol\ Al_2O_3}} \times \frac{27.0\ g\ Al}{1\ \cancel{mol\ Al}} = 309\ g\ Al$$
$$583\ \cancel{g\ Al_2O_3} \times \frac{1\ \cancel{mol\ Al_2O_3}}{102\ \cancel{g\ Al_2O_3}} \times \frac{3\ \cancel{mol\ O_2}}{2\ \cancel{mol\ Al_2O_3}} \times \frac{32.0\ g}{1\ \cancel{mol\ O_2}} = 274\ g\ O_2$$

Concept Challenge

87. The mole ratio is 2 mol KNO_3 for each 1 mol O_2. For example, for the first set of data:
$$0.840\ \cancel{g\ KNO_3} \times \frac{1\ \text{mol}\ KNO_3}{101.1\ \cancel{g\ KNO_3}} = 0.00831\ \text{mol}\ KNO_3$$
$$9.32\ \cancel{cL\ O_2} \times \frac{1\ \cancel{L\ O_2}}{100\ \cancel{cL\ O_2}} \times \frac{1\ \text{mol}\ O_2}{22.4\ \cancel{L\ O_2}} = 0.00416\ \text{mol}\ O_2$$
$$\frac{0.00831\ \text{mol}\ KNO_3}{0.00416\ \text{mol}\ O_2} = \frac{2\ \text{mol}\ KNO_3}{1\ \text{mol}\ O_2}$$

88. a. 1 mol NH_3 (the limiting reagent) $\rightarrow$ 1 mol NO.
$$P_{NO} = \frac{n \times R \times T}{V} = \frac{34.0\ \cancel{g\ NH_3} \times \dfrac{1\ \cancel{mol}}{17.0\ \cancel{g\ NH_3}} \times \dfrac{8.31\ \cancel{L} \times kPa}{\cancel{K} \times \cancel{mol}} \times (120 + 273)\ \cancel{K}}{40.0\ \cancel{L}} = 163\ kPa$$

b. $P_{H_2O} = \frac{6}{4} \times 163\ kPa = 244\ kPa$
$$P_{O_2} = \frac{96.0\ \cancel{g} \times \dfrac{1\ \cancel{mol}}{32.0\ \cancel{g}} \times \dfrac{8.31\ \cancel{L} \times kPa}{\cancel{K} \times \cancel{mol}} \times (120 + 273)\ \cancel{K}}{40\ \cancel{L}} - \left(\frac{5}{4} \times 163\ kPa\right)$$
$$= 244\ kPa - 203\ kPa = 41\ kPa$$
$$P_{total} = P_{NO} + P_{H_2O} + P_{O_2} = 163\ kPa + 244\ kPa + 41\ kPa = 448\ kPa$$

89. Two equations can be written for this reaction.

$C_2H_2 + \frac{5}{2}O_2 \rightarrow 2CO_2 + H_2O$

$CH_4 + 2O_2 \rightarrow CO_2 + 2H_2O$

Since V and T remain constant,

$$\frac{n_2}{P_2} = \frac{n_1}{P_1},\ n_{CO_2} = \frac{n_1 \times 25.6\ \cancel{kPa}}{16.8\ \cancel{kPa}} = 1.52n_1$$

From the two balanced equations above,

$n_{CO_2} = 2n_{C_2H_2} + n_{CH_4}$

By substitution,

$1.52n_1 = 2n_{C_2H_2} + n_{CH_4}$

Since $n_1 = n_{C_2H_2} + n_{CH_4}$

$1.52(n_{C_2H_2} + n_{CH_4}) = 2n_{C_2H_2} + n_{CH_4}$

$0.52n_{CH_4} = 0.48n_{C_2H_2}$

$n_{CH_4} = 0.48n_{C_2H_2}/0.52$

$$\text{Percent}_{CH_4} = \frac{\text{mol}_{CH_4}}{\text{mol}_{CH_4} + \text{mol}_{C_2H_2}} \times 100\%$$

$$= \frac{\frac{0.48\cancel{n}}{0.52}}{\frac{0.48\cancel{n}}{0.52} + \frac{0.52\cancel{n}}{0.48}} \times 100\% = 46\%$$

90. a. $$\text{Percent } H_2 = \frac{\text{volume of } H_2}{\text{volume of gas}} \times 100\%$$

$$= \frac{3.0 \times 10^{20}\ \cancel{\text{molec. } H_2} \times \frac{6.7 \times 10^{-24}\ \cancel{mL}}{1\ \cancel{\text{molec. } H_2}}}{0.100\ \cancel{L} \times \frac{1000\ mL}{1\ \cancel{L}}}$$

$\times\ 100\%$

$= 2.0 \times 10^{-3}\%$

b. $$\text{Percent } H_2 = \frac{\text{volume of } H_2}{\text{volume of gas}} \times 100\%$$

$$= \frac{0.100\ \cancel{L}}{1 \times 10^{-4}\ \cancel{L}} \times 2.0 \times 10^{-3}\% = 2.0\%$$

91. Because attractions between molecules in gases such as nitrogen and oxygen are insignificant, these gases have the molar volume of an ideal gas—22.41 L at STP. Based on their molar volumes at STP, attractions between molecules increase in strength and effect from methane to carbon dioxide to ammonia.

Standardized Test Prep

1. (b)
When students convert temperatures from °C to kelvins, they will find that the temperature has doubled from 150 K to 300 K. Thus, the volume should double from 120.0 mL to 240.0 mL.

2. (c)
The original pressure must be multiplied by 3/2 because the pressure is tripled in response to the temperature change and halved in response to the volume change.

3. (c)
Students need to find the gas with the lowest molar mass. NH_3 has a molar mass of 17 g. (The molar mass of Cl_2 is 71 g, of NO_2 is 46 g, and of N_2 is 28 g.)

4. (a)
Because the volume of hydrogen is constant, its pressure does not change. Because the volume of oxygen doubles, its pressure is cut in half.

5. (b)

6. (b)

7. Boiling the water fills the can with steam. When the can is plunged upside down into the cold water, the steam is trapped and quickly condenses, reducing gas pressure inside the can. Because the sides of the can are not very strong, the comparatively high atmospheric pressure crushes the can.

8. The results would be much less dramatic. The change in volume of heated air (and internal pressure) is much less than when steam condenses to a liquid.

9. (a)

10. (b)

11. (c)

12. (a) and (b)

13. There will be four green and four red spheres in each bulb.

14. Each bulb will contain 2 blue, 3 green, and 4 red spheres.

13 ELECTRONS IN ATOMS

Concept Practice

20. In his "plum-pudding" model of the atom, J.J. Thomson proposed that the atom consisted of a uniform sphere of positively charged matter in which negatively charged particles (later called electrons) were embedded.

21. Electrons have fixed energies. To move between energy levels, they must emit or absorb specific amounts of energy, called quanta.

22. In Rutherford's model, negatively charged electrons surround a dense, positively charged nucleus. In Bohr's model, electrons are assigned to circular orbits of fixed energy.

23. 90% of the time an electron is inside this boundary.

24. An atomic orbital is a region beyond the nucleus where there is a high probability of finding an electron.

25. The 1*s* orbital is spherical. The 2*s* orbital is spherical with a diameter larger than that of the 1*s* orbital. The dumbbell-shaped 2*p* orbitals reach beyond the diameter of the 2*s* orbital.

26. **a.** 2 **c.** 3
b. 1 **d.** 6

27. The *Aufbau principle* states that electrons occupy the lowest energy levels. The *Pauli exclusion principle* states that an atomic orbital can hold at most two electrons. *Hund's rule* states that one electron occupies each of a set of orbitals with equal energies before any pairing of electrons occurs. Those electrons all have the same spin.

28. **a.** $1s^22s^22p^63s^23p^3$
b. $1s^22s^2sp^63s^2$
c. $1s^22s^22p^5$
d. $1s^22s^22p^63s^23p^6$

29. The *p* orbitals in the third quantum level have three electrons.

30. **a.** valid **c.** invalid
b. invalid **d.** valid

31. **a.** 2 **e.** 6
b. 6 **f.** 2
c. 2 **g.** 14
d. 10 **h.** 6

32. **a.** 8
b. 8
c. 8

33. **a.** $1s^22s^22p^63s^23p^63d^{10}4s^24p^4$
b. $1s^22s^22p^63s^23p^63d^34s^2$
c. $1s^22s^22p^63s^23p^63d^84s^2$
d. $1s^22s^22p^63s^23p^64s^2$

34. violet, indigo, blue, green, yellow, orange, red

35. Frequency is the number of wave cycles that pass a given point per unit time. Frequency units are cycles, reciprocal seconds (s^{-1}), or hertz. Frequency and wavelength are inversely related.

36. *See answer below.*

36.

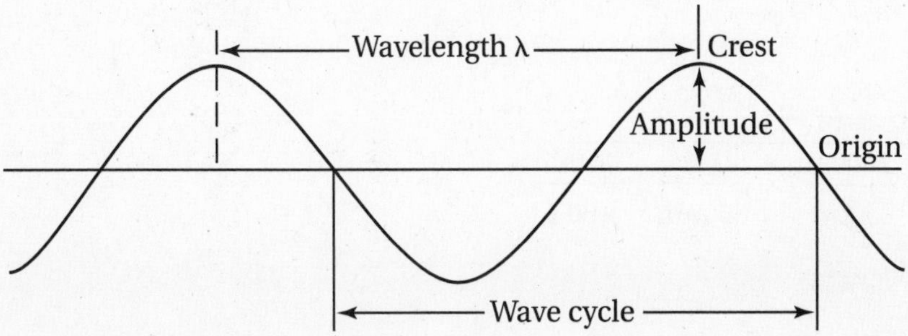

---

37. Classical physics viewed energy changes as continuous, occurring in any quantity. In the quantum concept, energy changes occur in discrete units called quanta.

38. $E = hv$

$E = 6.63 \times 10^{-34}\ \text{J}\cancel{\text{s}} \times \dfrac{5.80 \times 10^{14}}{\cancel{\text{s}}}$

$= 3.85 \times 10^{-19}\ \text{J}$

39. He showed that the quanta of radiation emitted depends on the frequency of radiation.

40. **a.** Emitted electrons have a low velocity.
b. More electrons are emitted; velocity stays low.
c. Emitted electrons have higher velocity.

41. A quantum is a discrete amount of energy. A photon is a quantum of light energy.

42. Its electron is raised to a higher energy level.

43. The outermost electron of sodium absorbs photons of wavelength 589 nm as it jumps to a higher orbital.

44. *See answer below.*

Concept Mastery

45. **a.** Ar
b. Ru
c. Gd

46. $1s^22s^22p^63s^23p^64s^23d^{10}4p^3$; Total 33; the first three levels are full; the fourth level is partially filled.

47. **a.** 2 **b.** 4 **c.** 10 **d.** 6

48. $1s^22s^22p^3$; nitrogen; 3 unpaired electrons

49. $\lambda = \dfrac{c}{v} = \dfrac{3.00 \times 10^{10}\ \dfrac{\text{cm}}{\cancel{\text{s}}}}{\dfrac{1.15 \times 10^6}{1\ \cancel{\text{s}}}}$

$\lambda = 2.61 \times 10^4\ \text{cm}$

50. **a.** $\lambda = (4.36 \times 10^{-7}\ \cancel{\text{m}}) \times \dfrac{100\ \text{cm}}{1\ \cancel{\text{m}}}$

$= 4.36 \times 10^{-5}\ \text{cm}$

b. visible

c. $v = \dfrac{c}{\lambda} = \dfrac{3.00 \times 10^8\ \cancel{\text{m}}/\text{s}}{4.36 \times 10^{-7}\ \cancel{\text{m}}}$

$= 6.88 \times 10^{14}\ \text{s}^{-1}$

51. $E = h \times v = h \times \dfrac{c}{\lambda}$

$= 6.62 \times 10^{34}\ \text{J}\ \cancel{\text{s}} \times \dfrac{3.00 \times 10^{10}\ \dfrac{\cancel{\text{cm}}}{1\ \cancel{\text{s}}}}{6.45 \times 10^{-5}\ \cancel{\text{cm}}}$

$= 3.08 \times 10^{-19}\ \text{J}$

Red light has lower energy than green light.

52. **a.** Na, sodium
b. N, nitrogen
c. Si, silicon
d. O, oxygen
e. K, potassium
f. Ti, titanium

Critical Thinking

53. **a.** 1
b. 4
c. 1

54. Answers will vary. Students may note that radio waves have the lowest energy in the electromagnetic spectrum, and thus would not be energetic enough to cook food. Others may reason that if microwaves cook food faster than infrared radiation, then radio waves would cook food even faster.

---

44. $\lambda = \dfrac{\text{h}}{mv}$

$= \dfrac{(6.6262 \times 10^{-34}\ \text{J}\ \cancel{\text{s}})}{(2500\ \cancel{\text{kg}}) \times \dfrac{75\ \cancel{\text{km}}}{\cancel{\text{h}}} \times \dfrac{1000\ \text{m}}{1\ \cancel{\text{km}}} \times \dfrac{1\ \cancel{\text{h}}}{60\ \cancel{\text{min}}} \times \dfrac{1\ \cancel{\text{min}}}{60\ \cancel{\text{s}}}}$

$= 1.3 \times 10^{-38}\ \text{m}$

55. The model of the atom uses the abstract idea of probability; light is considered a particle and a wave at the same time. Atoms and light cannot be compared with familiar objects because humans cannot experience them directly. Because matter and energy behave differently at the atomic level than at the level humans can observe directly.

Cumulative Review

56. $0.406\ \cancel{nm} \times \frac{1\ m}{1 \times 10^9\ \cancel{nm}} = 4.06 \times 10^{-10}\ m$

$0.406\ \cancel{nm} \times \frac{10^{-3}\ \mu m}{1\ \cancel{nm}} = 4.06 \times 10^{-4}\ \mu m$

The units are different, but the values are equal.

57. **a.** $2KNO_3 + H_2SO_4 \rightarrow K_2SO_4 + 2HNO_3$
b. $Cu_2O + H_2 \rightarrow 2Cu + H_2O$
c. $2NO + Br_2 \rightarrow 2NOBr$
d. $SnO_2 + 2CO \rightarrow Sn + 2CO_2$

58. $5.00\ L\ \cancel{C_2H_2} \times \frac{5\ L\ O_2}{2\ L\ \cancel{C_2H_2}} = 12.5\ L\ O_2$

59. **a.** $\frac{\text{gam Si}}{\text{gfm } SiO_2} \times 100\%$

$= \frac{28.1\ \cancel{g}}{28.1\ \cancel{g} + (2 \times 16.0)\ \cancel{g}} \times 100\%$

$= 46.8\%\ Si$

$\frac{2 \times \text{gam O}}{\text{gfm } SiO_2} \times 100\%$

$= \frac{2 \times 16.00\ \cancel{g}}{28.1\ \cancel{g} + (2 \times 16.0)\ \cancel{g}} \times 100\%$

$= 53.2\%\ O$

b. $\frac{\text{gam Fe}}{\text{gfm } FeCl_3} \times 100\%$

$= \frac{55.8\ \cancel{g}}{55.8\ \cancel{g} + (3 \times 35.5)\ \cancel{g}} \times 100\%$

$= 34.4\%\ Fe$

$\frac{3 \times \text{gam Cl}}{\text{gfm } FeCl_3} \times 100\%$

$= \frac{3 \times 35.5\ \cancel{g}}{55.8\ \cancel{g} + (3 \times 35.5)\ \cancel{g}} \times 100\%$

$= 65.6\%\ Cl$

c. $\frac{\text{2 gam H}}{\text{gfm } H_2O} \times 100\%$

$= \frac{2 \times 1.0\ \cancel{g}}{(2 \times 1.0)\ \cancel{g} + 16.0\ \cancel{g}} \times 100\%$

$= 11.1\%\ H$

$\frac{\text{2 gam O}}{\text{gfm } H_2O} \times 100\%$

$\frac{16.0\ \cancel{g}}{(2 \times 1.0)\ \cancel{g} + 16.0\ \cancel{g}} \times 100\% = 88.9\%\ O$

d. $\frac{2 \times \text{gam H}}{\text{gfm } H_2SO_4} \times 100\%$

$= \frac{2 \times 1.0\ \cancel{g}}{(2 \times 1.0)\ \cancel{g} + 32.1\ \cancel{g} + (4 \times 16.0)\ \cancel{g}}$
$\times 100\%$
$= 2.0\%\ H$

$\frac{\text{gam S}}{\text{gfm } H_2SO_4} \times 100\%$

$= \frac{32.1\ \cancel{g}}{(2 \times 1.0)\ \cancel{g} + 32.1\ \cancel{g} + (4 \times 16.0)\ \cancel{g}}$
$\times 100\%$
$= 32.7\%\ S$

$\frac{4 \times \text{gam O}}{\text{gfm } H_2SO_4} \times 100\%$

$= \frac{4 \times 16.0\ \cancel{g}}{2 \times 1.0\ \cancel{g} + 32.1\ \cancel{g} + 4 \times 16.0\ \cancel{g}}$
$\times 100\%$
$= 65.2\%\ O$

e. $\frac{\text{gam Ca}}{\text{gfm } CaCO_3} \times 100\%$

$= \frac{40.1\ g}{40.1\ g + 12.0\ g + (3 \times 16.0)\ g} \times 100\%$

$= 40.1\%\ Ca$

$\frac{\text{gam C}}{\text{gfm } CaCO_3} \times 100\%$

$= \frac{12.0\ g}{40.1\ g + 12.0\ g + (3 \times 16.0)\ g} \times 100\%$

$= 12.0\%\ C$

$\frac{3 \times \text{gam O}}{\text{gfm } CaCO_3} \times 100\%$

$= \frac{3 \times 16.0\ g}{40.1\ g + 12.0\ g + (3 \times 16.0)\ g} \times 100\%$

$= 48.0\%\ O$

60. **a.** Fe^{3+} **b.** Hg^{2+} **c.** N^{3-} **d.** HCO_3^- **e.** O^{2-} **f.** MnO_4^-

61. **a.** 55 protons, 55 electrons
b. 47 protons, 46 electrons
c. 48 protons, 46 electrons
d. 34 protons, 36 electrons

62. $P_2 = \frac{P_1 \times T_2}{T_1}$

$= \frac{1\ atm \times (125 + 273)\ \cancel{K}}{273\ \cancel{K}} = 1.46\ atm$

63. $\text{Density} = \frac{\text{Mass}}{\text{Volume}}\quad M = D \times V$

$M = 19.3 \times \frac{g}{\cancel{cm^3}} \times 8.00\ \cancel{cm^3} = 154\ g$

$$154.4\ \cancel{g} \times \frac{1\ \text{kg}}{10^3\ \cancel{g}} = 0.154\ \text{kg}$$

Concept Challenge

64. a. $v = \frac{E}{h}$

5.21×10^{12}
4.40×10^{13}
9.49×10^{13}
1.70×10^{14}
2.20×10^{14}
4.69×10^{14}

b.

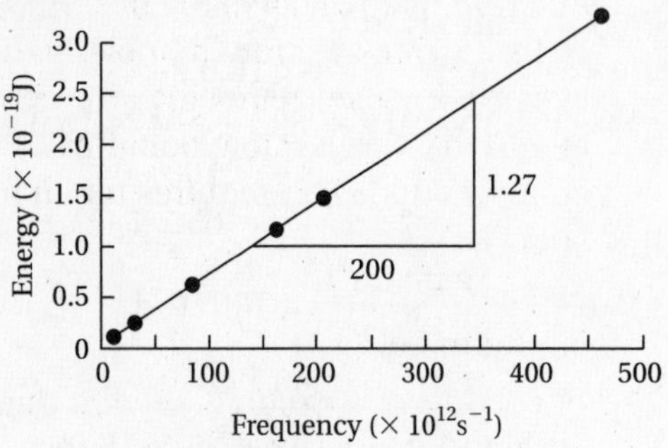

c. $\text{Slope} = \frac{\Delta\ \text{Energy}\ (\times 10^{-19}\ \text{J})}{\Delta\ \text{Frequency}\ (\times 10^{12}\ \text{s}^{-1})}$

$= \frac{1.27 \times 10^{-19}\ \text{J}}{200 \times 10^{12}\ \text{s}^{-1}}$

$= 6.3 \times 10^{-34}\ \text{Js}$

d. The slope is Planck's constant.

65. $2.08 \times 10^8\ \cancel{\text{km}} \times \frac{10^3\ \cancel{\text{m}}}{1\ \cancel{\text{km}}} \times \frac{1\ \text{s}}{3.00 \times 10^8\ \cancel{\text{m}}}$

$= 6.93 \times 10^2\ \text{s}$

66. Outermost electrons are ejected first. Then electrons at lower energy levels, which require greater escape energy, are ejected.

67. $E = \frac{Z^2 \times k}{n^2}$

For H:

$E = \frac{1^2 \times 1312\ \text{kJ/1 mol}}{1^2} = \frac{1312\ \text{kJ}}{\text{mol}}\ (n = 1)$

$E = \frac{1^2 + 1312\ \text{kJ/1 mol}}{2^2} = \frac{328.0\ \text{kJ}}{\text{mol}}\ (n = 2)$

For Li^{2+}:

$E = \frac{3^2 \times 1312\ \text{kJ/1 mol}}{1^2}$

$= \frac{1.181 \times 10^4\ \text{kJ}}{\text{mol}}\ (n = 1)$

Standardized Test Prep

1. (d)
2. (b)
3. (a)
4. (c)
5. (d)
6. (E)
7. (B)
8. (C)
9. (A)
10. (C)
11. (b)
12. (c)
13. (d)
14. (a)
15. (c)
16. (a)
17. (a)
18. According to the aufbau principle, electrons enter orbitals of lowest energy first. According to the Pauli exclusion principle, an orbital may contain at most two electrons. According to Hund's rule, one electron will enter each orbital of equal energy before electrons begin to pair up.

14 CHEMICAL PERIODICITY

Concept Practice

10. The noble gases are those elements listed in Group 0 of the periodic table. The representative elements are the Group A elements. The transition elements are the metallic elements in which the outermost *s* sublevel and the nearby *d* sublevel contain electrons; the transition elements are located in Groups 1B–8B. The inner transition elements are the lanthanide and actinide series of elements located in the *f*-block of the period table; a separate section between groups 2A and 3B.

11. **a.** $1s^22s^22p^1$
b. $1s^22s^22p^63s^2$
c. $1s^22s^22p^63s^23p^63d^{10}4s^24p^3$

12. Na, Mg, Cl

13. **a.** Ar: $1s^22s^22p^63s^23p^6$
b. Ge: $1s^22s^22p^63s^23p^63d^{10}4s^24p^2$
c. Ba: $1s^22s^22p^63s^23p^63d^{10}4s^24p^64d^{10}5s^25p^66s^2$

14. An element's outer electron configuration places it in a particular column (group) of the periodic table.

15. **a.** $1s^22s^22p^5$
b. $1s^22s^22p^63s^23p^63d^{10}4s^2$
c. $1s^22s^22p^63s^23p^1$
d. $1s^22s^22p^63s^23p^63d^{10}4s^24p^64d^{10}5s^25p^2$

16. **a.** H, Li, Na, K, Rb, Cs, Fr
b. O, S, Se, Te, Po
c. Zn, Cd, Hg, Uub

17. Fluorine has a smaller atomic radius than oxygen because fluorine has one more nuclear charge. Fluorine has a smaller radius than chlorine because fluorine has eight fewer electrons.

18. **a.** sodium
b. strontium
c. germanium
d. selenium

19. The first ionization energy is the energy needed to remove the outermost electron. The second ionization energy is the energy needed to remove the second-outermost electron.

20. **a.** boron
b. magnesium
c. aluminum

21. In a given row, nonmetals have higher ionization energies because the nuclear charge is greater and the shielding effect is the same, creating a stronger electron attraction.

22. **a.** Sr, Mg, Be
b. Cs, Ba, Bi
c. Na, Al, S

23. An atom of an alkali metal becomes stable by losing one electron. Removing the second electron involves removing an electron from an ion that has a stable noble-gas configuration. This requires much more energy.

24. **a.** Na **c.** I^-
b. S^{2-} **d.** Al

25. The radius of a cation is smaller than the atom from which it forms.

26. Noble gases generally do not form compounds.

27. **a.** fluorine **c.** magnesium
b. nitrogen **d.** arsenic

Concept Mastery

28. Mg^{2+} has a smaller radius than Na^+ because it has more protons. Therefore, there is a greater attraction by the nucleus for the remaining electrons in Mg^{2+}.

29. Zinc has more protons than calcium. This creates a stronger attraction for the 4*s* electrons.

30. **a.** The general trend is that the first ionization energy increases as electronegativity increases. This is true for both period 2 and period 3.
b. A positive correlation is expected because both properties measure the interaction between the nucleus and the surrounding electrons.

31. **a.** potassium, K, [Ar]$4s^1$
b. aluminum, Al, [Ne]$3s^23p^1$
c. sulfur, S, [Ne]$3s^23p^4$
d. barium, Ba [Xe]$6s^2$

32. **a.** Ca^{2+}
b. P^{3-}
c. Cu^+

33. scandium, Sc, $[Ar]3d^1 4s^2$
titanium, Ti, $[Ar]3d^2 4s^2$
vanadium, V, $[Ar]3d^3 4s^2$
chromium, Cr, $[Ar]3d^5 4s^1$
manganese, Mn, $[Ar]3d^5 4s^2$
iron, Fe, $[Ar]3d^6 4s^2$
cobalt, Co, $[Ar]3d^7 4s^2$
nickel, Ni, $[Ar]3d^8 4s^2$
copper, Cu, $[Ar]3d^{10} 4s^1$
zinc, Zn, $[Ar]3d^{10} 4s^2$

Critical Thinking

34. a. 2
b. 1
c. 3

35. Magnesium achieves a stable electron configuration by losing two electrons; aluminum achieves a stable electron configuration by losing three electrons.

36. a. 1851–1900; 25 elements
b. Mendeleev's periodic table helped scientists predict the existence of undiscovered elements.
c. None of these elements are found in nature

37. a. Possible cations are Rb^+ and Sr^{2+}; possible anions are Br^-, Se^{2-}, and As^{3-}.
b. No; a cation is isoelectronic with the noble gas in the preceding period; an anion is isoelectronic with the noble gas in the same period.

Cumulative Review

38. *See answer below.*

39. a. $2Ag + S \rightarrow Ag_2S$
b. $Na_2SO_4 + Ba(OH)_2 \rightarrow BaSO_4 + 2NaOH$
c. $Zn + 2HNO_3 \rightarrow Zn(NO_3)_2 + H_2$
d. $2H_2O + 2SO_2 + O_2 \rightarrow 2H_2SO_4$

40. $$\text{Mass}_{Fe} = \frac{55.8\text{ g Fe}}{1\ \cancel{\text{mol Fe}}} \times \frac{4\ \cancel{\text{mol Fe}}}{2\ \cancel{\text{mol Fe}_2\text{O}_3}} \times \frac{1\ \cancel{\text{mol Fe}_2\text{O}_3}}{159.6\ \cancel{\text{g Fe}_2\text{O}_3}} \times 100\ \cancel{\text{g Fe}_2\text{O}_3} = 69.9\text{ g Fe}$$

41. a. Li_2SO_4
b. $Zn_3(PO_4)_2$
c. $KMnO_4$
d. $SrCO_3$

42. $$V_2 = \frac{V_1 \times T_2}{T_1} = \frac{2.93\text{ L} \times (500 + 273)\ \cancel{\text{K}}}{(25 + 273)\ \cancel{\text{K}}} = 7.60\text{ L}$$

Concept Challenge

43. The radius of the ions decreases from S^{2-}, Cl^-, Ar, K^+, Ca^{2+}, to Sc^{3+} as the number of protons in the nucleus increases. The radius decreases from O^{2-}, F^-, Ne, Na^+, Mg^{2+}, to Al^{3+} for the same reason.

---

38. $$P_{CO_2} = \frac{n \times R \times T}{V} \text{ where } R = 8.31(\text{L} \times \text{kPa})/(\text{K} \times \text{mol}) = 0.0821\ (\text{atm} \times \text{L})/(\text{K} \times \text{mol})$$

$$= \frac{4.40\ \cancel{\text{g}} \times \frac{1\ \cancel{\text{mol}}}{44.0\ \cancel{\text{g}}} \times \frac{0.0821\text{ atm} \times \cancel{\text{L}}}{\cancel{\text{K}} \times \cancel{\text{mol}}} \times (27 + 273)\ \cancel{\text{K}}}{2.00\ \cancel{\text{L}}}$$

$$= 1.23\text{ atm}$$

$$P_{N_2} = \frac{2.00\ \cancel{\text{g}} \times \frac{1\ \cancel{\text{mol}}}{28.0\ \cancel{\text{g}}} \times \frac{0.0821\text{ atm} \times \cancel{\text{L}}}{\cancel{\text{K}} \times \cancel{\text{mol}}} \times (27 + 273)\ \cancel{\text{K}}}{2.00\ \cancel{\text{L}}}$$

$$= 0.880\text{ atm}$$

44. *See answer below.*

Standardized Test Prep

1. (a)

2. (c)

3. (b)

4. (a)

5.

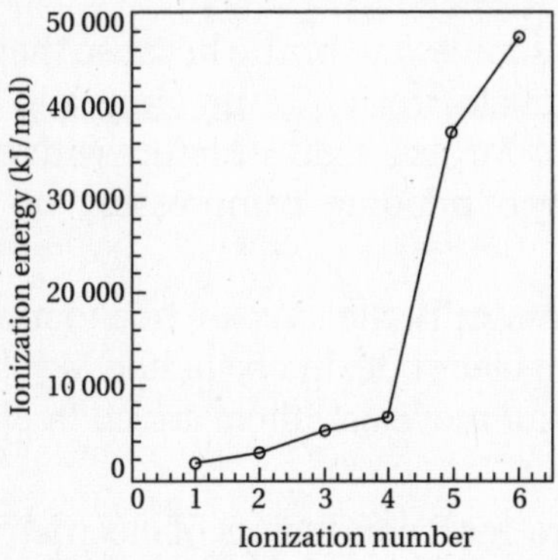

6. The largest increase is between ionization numbers 4 and 5 because carbon loses the first four electrons from the outermost (second) energy level. The fifth electron is removed from the first energy level.

7. (b)

8. (a)

9. Sphere (a) is the atom and sphere (b) is the anion.

10. inversely related

11. inversely related

12. directly related

13. True, True, correct explanation

14. True, False
Atoms of nonmetals are smaller than atoms of metals in the same period because, as the nuclear charge increases from left to right across the period, the outermost electrons are pulled closer to the nucleus.

15. True, False
Nonmetal ions are larger than the atoms from which they are formed, but metal ions are smaller than their corresponding atoms.

16. False, True
Of all the elements in a period, the noble gas has the largest ionization energy; it takes considerable energy to remove an electron from a filled energy level.

44.

	Density (g/cm^3)	Atomic Mass (amu)	Chlorides	Oxides	First Ionization Potential (kJ/mol)
Be	1.85	9.01	$BeCl_2$	BeO	900
Mg	1.74	24.31	$MgCl_2$	MgO	738
Ca	1.54	40.08	$CaCl_2$	CaO	590
Sr	2.64	87.62	$SrCl_2$	SrO	550
Ba	3.62	137.33	$BaCl_2$	BaO	503
Ra	5	226.03	$RaCl_2$	RaO	509

The table shows gradually increasing atomic masses and decreasing ionization potentials for these elements. All need two atoms of chlorine or one atom of oxygen for compounds.

15 IONIC BONDING AND IONIC COMPOUNDS

Concept Practice

20. *Valence electrons* are the electrons in the highest occupied energy level of an element's atoms.

21. The halogens are in Group 7A of the periodic table. They have seven valence electrons. The first four halogens are fluorine (F), chlorine (Cl), bromine (Br), and iodine (I).

22. **a.** 7 electrons; Group 5A
b. 3 electrons; Group 1A
c. 15 electrons; Group 5A
d. 56 electrons; Group 2A

23. **a.** :C̤l· **c.** ·Ȧl·
b. :Ṣ· **d.** Li·

24. Noble gas atoms are stable (exceptionally unreactive) because their outermost energy levels are filled.

25. **a.** 2 **c.** 1
b. 3 **d.** 2

26. **a.** Al^{3+} **d.** K^+
b. Li^+ **e.** Ca^{2+}
c. Ba^{2+} **f.** Sr^{2+}

27. **a.** $1s^22s^22p^63s^23p^63d^3$
b. $1s^22s^22p^63s^23p^63d^4$
c. $1s^22s^22p^63s^23p^63d^5$

28. Most nonmetals gain 1, 2, or 3 electrons to achieve a noble-gas electron configuration.

29. **a.** S^{2-} **c.** F^-
b. Na^+ **d.** P^{3-}

30. **a.** 3 **c.** 1
b. 2 **d.** 3

31. **a.** Br^- **c.** As^{3-}
b. H^- **d.** Se^{2-}

32. All are $1s^22s^22p^6$. All have the same configuration as neon.

33. Ionic compounds are neutral since the positive charges of the cations equal the negative charges of the anions.

34. Most ionic compounds contain metal and nonmetal atoms. Thus, the pairs of elements in **a., b.,** and **d** are not expected to form ionic compounds.

35. **a.** K^+ and Cl^- **c.** $Mg^{2+}$and Br^-
b. Ba^{2+} and $SO_4{}^{2-}$ **d.** Li^+ and $CO_3{}^{2-}$

36. No; the packing of ions in a crystalline structure depends on a number of factors, including the relative sizes of the ions. The coordination number of an element can vary from compound to compound.

37. Ionic substances are brittle because their network of electrostatic attractions and repulsions forms a rigid structure with no possibility of bending, compressing, or twisting.

38. In molten $MgCl_2$, the ions are free to move toward an electrode. In crystalline $MgCl_2$ the ions cannot move and there are no free electrons.

39. Metals are good conductors of electricity because they have many free electrons. The electrons that leave the metal are replaced by the ones in the entering current.

40. Body-centered cubic: Na, K, Fe, Cr, or W
Face-centered cubic: Cu, Ag, Au, Al, or Pb
Hexagonal close-packed: Mg, Zn, or Cd

41. Answers will vary and could include tableware, steel in cars and buses, high-speed dental drill bits, solder in stereos and televisions, and structural steel in buildings.

42. The properties of steel vary according to its composition. In addition to iron, steel can contain varying amounts of carbon and such metals as chromium, nickel, and molybdenum.

43. Brass is a mixture of copper and zinc. The properties of a particular sample of brass will vary with the relative proportions of the two metals.

Concept Mastery

44. **a., c, e,** and **f.**

45.

Group number	1A	2A	3A	5A	6A	7A
Valence electrons lost or gained	1	2	3	3	2	1
Ion formula	Na^+	Ca^{2+}	Al^{3+}	N^{3-}	S^{2-}	Br^-

46. **a.** ·Ċ· **d.** :F̤·
b. ·Be· **e.** Na·
c. :Ö· **f.** ·Ṗ·

47. For the representative elements, the number of electrons in the electron dot structure is the group number of the element.

48. A cation has a positive charge because it has lost valence electrons and therefore has more protons than electrons.

49. An anion has a negative charge because it has gained valence electrons. It has more electrons than protons.

50. In a hexagonal close-packed arrangement, every atom has twelve neighbors.

51. a. $1s^22s^22p^63s^23p^63d^6$
    b. $1s^22s^22p^63s^23p^63d^7$
    c. $1s^22s^22p^63s^23p^63d^8$

52. All have the noble gas configuration of argon: $1s^22s^22p^63s^23p^6$.

53. Hexagonal close-packed unit cells have 12 neighbors for every atom or ion. Face-centered cubic unit cells also have 12 neighbors for every atom or ion, with an atom or ion in the center of each face. Body-centered cubic units cells have 8 neighbors for every atom or ion, with an atom or ion at the center of each cube.

54. a. For nonmetals, an atom is smaller than its corresponding ion. Within a group, atoms and ions increase in size with increasing atomic number: oxygen atom, sulfur atom, oxide ion, sulfide ion.
    b. For metals, an atom is larger than its corresponding ion. Within a group, both atoms and ions increase in size with increasing atomic number: sodium ion, potassium ion, sodium atom, potassium atom.

55. a. $1s^22s^22p^63s^23p^6$
    b. $1s^22s^22p^6$
    Each atom and ion has a noble-gas electron configuration.

Critical Thinking

56. a. 4
    b. 1
    c. 3

57. Both are composed of ions and are held together by electrostatic bonds. Metals always conduct electricity, but ionic compounds conduct only when melted or in aqueous solution. Ionic compounds are composed of cations and anions, but metals are composd of cations and free-floating valence electrons. Metals are malleable, but ionic compounds are brittle.

Cumulative Review

58. Two moles of hydrogen produce two moles of water. Therefore 0.50 mol of H_2 is needed to make 0.50 mol H_2O.

$$0.50\ \cancel{\text{mol H}_2} \times \frac{22.4\ \text{L H}_2}{1\ \cancel{\text{mol H}_2}} = 11\ \text{L H}_2$$

59. Gases and liquids assume the shapes of their containers. Solids have a definite shape. Liquids and solids have a definite volume; gases do not. Gases have a low density; liquids have an intermediate density; solids have a high density. The molecules in a gas move freely and randomly. The molecules of a liquid flow. The molecules of a solid vibrate and rotate around a fixed position.

60. $$8.0\ \cancel{\text{g O}_2} \times \frac{1\ \text{mol O}_2}{32.0\ \cancel{\text{g O}_2}} = 0.25\ \text{mol O}_2$$

$$0.25\ \cancel{\text{mol O}_2} \times \frac{22.4\ \text{L O}_2}{1\ \cancel{\text{mol O}_2}} = 5.6\ \text{L O}_2$$

61. Raising the temperature of a gas increases the average kinetic energy and speed of the gas molecules. They also collide more often with the container walls. The pressure therefore increases if volume remains constant.

62. $$V_2 = \frac{P_1 \times V_1 \times T_2}{P_2 \times T_1} = \frac{1.6\ \cancel{\text{kPa}} \times 750\ \text{cm}^3 \times 273\ \cancel{\text{K}}}{101.3\ \cancel{\text{kPa}} \times (27 + 273)\ \cancel{\text{K}}} = 11\ \text{cm}^3$$

63. a. At 40 °C, more water molecules have energies that allow them to overcome the intermolecular attractions than at 20 °C, and water evaporates faster.
    b. Steam at 100 °C has the same kinetic energy as water at 100 °C but has more potential energy holding the molecules apart against their attractions. This additional energy increases the severity of the burn.

c. The temperature of the root beer increases in a sealed trunk. The molecules have more kinetic energy, creating a greater vapor pressure. This pops the can.
d. Because water molecules require more energy to evaporate than do ether molecules, the attractions between water molecules must be greater than those between ether molecules.
e. Ice absorbs energy to overcome the attractions between its molecules. The kinetic energy of the tea decreases, and its temperature drops.
f. The goal is to change liquid water to water vapor without destroying chemical bonds by heating; lowering the external pressure lowers the temperature at which liquid water molecules have enough energy to vaporize.

64. **a.** decreases
b. increases
c. decrease
d. increase
e. decrease
f. increase, decrease, or stay the same depending on the relative sizes of the changes of *T* and *P*.

65. $P_{\text{total}} = P_{O_2} + P_{N_2} = P_{O_2} + \dfrac{n_{N_2} \times P_{O_2}}{n_{O_2}}$

$= 63.3 \text{ kPa}$

$$+ \frac{1.50 \text{ g } N_2 \times \dfrac{1 \text{ mol}}{28.0 \text{ g } N_2} \times 63.3 \text{ kPa}}{1.50 \text{ g } O_2 \times \dfrac{1 \text{ mol}}{32.0 \text{ g } O_2}}$$

$= 136 \text{ kPa}$

66. Average kinetic energy is directly proportional to Kelvin temperature. Because 25 °C equals 298 K, the average kinetic energy will be double at 596 K, or 323 °C.

67. **a.** 0.0147 mol, 0.0373 mol, 0.0639 mol, 0.0879 mol
b.

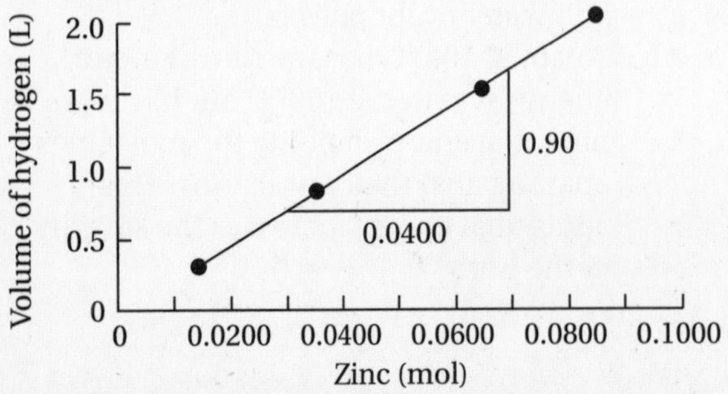

c. $\text{Slope} = \dfrac{\Delta \text{ Volume of } H_2 \text{ (L)}}{\Delta \text{ Zinc (mol)}}$

$= \dfrac{0.90 \text{ L}}{0.0400 \text{ mol}}$

$= 23 \text{ L/mol}$

d. One mole of H_2 is produced for each mole of Zn that reacts.

Concept Challenge

68. Sodium and cesium ions differ greatly in size. Sodium and chloride ions are similar in size to manganese and sulfide ions.

69. In the face of the face-centered cubic unit cell the three atoms along the diagonal are touching. The length of the diagonal is $0.4086 \text{ nm} \times \sqrt{2}$.

$\text{Radius}_{Ag} = \dfrac{\text{length of diagonal}}{4}$

$= \dfrac{0.4086 \text{ nm} \times \sqrt{2}}{4} = 0.1444 \text{ nm}$

70. **a.** cation: lose $1e^-$
b. cation: lose $1e^-$
c. unreactive
d. cation: lose $2e^-$
e. anion: gain $1e^-$

71. **a.** iron(II); Fe^{2+}
b. iron(III); Fe^{3+}
c. copper(II); Cu^{2+}
d. copper(I); Cu^+
e. cobalt(III); Co^{3+}

72. **a.** copper and zinc
b. silver and copper
c. copper and tin
d. iron, chromium, carbon, nickel
e. iron, chromium, nickel, molybdenum
f. iron, chromium, carbon

Standardized Test Prep

1. (c)
2. (d)
3. (a)
4. (c)
5. (c)
6. (d)
7. (E)
8. (B)
9. (D)
10. (C)
11. Because the atomic radius increases moving down the halogen group, the lattice energy decreases.
12. Lattice energy decreases as the atomic radius of the alkali metal increases.
13. decreases
14. The spheres are more closely packed in circle (a) because it has about 26 spheres compared to about 22 spheres in circle (b).

16 COVALENT BONDING

Concept Practice

27. Neon already has a stable electron configuration. A chlorine atom can achieve a stable electron configuration by sharing an electron with another chlorine atom.

28. **a.** ionic **c.** covalent
b. ionic **d.** covalent

29. Ionic bonds depend on electrostatic attraction between ions. Covalent bonds depend on electrostatic attraction between shared electrons and nuclei of combining atoms.

30. A double covalent bond has four shared electrons; a triple covalent bond has six shared electrons.

31. A single atom of an element is usually the central atom.

32. **a.** :I:I: **c.** H:S:H
b. :F:O:F: **d.** :I:N:I: / :I:

33. **a.** :F:F: **c.** H:C::C:H
b. H:Cl: **d.** H:C::N:

34. A bond in which one atom contributes both bonding electrons in a covalent bond is called a coordinate covalent bond. Sulfur dioxide has a coordinate covalent bond in which sulfur donates a pair of electrons for bonding to one of the oxygen atoms. (See Table 16.2.)

35. An unshared pair of electrons is needed for a coordinate covalent bond. There are no unshared pairs in C—H or C—C bonds.

36. Molecules of each compound can be described by more than one electron dot structure.

37. *See answer below.*

38. $[:O:N::O:]^{-} \leftrightarrow [:O::N:O:]^{-}$

39. The measured mass of a paramagnetic substance appears greater when measured in the presence of a magnetic field than when measured in the absence of a magnetic field.

40. **a.** 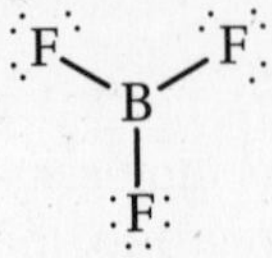 diamagnetic

b. :O—O: paramagnetic

c. O=N—O· paramagnetic

d. :F—F: diamagnetic

41. Phosphorus and sulfur sometimes expand octets because they are larger atoms than nitrogen and oxygen and have unfilled *d* orbitals that can be used to accommodate additional electrons.

42. **a.** $[:O:N::O: / :O:]^{-}$ diamagnetic

b. $[:O:H]^{-}$ diamagnetic

c. H:O:H diamagnetic

d. :O:S::O: / :O: diamagnetic

43. Increasing bond dissociation energy is linked to lower chemical reactivity.

44. Bond dissociation energy is defined as the energy needed to break one covalent bond.

45. H:C:::C:H There are 2 C—H bonds and 1 C ≡ C bond. $2(393) + 908 = 1694$ kJ/mol

---

37. 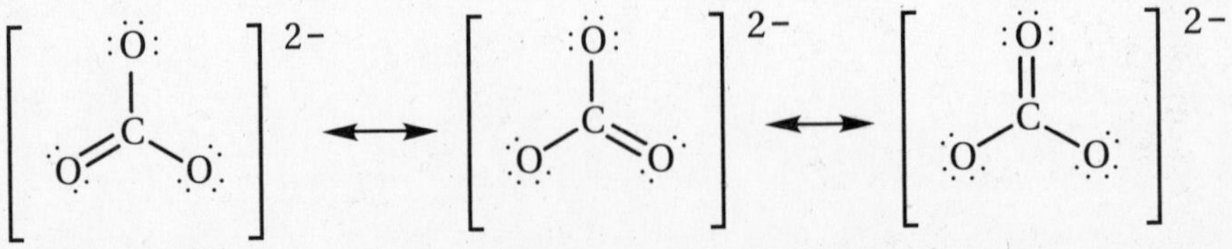

46.

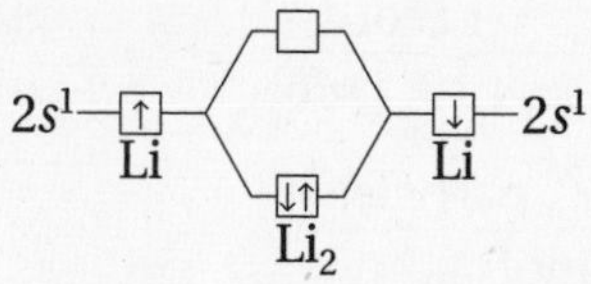

The lithium molecule has two electrons in a bonding molecular orbital. Lithium theoretically should exist as a diatomic molecule. The Li_2 molecule is moderately stable in the gaseous state.

47. a. 2 sigma bonds, 2 pi bonds
   b. 6 sigma bonds, 2 pi bonds

48. a. linear
   b. tetrahedral
   c. trigonal planar
   d. bent
   e. linear
   f. bent

49. The $2s$ and $2p$ orbitals form two sp^2 hybrid orbitals in the carbon atom. One sp^2 hybrid orbital from each oxygen atom forms a sigma bond with the sp orbital of the carbon atom. Pi bonds between each oxygen atom and the carbon are formed by the unhybridized $2p$ orbitals.

50. a. sp^3
   b. sp^2
   c. sp
   d. sp

51. The two atoms involved must have different electronegativities.

52. c., d., a., f., b., e.

53. b., d., e., a., c., f.

54. a. polar   **c.** nonpolar
   b. polar   **d.** nonpolar

55.

$\cdot\overset{\cdot\cdot}{O}\!-\!H$ H

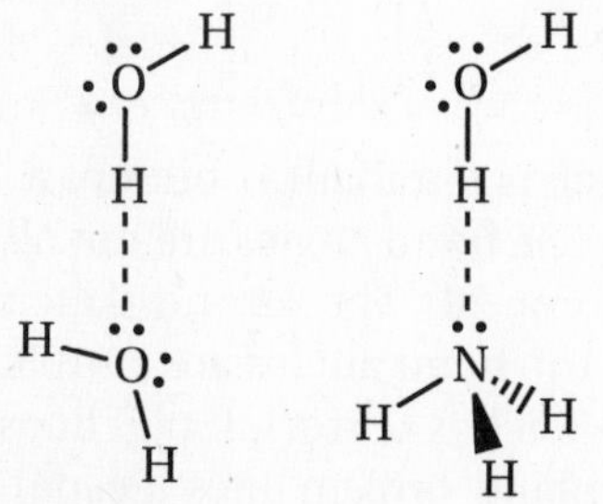

Hydrogen bonding between molecules is represented by a dashed line.

56. a. H_2O **c.** HCl
   b. HF   **d.** H_2O

57. A hydrogen bond is formed by an electrostatic attraction between a hydrogen atom covalently bonded to a very electronegative atom and an unshared electron pair of an electronegative atom in the same molecule or one nearby.

58. Compounds with stronger intermolecular forces require more energy to separate the molecules. Higher boiling points result from the need for a higher average kinetic energy to separate the molecules.

Concept Mastery

59. The $3s$ and three $3p$ orbitals of phosphorous hybridize to form four sp^3 hybrid orbitals. Three of these overlap with one p orbital of each chlorine to make three sigma bonds. The fourth hybrid orbital of phosphorous is an unshared pair of electrons that repels the other three orbitals slightly more. The resulting shape is pyramidal with a bond angle of $107°$ between the sigma bonds.

60. $\overset{\cdot\cdot}{N}\!:\!:\!N\!:\!:\!\overset{\cdot\cdot}{O}:$ $:\!N\!:\!:\!N\!:\!\overset{\cdot\cdot}{\underset{\cdot\cdot}{O}}:$

This molecule is linear. It is diamagnetic, with no unpaired electrons.

61. $:\!\overset{\cdot\cdot}{\underset{\cdot\cdot}{Cl}}\!:\!\overset{\cdot\cdot}{S}\!:\!\overset{\cdot\cdot}{\underset{\cdot\cdot}{Cl}}\!:$
$:\!\overset{\cdot\cdot}{\underset{\cdot\cdot}{O}}:$

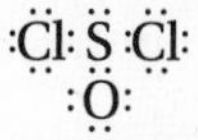

62. a. Carbon does not have an octet.

   $[:\!C\!:\!:\!N\!:]^-$

   b. A fluorine atom has 10 electrons.

   $:\!\overset{\cdot\cdot}{F}\!:\!\overset{\cdot\cdot}{P}\!:\!\overset{\cdot\cdot}{F}\!:$
   $:\!\overset{\cdot\cdot}{\underset{\cdot\cdot}{F}}\!:$

   c. Carbon has too many e^- (10) and oxygen too few (4).

   $H\!:\!C\!:\!:\!\overset{\cdot\cdot}{O}:$
   $:\!\overset{\cdot\cdot}{\underset{\cdot\cdot}{Cl}}:$

   d. The atoms in boron trifluoride have 24 electrons to contribute, not 26.

   $:\!\overset{\cdot\cdot}{F}\!:\!B\!:\!\overset{\cdot\cdot}{F}\!:$
   $:\!\overset{\cdot\cdot}{\underset{\cdot\cdot}{F}}\!:$

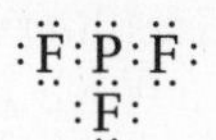

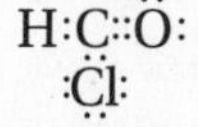

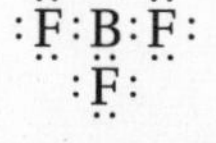

63. a. tetrahedral, 109.5°
   b. trigonal planar, 120°
   c. tetrahedral, 109.5°
   d. bent, 105°

64. a. The percent ionic character increases as the difference in electronegativities increases.
   b. 1.6
   c. (1) 85% (2) 10% (3) 62% (4) 23%

65. $\Delta H = \text{bond energy}_{C\equiv O} + (2 \times \text{bond energy})_{H-H} - (3 \times \text{bond energy})_{C-H} - \text{bond energy}_{C-O} - \text{bond energy}_{O-H}$

$$= \frac{1074 \text{ kJ}}{1 \text{ mol}} + 2 \times \frac{435 \text{ kJ}}{1 \text{ mol}} - 3 \times \frac{393 \text{ kJ}}{1 \text{ mol}} - \frac{356 \text{ kJ}}{1 \text{ mol}} - \frac{464 \text{ kJ}}{1 \text{ mol}} = -55 \frac{\text{kJ}}{\text{mol}}$$

66. **a.** 109.5°
b. 120°
c. 180°

67. An antibonding orbital has a higher energy because the atomic orbitals overlap on opposite sides of the nuclei, not between them.

Critical Thinking

68. **a.** 3
b. 3

69. C, O, H, S, N, F, Cl, I, Br; These elements are all nonmetals.

70. Answers will vary. **Table 16.4** suggests there is no clear difference. The student's argument could be based on chemical properties, such as conductivity of the compound in the liquid state.

Cumulative Review

71. a., b., c., d.

72. $BaCl_2(aq) + Na_2SO_4(aq) \rightarrow 2NaCl(aq) + BaSO_4(s)$
$BaCl_2$ is the limiting reagent:
0.10 mol $BaCl_2 \rightarrow$ 0.10 mol $BaSO_4$

$$\text{Mass}_{BaSO_4} = 0.10 \cancel{\text{mol}} \times \frac{233.4 \text{ g}}{1 \cancel{\text{mol}}} = 23 \text{ g } BaSO_4$$

73. **a.** $1s^2 2s^2 2p^6 3s^1$
b. $1s^2 2s^2 2p^6 3s^2 3p^4$
c. $1s^2 2s^2 2p^6 3s^2 3p^3$
d. $1s^2 2s^2 2p^3$

74. **a.** gfm = [40.1 + 32.1 + (4 × 16.0)] = 136.2 g
b. gfm = [(2 × 1.0) + 32.1 + (4 × 16.0)] = 98.1 g
c. gfm = [14.0 + (3 × 126.9)] = 394.7 g
d. gfm = [55.8 + (3 × 35.5)] = 162.3 g

75. **a.** $2.00 \cancel{\text{cmol}} \times \frac{1 \cancel{\text{mol}}}{1 \times 10^2 \cancel{\text{cmol}}} \times \frac{6.02 \times 10^{23} \text{ particles}}{1 \cancel{\text{mol}}} = 1.20 \times 10^{22} \text{ particles}$

b. $1.54 \cancel{\text{mmol}} \times \frac{1 \cancel{\text{mol}}}{1 \times 10^3 \cancel{\text{mmol}}} \times \frac{6.02 \times 10^{23} \text{ particles}}{1 \cancel{\text{mol}}} = 9.27 \times 10^{20} \text{ particles}$

c. $8.73 \cancel{\text{nmol}} \times \frac{1 \cancel{\text{mol}}}{1 \times 10^9 \cancel{\text{nmol}}} \times \frac{6.02 \times 10^{23} \text{ particles}}{1 \cancel{\text{mol}}} = 5.26 \times 10^{15} \text{ particles}$

d. $3.00 \cancel{\mu\text{mol}} \times \frac{1 \cancel{\text{mol}}}{1 \times 10^6 \cancel{\mu\text{mol}}} \times \frac{6.02 \times 10^{23} \text{ particles}}{1 \cancel{\text{mol}}} = 1.81 \times 10^{18} \text{ particles}$

76. **a.** manganese (Mn)
b. indium (In)
c. francium (Fr)
d. polonium (Po)

Concept Challenge

77.
```
  H
H:C:H
  H
```

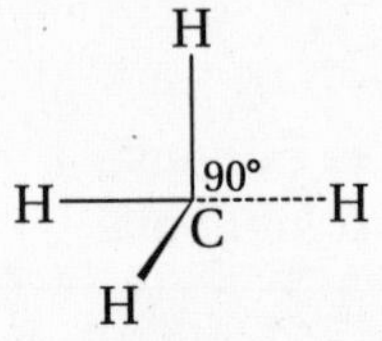

Sketch 1

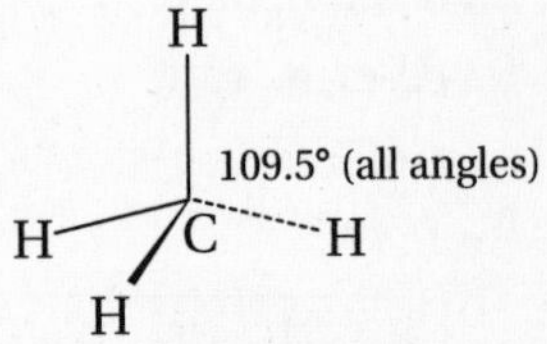

Sketch 2

The first sketch is tetrahedral, but not a tetrahedron. The bond angles are not all equal, with some 90°. The second sketch is a tetrahedron; the bond angles are all 109.5°. The second sketch is correct. (Solid lines lie in the paper plane, broken lines recede, and wedged lines come out of the paper plane.)

78. 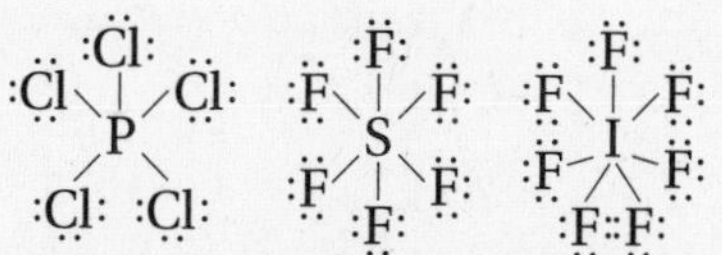

In each compound, each electron makes a hybrid orbital for sigma bonding to halogen. P forms 5 hybrid orbitals (*dsp*^{3}), S forms 6 hybrid orbitals (*d*^{2}*sp*^{3}), and I forms 7 hybrid orbitals (*d*^{3}*sp*^{3}).

Standardized Test Prep

1. (c)
2. (d)
3. (b)
4. (a)
   The polyatomic ammonium ion contains covalent bonds.
5. (c)
   Fluorine is the most electronegative element.
6. 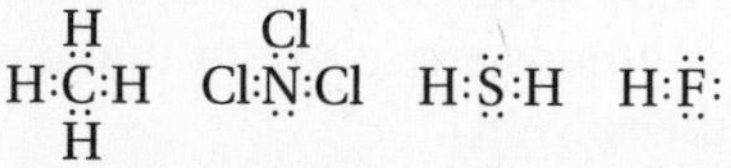
7. Each central atom has four pairs of electrons that, according to VSEPR theory, assume a tetrahedral shape.
8. The two nonbonding pairs repel the bonding pairs; there are still four pairs of electrons around the sulfur atom.
9. The arrangement of electron pairs is tetrahedral. The electron dot structure shows three bonding electron pairs and one nonbonding electron pair; thus, the predicted molecular shape is pyramidal.
10. hydrogen bonding
11. primarily dispersion forces
12. hydrogen bonding
13. 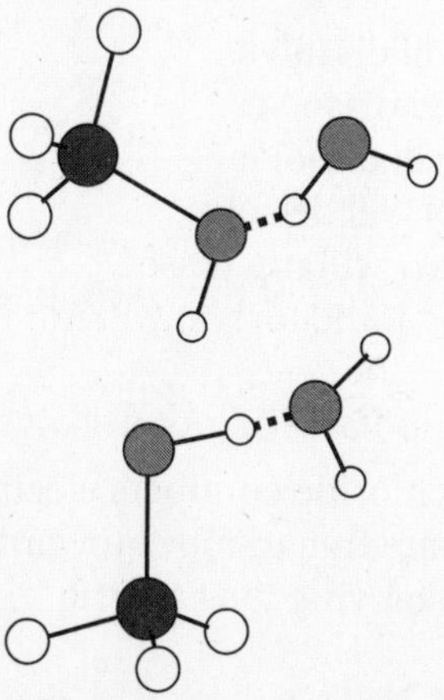
14. True, True
15. True, True
16. False, True
    Because dispersion forces between xenon atoms are stronger than those between neon atoms, xenon has a higher boiling point than neon.
17. True, False
    The actual bonds in a nitrate ion are hybrids of single and double bonds.

17 WATER AND AQUEOUS SYSTEMS

Concept Practice

19. Water molecules are polar because oxygen is more electronegative than hydrogen. Because of the bent shape of the molecule, the bond polarities do not cancel.

20. Surface molecules are attracted to the liquid molecules below but not to the air. Molecules inside the liquid are attracted in all directions.

21. Some water molecules have sufficient energy to leave the surface of the liquid. Vapor pressure is the pressure of the water vapor above the liquid.

22. The surface tension of a liquid tends to hold a drop of the liquid in a spherical shape. It also makes it possible for certain objects denser than a liquid to float on the surface.

23. A surfactant physically interferes with hydrogen bonding between water molecules and reduces surface tension. Surfactants also replace water molecules at the surface.

24. No; the specific heat capacity is expressed per gram of water and is essentially constant at 4.18 J/(g × °C) at temperatures between 0 °C and 100 °C.

25. $\Delta H = m \times C \times \Delta T$

$$256\ \cancel{\text{g H}_2\text{O}} \times \frac{4.18\ \text{J}}{\cancel{\text{g H}_2\text{O}} \times \cancel{°\text{C}}} \times (99\ \cancel{°\text{C}} - 20\ \cancel{°\text{C}}) = 8.5 \times 10^4\ \text{J}$$

$$256\ \cancel{\text{g Fe}} \times \frac{0.447\ \text{J}}{\cancel{\text{g Fe}} \times \cancel{°\text{C}}} \times (99\ \cancel{°\text{C}} - 20\ \cancel{°\text{C}}) = 9.0 \times 10^3\ \text{J}$$

26. ΔH_{vap} (water) = 2.26 kJ/g

$$5.0\ \cancel{\text{mg H}_2\text{O}(l)} \times \frac{1\ \cancel{\text{g H}_2\text{O}(l)}}{10^3\ \cancel{\text{mg H}_2\text{O}(l)}} \times \frac{2.26\ \text{kJ}}{1\ \cancel{\text{g H}_2\text{O}(l)}} = 1.1 \times 10^{-2}\ \text{kJ}$$

27. Ammonia molecules form hydrogen bonds, whereas methane molecules do not. Substances whose molecules form hydrogen bonds tend to have higher boiling points.

28. $\Delta H = m \times \Delta H_{vap}$

$$= 24\ \cancel{\text{g}}\ \text{H}_2\text{O} \times \frac{2.26\ \cancel{\text{kJ}}}{1\ \cancel{\text{g H}_2\text{O}(g)}} \times \frac{10^3\ \cancel{\text{J}}}{1\ \cancel{\text{kJ}}} \times \frac{1\ \text{cal}}{4.184\ \cancel{\text{J}}}$$
$$= 1.3 \times 10^4\ \text{cal}$$

29. Ice has an open, honeycomb-like structure of hydrogen-bonded water molecules. Water has a less rigid structure in which water molecules are closer together. The density of ice is less than that of water because of ice's lattice structure. As a result, ice floats on water.

30. ΔH_{fus} (ice) = 6.01 kJ/mol

$$24\ \cancel{\text{g H}_2\text{O}(s)} \times \frac{334\ \cancel{\text{J}}}{1\ \cancel{\text{g H}_2\text{O}(s)}} \times \frac{1\ \text{kJ}}{10^3\ \cancel{\text{J}}} = 8.0\ \text{kJ}$$

31. Bodies of water would freeze from the bottom up. This would kill many forms of aquatic life.

32. Solutions are homogeneous mixtures in which a solute is dissolved in a solvent. Aqueous solutions are solutions that have water as the solvent.

33. The polar water molecules electrostatically attract ions and polar covalent molecules. Polar compounds will dissolve but nonpolar compounds are unaffected because they have no charges.

34. No. In a solution, each solute molecule is surrounded by solvent molecules. Solute and solvent molecules pass through the filter because molecules and ions are smaller than the pores of the filter.

35. The positive ions are attracted by the negatively charged end of the polar water molecule; the negative ions are attracted by the positively charged end. As the ions are pulled away from the crystal, they are surrounded by the water molecules.

36. **a.** HCl (polar) will dissolve.
b. NaI (ionic) will dissolve.
c. NH_3 (polar) will dissolve.
d. $MgSO_4$ (ionic) will dissolve.
e. CH_4 (nonpolar) will not dissolve.
f. $CaCO_3$ (strong ionic forces) will not dissolve.
g. Gasoline (nonpolar) will not dissolve.

37. Molten sodium chloride conducts electricity because its ions are free to move toward an electrode. These moving ions are the current.

38. At the same concentrations, an aqueous solution of a strong electrolyte is almost totally ionized.

39. The water of hydration is the water molecules that are an integral part of a crystal structure of a substance.

40. **a.** $Na_2SO_4 \cdot 10H_2O$
b. $MgSO_4 \cdot 7H_2O$
c. $Ba(OH)_2 \cdot 8H_2O$

41. **a.** tin(IV) chloride pentahydrate
b. iron(II) sulfate heptahydrate
c. barium bromide tetrahydrate
d. iron(III) phosphate tetrahydrate

42. $MgSO_4 \cdot 7H_2O \xrightarrow{150\ ^\circ C} MgSO_4 \cdot H_2O + 6H_2O$

43. A suspension is a mixture with large particles that settle on standing. A colloid is a mixture with particles of intermediate size that do not settle.

44. The molecules or ions are too small to have reflective surfaces.

45. The random motion of the dispersion medium molecules causes them to collide with the molecules of the dispersed phase. The colloidal particles are so small that this force is enough to overcome gravity and keep the particles in suspension.

46. Brownian motion is the random movement of colloidal particles caused by collisions with molecules of the medium in which they are dispersed.

Concept Mastery

47. As liquid water cools to 4 °C, the kinetic energy of the molecules decreases allowing the intermolecular attractive forces to hold molecules closer together. As a result, the liquid contracts until it reaches a maximum density at 4 °C. Below 4 °C, the liquid solidifies. In the solid state the water molecules are held in fixed positions by hydrogen bonds. The maximum number of hydrogen bonds form when the molecules are arranged in a more open honeycomb arrangement. As a result, ice has a lower density than liquid water, and will float in its liquid.

48. hexane, ethanol, water

49. **a.** *See answer below.*
b. *See answer below.*

50. **a.** $\Delta H = \Delta H_{vap} \times m + [m \times C \times \Delta T]$

$$= \left(\frac{540\ \text{cal}}{\text{g } H_2O(g)} \times 5.0\ \text{g } H_2O(g)\right) + \left[5.0\ \text{g } H_2O(g) \times \frac{1.0\ \text{cal}}{\text{g } H_2O(g) \times {}^\circ C} \times (100\ {}^\circ C - 50\ {}^\circ C)\right]$$

$$= 2.95 \times 10^3\ \text{cal}$$

b. $2.95 \times 10^3\ \text{cal} \times \dfrac{1\ \text{kcal}}{1000\ \text{cal}} = 2.95\ \text{kcal}$

51. Ions in solution are surrounded by water molecules. Negative ions are attracted to the hydrogen atoms and positive ions are attracted to the oxygen atoms.

---

49. **a.** sodium carbonate monohydrate:

$$\%\ H_2O = \frac{\text{gfm } H_2O}{\text{gfm } Na_2CO_3 \cdot H_2O} \times 100\% = \frac{18.0\ \text{g}}{(2 \times 23.0)\ \text{g} + 12.0\ \text{g} + (3 \times 16.0)\ \text{g} + 18.0\ \text{g}} \times 100\%$$
$$= 14.5\%\ H_2O$$

b. magnesium sulfate heptahydrate:

$$\%\ H_2O = \frac{7 \times \text{gfm } H_2O}{\text{gfm } MgSO_4 \cdot 7H_2O} \times 100\% = \frac{7 \times 18.0\ \text{g}}{24.3\ \text{g} + 32.1\ \text{g} + (4 \times 16.0)\ \text{g} + (7 \times 18.0)\ \text{g}} \times 100\%$$
$$= 51.1\%\ H_2O$$

52. $\Delta H = \Delta H_{fus} \times m$

$$= \frac{80\ \text{cal}}{1\ \cancel{g}\ H_2O(s)} \times 176.0\ \cancel{g}\ H_2O(s) \times \frac{25}{100}$$

$$= 3.52 \times 10^3\ \text{cal}$$

$$3.52 \times 10^3\ \cancel{\text{cal}} \times \frac{1\ \text{kcal}}{1000\ \cancel{\text{cal}}} = 3.52\ \text{kcal}$$

$$3.52 \times 10^3\ \cancel{\text{cal}} \times \frac{4.184\ \text{J}}{1\ \cancel{\text{cal}}} = 1.47 \times 10^4\ \text{J}$$

$$1.47 \times 10^4\ \cancel{\text{J}} \times \frac{1\ \text{kJ}}{1000\ \cancel{\text{J}}} = 14.7\ \text{kJ}$$

$$\text{Mass remaining} = 176.0\ \text{g}\ H_2O(s) \times \frac{75}{100}$$

$$= 132.0\ \text{g}\ H_2O(s)$$

53. **a.** no
b. tasting, drying to examine the crystals, testing for electrical conductivity, doing a flame test

54. **a.** water
b. water
c. gasoline
d. water

55. **a.** 1, 3, 6, 8
b. 1, 2, 5, 6, 7, 9
c. 2, 4, 5

56. **a.** Water expands when it turns to ice.
b. Water is polar and wax is nonpolar, and water has a high surface tension.
c. Sweat evaporates to carry away the heat of vaporization.
d. Freezing damages plants because water inside them expands as it freezes. Water on the surface gives off the heat of fusion to the plants when it freezes.
e. Steam carries the heat of vaporization. It also has more heat than an equal mass of water. This heat energy is released as steam condenses to water.

57. Ethyl alcohol has a polar hydroxyl end (—OH) that dissolves in water, and a nonpolar hydrocarbon end (C_2H_5—) that dissolves in gasoline.

58. $$\text{Mass} = \frac{0.997\ \text{g}}{\cancel{\text{cm}^3}} \times \frac{1 \times 10^6\ \cancel{\text{cm}^3}}{1\ \cancel{\text{m}^3}} \times 25.0\ \cancel{\text{m}}$$

$$\times 10.0\ \cancel{\text{m}} \times 1.70\ \cancel{\text{m}} = 4.24 \times 10^8\ \text{g}$$

$$\Delta H = \Delta H_{fus} \times m + [m \times C \times \Delta T]$$

$$= \left[\frac{80\ \text{cal}}{\cancel{g}} \times (4.24 \times 10^8\ \cancel{g})\right]$$

$$+ \left[\left(4.24 \times 10^8\ \cancel{g}\right) \times \frac{1\ \text{cal}}{\cancel{g} \times \cancel{°C}}) \times 25\ \cancel{°C}\right]$$

$$= 4.5 \times 10^{10}\ \text{cal} = 4.5 \times 10^7\ \text{kcal}$$

$$= 4.5 \times 10^7\ \cancel{\text{kcal}} \times \frac{4.18\ \text{kJ}}{1\ \cancel{\text{kcal}}} = 1.9 \times 10^8\ \text{kJ}$$

59. Not all liquids are soluble in each other. Nonpolar liquids do not dissolve in polar liquids. The polar molecules are attracted to each other but not to nonpolar molecules.

60. **a.** $NH_4Cl \xrightarrow{H_2O} NH_4^+(aq) + Cl^-(aq)$
b. $Cu(NO_3)_2 \xrightarrow{H_2O} Cu^{2+}(aq) + 2NO_3^-(aq)$
c. $HC_2H_3O_2 \xrightarrow{H_2O} H^+(aq) + C_2H_3O_2^-(aq)$
d. $HgCl_2 \xrightarrow{H_2O} Hg^{2+}(aq) + 2Cl^-(aq)$

61. **a.** 1.0001 g/mL
b. 4 °C
c. No; the density of ice is 0.917 g/mL at 0 °C. There would be a break in the curve at 0 °C as liquid water at 0 °C changes to solid water (ice) at 0 °C.

Critical Thinking

62. **a.** 1
b. 3
c. 2

63. The blood and all of the body's cells contain large amounts of water. Most of the important chemical reactions of life take place in aqueous solution inside cells.

64. The nonpolar liquid would form a layer in the water. The layer would be on top of the water if its density were less than that of water and on the bottom if its density were greater. A temporary emulsion would form if the mixture were shaken.

Cumulative Review

65. **a.** Mass = density × volume

$$= \text{density} \times \pi r^2 h$$

$$= \frac{0.988\ \text{g}}{1\ \cancel{\text{cm}^3}} \times 3.14 \times (1.50\ \cancel{\text{cm}})^2 \times 28.0\ \cancel{\text{cm}}$$

$$= 195\ \text{g}$$

b. $195\ \cancel{g} \times \dfrac{1000\ \text{mg}}{1\ \cancel{g}} = 1.95 \times 10^5\ \text{mg}$

c. $195\ \cancel{g} \times \dfrac{1\ \text{kg}}{1000\ \cancel{g}} = 0.195\ \text{kg}$

66. $$P_2 = \frac{P_1 \times T_2}{T_1} = \frac{1\ \text{atm} \times (200 + 273)\ \cancel{K}}{(100 + 273)\ \cancel{K}}$$

$$= 1.27\ \text{atm}$$

67. **a.** An increase in pressure on a water surface raises the boiling point of the water because it tends to hold the water molecules together, making escape difficult.
b. A decrease in pressure lowers the boiling point because less kinetic energy is needed for molecules to escape.

68. At STP, 2.00×10^{-3} mol $H_2O_2 \rightarrow$
2.00×10^{-3} mol H_2O + 1.00×10^{-3} mol O_2.

$$2.00 \times 10^{-3} \cancel{\text{mol } H_2O(l)} \times \frac{18.0 \text{ g } H_2O(l)}{1 \cancel{\text{mol } H_2O(l)}} = 3.60 \times 10^{-2} \text{ g } H_2O(l)$$

$$1.00 \times 10^{-3} \cancel{\text{mol } O_2(g)} \times \frac{22.4 \text{ L } O_2(g)}{1 \cancel{\text{mol } O_2(g)}} = 2.24 \times 10^{-2} \text{ L } O_2(g)$$

69. $2H_2 + O_2 \rightarrow 2H_2O$
4.50 mol water requires 4.50 mol H_2 and 2.25 mol O_2.

$$4.50 \cancel{\text{mol } H_2} \times \frac{2.0 \text{ g } H_2}{1 \cancel{\text{mol } H_2}} = 9.00 \text{ g } H_2$$

$$2.25 \cancel{\text{mol } O_2} \times \frac{32.0 \text{ g } O_2}{1 \cancel{\text{mol } O_2}} = 72.0 \text{ g } O_2$$

70. $C_3H_8 + 5O_2 \rightarrow 3CO_2 + 4H_2O$
Combustion of one mole of propane will produce 4 moles of water.

$$8.0 \cancel{\text{L } C_3H_8} \times \frac{1 \cancel{\text{mol } C_3H_8}}{22.4 \cancel{\text{L } C_3H_8}} \times \frac{4 \cancel{\text{mol } H_2O}}{1 \cancel{\text{mol } C_3H_8}} \times \frac{18.0 \text{ g } H_2O}{\cancel{\text{mol } H_2O}} = 25.7 \text{ g } H_2O$$

71. $C_2H_2 + H_2O \rightarrow C_2H_4O$
One mole of water makes one mole of acetaldehyde.

$$2.60 \times 10^2 \cancel{\text{g } H_2O} \times \frac{1 \cancel{\text{mol } H_2O}}{18.0 \cancel{\text{g } H_2O}} \times \frac{1 \text{ mol } C_2H_4O}{1 \cancel{\text{mol } H_2O}} \times \frac{44.0 \text{ g } C_2H_4O}{1 \cancel{\text{mol } C_2H_4O}} = 636 \text{ g } C_2H_4O$$

Concept Challenge

72. **a.** pink
b. pink
c. blue
d. gfm $CoCl_2 \cdot 6H_2O$ = 237.9 g

$$\%H_2O = \frac{6 \times \text{gfm } H_2O}{\text{gfm } CoCl_2 \cdot 6H_2O} \times 100\% = \frac{108 \cancel{\text{ g}}}{237.9 \cancel{\text{ g}}} \times 100\% = 45.4\ \%$$

e. Cobalt chloride paper is used to test for the presence of water.

73. **a.** As the molar mass increases, the boiling point increases.
b. The boiling point more than doubles.

74. **a.** The volume of 1 g ice at 0 °C is greater than the volume of 1 g of liquid water at 0 °C.
b. The volume of 1 g liquid water at 100 °C is less than the volume of 1 g of steam at 100 °C.

75. $2H_2 + O_2 \rightarrow 2H_2O$
a. Hydrogen gas is the limiting reagent because 2 volumes of H_2 are needed for 1 volume of O_2, but only 1.5 volumes of H_2 are available.
b.

$$60 \cancel{\text{cm}^3 H_2} \times \frac{1 \cancel{\text{L } H_2}}{10^3 \cancel{\text{cm}^3 H_2}} \times \frac{1 \cancel{\text{mol } H_2}}{22.4 \cancel{\text{L } H_2}} \times \frac{1 \cancel{\text{mol } H_2O}}{1 \cancel{\text{mol } H_2}} \times \frac{18.0 \text{ g } H_2O}{1 \cancel{\text{mol } H_2O}} = 4.8 \times 10^{-2} \text{ g } H_2O$$

c. Oxygen is in excess.
d. Because only 30 cm^3 O_2 is used, 10 cm^3 O_2 remains.

Standardized Test Prep

1. (d)
2. (b)
3. (b)
4. (b)
5. When water is purified by distillation, dissolved ions are removed. Ethanol is a molecular compound that does not ionize in water.
6. KCl and NaOH have similar conductivities because they provide two moles of ions per mole of compound. $CaCl_2$ and $MgBr_2$ have similar conductivities because they provide three moles of ions per mole of compound.
7. Aluminum chloride provides twice as many ions per mole as potassium chloride.
8. (b)
When the solvent is doubled, the concentration of the solute per unit volume is cut in half.
9. True, True, correct explanation
10. False, True
Methanol is a nonelectrolyte.
11. False, True
The intermediate-sized colloid particles are interspersed throughout the mixture and do not settle out.
12. True, True

18 SOLUTIONS

Concept Practice

40. A solution is composed of a solvent and one or more solutes. The dissolving medium, and the component in greater amount, is the solvent. The dissolved particles, and the component present in smaller amount, is the solute.

41. Each of the molecules or ions of the dissolved component is surrounded by molecules of the solvent. Random collisions of the solvent molecules with the solute molecules or ions provide enough force to overcome gravity. As a result, no solute particles settle out.

42. Fluids that mix with, or dissolve in each other in all proportions are miscible. Fluids that do not mix with, and are not soluble in each other are immiscible.

43. Solubility is the amount of solute dissolved in a given amount of solvent to form a saturated solution at a given temperature. A saturated solution contains the maximum possible amount of solute at that temperature. An unsaturated solution contains less dissolved solute than a saturated solution.

44. Mass $AgNO_3$ = solubility $AgNO_3$ $\times$ mass solvent (H_2O)

$$= \frac{222.0 \text{ g } AgNO_3}{100 \text{ g } \cancel{H_2O}} \times 250 \text{ g } \cancel{H_2O}$$

$$= 555 \text{ g } AgNO_3$$

45. The solution becomes cloudy as particles of solute crystallize and become large enough to reflect light. Some of the crystallized solute particles fall to the bottom of the container as they increase in size.

46. No; if there were undissolved solute, the excess solute would come out of solution.

47. When the pressure is increased, the solubility of a gas in a liquid is increased.

48. $S_2 = \frac{S_1 \times P_2}{P_1}$

a. $$\frac{\frac{0.026 \text{ g}}{\text{L}} \times 0.60 \cancel{\text{atm}}}{1.00 \cancel{\text{atm}}} = 0.016 \text{ g/L}$$

b. $$\frac{\frac{0.026 \text{ g}}{\text{L}} \times 1.80 \cancel{\text{atm}}}{1.00 \cancel{\text{atm}}} = 0.047 \text{ g/L}$$

49. Molarity provides the exact number of moles of solute per liter of solution. Dilute and concentrated are relative terms and are not quantitative.

50. $M = \frac{\text{mol}}{\text{L}}$

a. $750 \cancel{\text{mL}} \times \frac{1 \text{ L}}{1000 \cancel{\text{mL}}} = 0.75 \text{ L}$

$$\frac{1.0 \text{ mol KCl}}{0.75 \text{ L}} = 1.3M \text{ KCl}$$

b. $\frac{0.50 \text{ mol } MgCl_2}{1.5 \text{ L}} = 0.33M \text{ } MgCl_2$

51. Molarity is the number of moles of solute dissolved in one liter of solution.

52. Mol = $M \times L$

a. $\frac{0.50 \text{ mol NaCl}}{\cancel{\text{L}}} \times 1.0 \cancel{\text{L}} = 0.50 \text{ mol NaCl}$

$$0.50 \cancel{\text{mol NaCl}} \times \frac{58.5 \text{ g NaCl}}{\cancel{\text{mol NaCl}}} = 29 \text{ g NaCl}$$

b. $500 \cancel{\text{mL}} \times \frac{1 \cancel{\text{L}}}{1000 \cancel{\text{mL}}} \times \frac{2.0 \text{ mol } KNO_3}{\cancel{\text{L}}}$

$= 1.0 \text{ mol } KNO_3$

$$1.0 \cancel{\text{mol } KNO_3} \times \frac{101.1 \text{ g } KNO_3}{\cancel{\text{mol } KNO_3}}$$

$= 1.0 \times 10^2 \text{ g } KNO_3$

c. $250 \cancel{\text{mL}} \times \frac{1 \cancel{\text{L}}}{1000 \cancel{\text{mL}}} \times \frac{0.10 \text{ mol } CaCl_2}{1 \cancel{\text{L}}}$

$= 0.025 \text{ mol } CaCl_2$

$$0.025 \cancel{\text{mol } CaCl_2} \times \frac{111.1 \text{ g } CaCl_2}{\cancel{\text{mol } CaCl_2}}$$

$= 2.8 \text{ g } CaCl_2$

d. $2.0 \cancel{\text{L}} \times \frac{0.30 \text{ mol } Na_2SO_4}{\cancel{\text{L}}}$

$= 0.60 \text{ mol } NaSO_4$

$$0.60 \cancel{\text{mol } Na_2SO_4} \times \frac{142.1 \text{ g } Na_2SO_4}{\cancel{\text{mol } Na_2SO_4}}$$

$= 85 \text{ g } Na_2SO_4$

53. a. $2.5 \cancel{\text{L}} \times \frac{10^3 \cancel{\text{mL}}}{1 \cancel{\text{L}}} \times \frac{0.90 \text{ g NaCl}}{10^2 \cancel{\text{mL}}}$

$= 23 \text{ g NaCl}$

b. $50 \cancel{\text{mL}} \times \frac{4.0 \text{ g } MgCl_2}{100 \cancel{\text{mL}}} = 2.0 \text{ g } MgCl_2$

54. a. $\frac{20\text{ g KCl}}{600\text{ mL}} \times 100\% = 3.3\%\text{ KCl}$

b. $\frac{32\text{ g NaNO}_3}{2.0\text{ }\cancel{L}} \times \frac{1\text{ }\cancel{L}}{1000\text{ mL}} \times 100\%$
$= 1.6\%\text{ NaNO}_3$

55. The boiling point of water increases by 0.512 °C for every mole of particles that the solute forms when dissolved in 1000 g of water.

a. $0.50\text{ }\cancel{\text{mol particles}} \times \frac{0.512\text{ °C}}{1\text{ }\cancel{\text{mol particles}}}$
$= 0.26\text{ °C}$

Boiling point of solution
$= 100\text{ °C} + 0.26\text{ °C} = 100.26\text{ °C}$

b. $3.0\text{ }\cancel{\text{mol particles}} \times \frac{0.512}{1\text{ }\cancel{\text{mol particles}}}$
$= 1.54\text{ °C}$

Boiling point of solution
$= 100\text{ °C} + 1.54\text{ °C} = 101.54\text{ °C}$

56. $X_{Me} = \frac{n_{Me}}{n_{H_2O} + n_{Me}}$

$0.40 = \frac{n_{Me}}{n_{H_2O} + n_{Me}}$

$n_{H_2O} = 1.5\text{ mol H}_2\text{O}$
$= 27\text{ g H}_2\text{O}$

$n_{Me} = 1.0\text{ mol CH}_3\text{OH}$
$= 32\text{ g CH}_3\text{OH}$

Add 27.0 g H_2O to 32.0 g CH_3OH.

57. A 1*M* solution is 1 mol of solute dissolved in 1 liter of solution. A 1*m* solution is 1 mol of solute dissolved in 1000 g, or 1 kg, of solvent.

58. a. Molality of $Na_2SO_4 = \frac{1.40\text{ mol Na}_2\text{SO}_4}{1750\text{ }\cancel{\text{g H}_2\text{O}}}$
$\times 1000\text{ }\cancel{\text{g H}_2\text{O}}$
$= 0.800m\text{ Na}_2\text{SO}_4$

Each mol of Na_2SO_4 that dissolves yields 3 mol of particles.
Molality of total particles
$= 3 \times 0.800m = 2.40m$

$\Delta T_f = K_f \times m$
$= 1.86\text{ °C}/m \times 2.40m$
$= 4.46\text{ °C}$

Freezing point of solution
$= 0\text{ °C} - 4.46\text{ °C} = -4.46\text{ °C}$

b. Molality of $MgSO_4 = \frac{0.60\text{ mol MgSO}_4}{100\text{ }\cancel{\text{g H}_2\text{O}}}$
$\times 1000\text{ }\cancel{\text{g H}_2\text{O}}$
$= 6.0m\text{ MgSO}_4$

Each mol of $MgSO_4$ that dissolves yields 2 mol of particles.
Molality of total particles
$= 2 \times 6.0m = 12m$

$\Delta T_f = K_f \times m$
$= 1.86\text{ °C}/m \times 12m = 22\text{ °C}$

Freezing point of solution
$= 0\text{ °C} - 22\text{ °C} = -22\text{ °C}$

59. a. Molality of total particles
$= 3 \times 0.20m = 0.60m$

$\Delta T_f = K_f \times m$
$= 1.86\text{ °C}/m \times 0.60m = 1.1\text{ °C}$

Freezing point of solution
$= 0\text{ °C} - 1.1\text{ °C} = -1.1\text{ °C}$

b. Molarity of total particles
$= 2 \times 0.20m = 0.40m$

$\Delta T_f = K_f \times \text{m}$
$= 1.86\text{ °C}/m \times 0.40m = 0.74\text{ °C}$

Freezing point of solution
$= 0\text{ °C} - 0.74\text{ °C}$
$= -0.74\text{ °C}$

c. Molarity of total particles
$= 4 \times 0.20m = 0.80m$

$\Delta T_f = K_f \times m$
$= 1.86\text{ °C}/\cancel{m} \times 0.80\cancel{m} = 1.5\text{ °C}$

Freezing point of solution $= 0\text{ °C} - 1.5\text{ °C}$
$= -1.5\text{ °C}$

60. Measure the mass of the solute, the mass of the solvent, the boiling point of the solvent, and the boiling point of the solution.

Concept Mastery

61. a. The freezing-point depression is twice as great for solute B; solute B must provide twice as many particles in solution.

b. Solute A forms a saturated solution.

62. $12.0\text{ }\cancel{g}\text{ C}_{10}\text{H}_8 \times \frac{1\text{ mol}}{128.0\text{ }\cancel{g}} = 0.0938\text{ mol C}_{10}\text{H}_8$

$m = \frac{0.0936\text{ mol C}_{10}\text{H}_8}{50.0\text{ }\cancel{g}\text{ C}_6\text{H}_6 \frac{1\text{ kg}}{1000\text{ }\cancel{g}}} = 1.88m\text{ C}_{10}\text{H}_8$

$\Delta T_f = K_f \times m = \frac{-5.12\text{ °C}}{1\text{ }\cancel{m}} \times 1.88\cancel{m}\text{ C}_{10}\text{H}_8$
$= -9.63\text{ °C}$

$\Delta T_b = K_b \times m = \frac{2.53\text{ °C}}{1\text{ }\cancel{m}} \times 1.88\cancel{m}\text{ C}_{10}\text{H}_8$
$= 4.76\text{ °C}$

63. $x_{acetone} = \dfrac{n_{acetone}}{n_{H_2O} + n_{acetone}}$

$0.25 = \dfrac{n_{acetone}}{n_{H_2O} + n_{acetone}}$

$n_{H_2O} = 3.0 \text{ mol}$

$n_{acetone} = 1.0 \text{ mol}$

$\dfrac{3.0 \text{ mol } H_2O}{1.0 \text{ mol acetone}} = \dfrac{54.0 \text{ g } H_2O}{58.0 \text{ g } C_2H_6O}$

$= \dfrac{0.931 \text{ g } H_2O}{1 \text{ g } C_2H_6O}$

Add 0.93 g H_2O per gram of acetone.

64. $9.6 \text{ g } NaHCO_3 \times \dfrac{1 \text{ mol}}{84.0 \text{ g}} = 0.11 \text{ mol } NaHCO_3$

$100 \text{ g } H_2O \times \dfrac{1 \text{ mol}}{18.0 \text{ g}} = 5.56 \text{ mol } H_2O$

$X_{NaHCO_3} = \dfrac{n_{NaHCO_3}}{n_{NaHCO_3} + n_{H_2O}}$

$= \dfrac{0.11 \text{ mol } NaHCO_3}{0.11 \text{ mol } NaHCO_3 + 5.56 \text{ mol } H_2O}$

$= 0.019$

$m = \dfrac{0.11 \text{ mol } NaHCO_3}{100 \text{ g } H_2O \times \dfrac{1 \text{ kg}}{1000 \text{ g}}}$

$= 1.1m \; NaHCO_3$

65. $X_{NaCl} = \dfrac{n_{NaCl}}{n_{NaCl} + n_{H_2O}} \quad X_{H_2O} = \dfrac{n_{H_2O}}{n_{NaCl} + n_{H_2O}}$

Determine the number of moles of water in the solution.

$\text{mol } H_2O = \dfrac{1000 \text{ g } H_2O}{18 \dfrac{\text{g}}{\text{mol}}} - 55.56 \text{ mol } H_2O$

$X_{NaCl} = \dfrac{0.150 \text{ mol}}{0.150 \text{ mol} + 55.56 \text{ mol}} = 0.00269$

$X_{H_2O} = \dfrac{55.56 \text{ mol}}{0.150 \text{ mol} + 55.56 \text{ mol}} = 0.997$

66. If the solution is supersaturated, one crystal of KNO_3 causes crystallization. If it is saturated, the crystal does not dissolve: if unsaturated, the crystal dissolves.

67. **a.** about 1.145
b. about −6.8 °C
c. about −9.5 °C

68. $\text{Molarity} = \dfrac{\text{moles of solute}}{1000 \text{ g solvent}}$

$= \dfrac{15.0 \text{ g } CH_4N_2O \times \dfrac{1 \text{ mol}}{60.0 \text{ g}}}{250 \text{ g } H_2O \times \dfrac{1 \text{ kg } H_2O}{1000 \text{ g } H_2O}}$

$= 1.00m \; CH_4N_2O$

$\Delta T_b = K_f \times m = \dfrac{-1.86 \text{ °C}}{1 \; m} \times 1.00m \; CH_4N_2O$

$= -1.86 \text{ °C}$

Freezing point = −1.86 °C

$\Delta T_b = K_b \times m = \dfrac{0.512 \text{ °C}}{1 \; m} \times 1.00m \; CH_4N_2O$

$= 0.512 \text{ °C}$

Boiling point

$= 100 \text{ °C} + 0.512 \text{ °C} = 100.512 \text{ °C}$

69. $25.0 \text{ g } C_2H_5OH \times \dfrac{1 \text{ mol}}{46.0 \text{ g}}$

$= 0.543 \text{ mol } C_2H_5OH$

$40.0 \text{ g } H_2O \times \dfrac{1 \text{ mol}}{18.0 \text{ g}} = 2.22 \text{ mol } H_2O$

$X_{C_2H_5OH} =$

$\dfrac{0.543 \text{ mol } C_2H_5OH}{0.543 \text{ mol } C_2H_5OH + 2.22 \text{ mol } H_2O}$

$= 0.197$

$X_{H_2O} =$

$\dfrac{2.22 \text{ mol } H_2O}{0.543 \text{ mol } C_2H_5OH + 2.22 \text{ mol } H_2O}$

$= 0.804$

70. $\text{Modality} = \dfrac{20.0 \text{ g } C_6H_{12}O_6 \times \dfrac{1 \text{ mol}}{180.0 \text{ g}}}{500.0 \text{ g } H_2O \times \dfrac{1 \text{ kg } H_2O}{1000 \text{ g } H_2O}}$

$= 0.222m \; C_6H_{12}O_6$

$\Delta T_b = K_f \times m = \dfrac{-186 \text{ °C}}{1 m}$

$\times 0.222m \; C_6H_{12}O_6$

$= -0.413 \text{ °C}$

Freezing point = −0.413 °C

71.

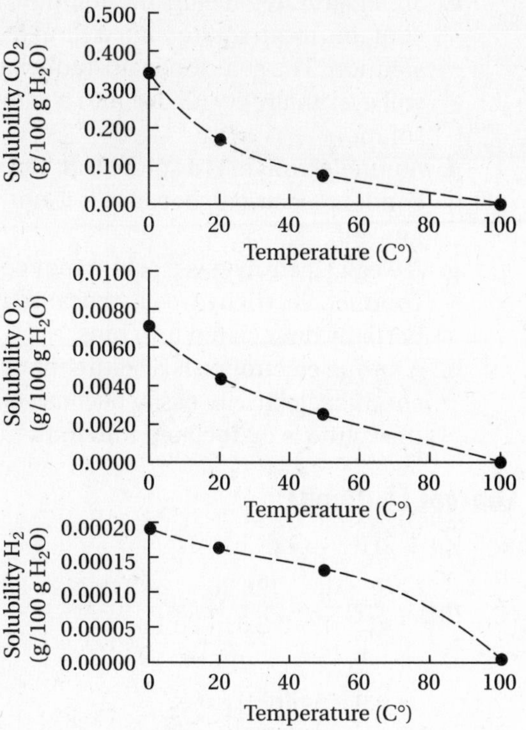

72. a. At 20 °C, the solubility of KCl in water is 34.0 g/100 g, or 44.2 g/130 g. Therefore, 44.2 g remain dissolved.

b. 50.0 g − 44.2 g = 5.8 g KCl

73. a. 0.30 mol **b.** 0.40 mol **c.** 0.50 mol **d.** 0.20 mol

74. *Row* 1: $12.5\ \text{g}\ C_6H_{12}O_6 \times \dfrac{1\ \text{mol}}{180.0\ \text{g}}$

$= 0.0694\ \text{mol}\ C_6H_{12}O_6$

$219\ \text{mL} \times \dfrac{1\ \text{L}}{1000\ \text{mL}} = 0.219\ \text{L}$

$M = \dfrac{0.0694\ \text{mol}\ C_6H_{12}O_6}{0.219\ \text{L}} = 0.317M\ C_6H_{12}O_6$

Row 2: $1.08\ \text{mol}\ C_6H_{12}O_6 \times \dfrac{180.0\ \text{g}}{1\ \text{mol}}$

$= 194\ \text{g}\ C_6H_{12}O_6$

$V = \dfrac{1.08\ \text{moles}}{\dfrac{0.519\ \text{moles}}{1\ \text{L}}} = 2.08\ \text{L}$

Row 3: $\dfrac{1.08\ \text{moles}}{1\ \text{L}} \times 1.62\ \text{L}$

$= 1.75\ \text{mol}\ C_6H_{12}O_6$

$1.75\ \text{mol}\ C_6H_{12}O_6 \times \dfrac{180.0\ \text{g}}{1\ \text{mol}} = 315\ \text{g}\ C_6H_{12}O_6$

Mass Solute	Moles Solute	Volume of solution	Molarity
12.5 g	0.0694	219 mL	0.317
194 g	1.08	2.08 L	0.519
315 g	1.75	1.62 L	1.08

75. $\text{Solubility} = \dfrac{36.0\ \text{NaCl}}{100\ \text{g}\ H_2O} \times \dfrac{0.75}{0.75} = \dfrac{27\ \text{g NaCl}}{75\ \text{g}\ H_2O}$

The solution has 26.5 g NaCl/75 g H_2O and is therefore unsaturated.

76. $\Delta T_f = K_f \times m$

$m = \dfrac{\Delta T_f}{K_f} = \dfrac{-2.47\ °\text{C}}{-1.86\ °\text{C}/m} = 1.33m$

$\Delta T_f = K_b \times m$

$= 0.512\ °\text{C}/m \times 1.33m$

$= 0.681\ °\text{C}$

Boiling point of solution = 100 °C + 0.681 °C

= 100.681 °C

77. a. $m = \dfrac{3.0\ \text{g}\ H_2O_2}{100\ \text{mL}} \times 250\ \text{mL} = 7.5\ \text{g}\ H_2O_2$

b. $250\ \text{mL} \times \dfrac{1\ \text{L}}{1000\ \text{mL}} = 0.250\ \text{L}$

$$M = \dfrac{7.5\ \text{g}\ H_2O_2 \times \dfrac{1\ \text{mol}}{34.0\ \text{g}\ H_2O_2}}{250\ \text{mL} \times \dfrac{1\ \text{L}}{1000\ \text{mL}}}$$

$= 0.88M\ H_2O_2$

78. 50 °C: $\dfrac{114.0\ \text{g}\ NaNO_3}{100\ \text{g}\ H_2O} = \dfrac{228.0\ \text{g}\ NaNO_3}{200\ \text{g}\ H_2O}$

20 °C: $\dfrac{88.0\ \text{g}\ NaNO_3}{100\ \text{g}\ H_2O} = \dfrac{176.0\ \text{g}\ NaNO_3}{200\ \text{g}\ H_2O}$

228.0 g − 176.0 g = 52.0 g $NaNO_3$ will precipitate

79. $m = \dfrac{\Delta T_f}{K_f} = \dfrac{0.460\ °\text{C}}{\dfrac{5.12\ °\text{C}}{1m}} = 0.0898m$ compound

$= \dfrac{0.0898\ \text{mol compound}}{1000\ \text{g benzene}}$

Mass of compound in 1000 g benzene

$= \dfrac{5.76\ \text{g compound}}{750\ \text{g benzene}} \times 1000\ \text{g benzene}$

$= 7.68$ g compound

Molecular mass $= \dfrac{7.68\ \text{g compound}}{0.0898\ \text{mol compound}}$

= 85.5 g/mol

80. $1000\ \text{g H}_2\text{O} \times \frac{1\ \text{mol}}{18.0\ \text{g}} = 55.6\ \text{mol H}_2\text{O}$

$m_{C_{12}H_{22}O_{11}} = 1.62m$

$$X_{H_2O} = \frac{55.6\ \text{mol H}_2\text{O}}{55.6\ \text{mol H}_2\text{O} + 1.62\ \text{mol C}_{12}\text{H}_{12}\text{O}_{11}}$$

$= 0.972$

$$X_{C_{12}H_{22}O_{11}} = \frac{1.62\ \text{mol C}_{12}\text{H}_{22}\text{O}_{11}}{55.6\ \text{mol H}_2\text{O} + 1.62\ \text{mol C}_{12}\text{H}_{22}\text{O}_{11}}$$

$= 0.0283$

81. **a.** 4
b. 1

82. With moles per liter, it is easier to produce two solutions with equal numbers of representative particles per a given volume.

83. One mol of $CaCl_2$ supplies 3 mol of particles, whereas 1 mol of NaCl supplies only 2 mol of particles. The freezing point depression is proportional to the number of solute particles.

Cumulative Review

84. **a.** $NH_4Cl \rightarrow NH_4^+(aq) + Cl^-(aq)$
b. $Cu(NO_3)_2 \rightarrow Cu^{2+}(aq) + 2NO_3^-(aq)$
c. $HNO_3 \rightarrow H^+(aq) + NO_3^-(aq)$
d. $HC_2H_3O_2 \rightarrow H^+(aq) + C_2H_3O_2^-(aq)$
e. $Na_2SO_4 \rightarrow 2Na^+(aq) + SO_4^{2-}(aq)$
f. $HgCl_2 \rightarrow Hg^{2+}(aq) + 2Cl^-(aq)$

85. The stronger the intermolecular attractions in a liquid, the greater the surface tension. Surface tension depends on an imbalance of forces at the surface of the liquid.

86. Hydrogen chloride is polar. Polar water molecules attract HCl molecules, causing ionization and high solubility. Nonpolar solvents such as benzene have virtually no interaction with HCl.

87. Hydrogen bonding between molecules raises the boiling point of a substance.

88. Soaps and detergents are emulsifying agents that form colloidal dispersions in water.

89. **a.** A solute is the substance that is dissolved.
b. A solvent is the substance used for dissolving.
c. Saturated means no additional solute can be dissolved.
d. Unsaturated means more solute can be dissolved.
e. Supersaturated means the solution contains more solute than a saturated solution. The solution is unstable and will eventually crystallize into a saturated solution.
f. A nonelectrolyte is a solute that cannot conduct electricity because it is not ionized.
g. A weak electrolyte is a solute that can conduct electricity weakly because it is partially dissociated into ions.
h. A strong electrolyte is a solute that can conduct electricity easily because all of the solute is dissociated into ions.

Concept Challenge

90. $Zn + 2HCl \rightarrow ZnCl_2 + H_2$

$$n_{H_2} = \frac{P \times V}{R \times T} = \frac{(98.36 - 2.48)\ \text{kPa} \times 1.21\ \text{L}}{8.31\ \frac{\text{kPa L}}{\text{mol K}} \times (21 + 273)\ \text{K}}$$

$= 0.0475\ \text{mol H}_2$

$$n_{HCl} = 0.475\ \text{mol H}_2 \times \frac{2\ \text{mol HCl}}{1\ \text{mol H}_2}$$

$= 0.0950\ \text{mol HCl}$

$$M_{HCl} = \frac{0.0950\ \text{mol HCl}}{0.800\ \text{L}} = 0.119M\ \text{HCl}$$

91. Eight moles of HNO_3 react with three moles of Cu.

$$V = 3.94\ \text{g Cu} \times \frac{1\ \text{mol Cu}}{63.5\ \text{g Cu}} \times \frac{8\ \text{mol HNO}_3}{3\ \text{mol Cu}} \times \frac{1000\ \text{mL}}{1.5\ \text{mol HNO}_3} = 1.10 \times 10^2\ \text{mL}$$

92. **a.** Solubility of KNO_3 at 76 °C is approximately 15 mol/kg. Solubility of KNO_3 at 33 °C is approximately 5 mol/kg.
b. Temperature at which solubility is 17.6 mol/kg is approximately 82 °C.
c. Temperature at which solubility is 4.24 mol/kg is approximately 30 °C.

93. $Na_2SO_4(aq) + BaCl(aq) \rightarrow BaSO_4(s) + 2NaCl(aq)$

$$5.28\ \text{g BaSO}_4(s) \times \frac{1\ \text{mol BaSO}_4(s)}{233.4\ \text{g BaSO}_4(s)} \times \frac{1\ \text{mol Na}_2\text{SO}_4(aq)}{1\ \text{mol BaSO}_4(s)}$$

$= 0.0226\ \text{mol Na}_2\text{SO}_4$

$$\text{Molarity Na}_2\text{SO}_4(aq) = \frac{0.0226\ \text{mol Na}_2\text{SO}_4}{250 \times 10^{-3}\ \text{L}}$$

$= 0.0904M\ \text{Na}_2\text{SO}_4$

94. Calculate the percent by mass of each ion in sea water.
mass of chloride ion in 1 kg of solvent
$= 1\ \cancel{kg} \times \frac{0.568\ \cancel{mol\ Cl^-}}{1\ \cancel{kg}} \times \frac{35.5\ g\ Cl^-}{1\ \cancel{mol\ Cl^-}}$
$= 20.2\ g$
percent by mass =
$\frac{\text{mass of solute (g)}}{\text{mass of solution (g)}} \times 100\%$

$\%\ (m/m)\ \text{chloride ion} = \frac{20.2\ g}{1000\ g + 20.2\ g}$
$\times 100\% = 1.98\%$
Thus, the mass of chloride ion in 5.00 L of sea water =
$0.0198 \times 5.00\ \cancel{L} \times \frac{10^3\ \cancel{mL}}{1\ \cancel{L}} \times \frac{1.024\ g}{1\ \cancel{mL}} = 101\ g$
Proceeding as given above for each of the ions gives the following.

Ion	Mass contained in 5.00 L of sea water (g)
Chloride	101
Sodium	56.2
Magnesium	7.1
Sulfate	14
Calcium	2.3
Potassium	2.0
Hydrogen carbonate	0.6

Standardized Test Prep

1. (c)
Students must subtract 65% alcohol from 100% to get 35% water.
$0.35 \times 95\ mL = 33\ mL$

2. (b)
Stirring and grinding into a powder can affect the rate of the reaction, but only heating will affect the amount of solute that can be dissolved.

3. (a)
$0.28\ mol/\cancel{L} \times 1\ \cancel{L}/1000\ \cancel{mL} \times 650\ \cancel{mL}$
$= 0.18\ mol$

4. (b)

5. (a)
45 g of water equals 2.5 mol water. Thus, the total number of moles in solution is 2.0 plus 2.5 or 4.5 mol.
$\frac{2.0\ \cancel{mol}}{4.5\ \cancel{mol}} = 0.44$

6. (C)

7. (E)

8. (B)

9. (A)

10.

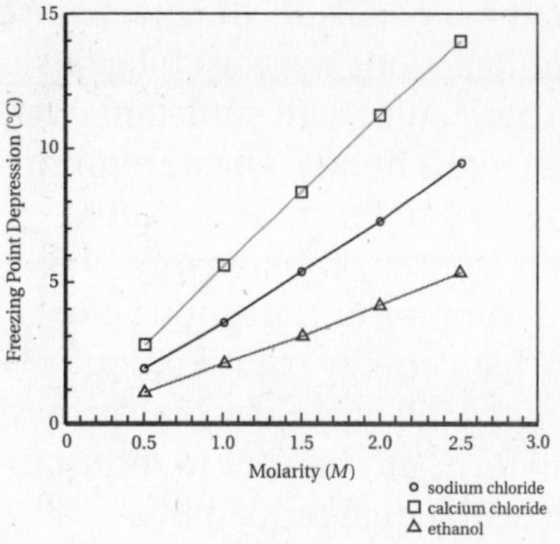

11. As the molarity increases the freezing point depression increases.

12. The slopes are in an approximate 1 : 2 : 3 ratio that reflects the relative number of particles per mole of each solute in solution.

13. NaCl, because KOH and NaCl release the same number of particles per mole into a solution.

14. (b)

15. (a)

16. (c)

17. Transfer 25 mL of the stock solution to a 100-mL volumetric flask and add water to make 100 mL of solution.

19 REACTION RATES AND EQUILIBRIUM

Concept Practice

38. Collision theory explains the mechanism of reactions. Reactions require collisions between molecules with sufficient energy to break and make bonds. The minimum energy needed to form the activated complex is the activation energy. The activated complex or transition state is an unstable, high energy combination of the two reactants. The complex breaks down rapidly to form products or to return to reactants with equal probability.

39. Reactant particles must collide with a certain minimum amount of energy to react to form product, just as it takes a certain minimum amount of energy to climb over a wall or barrier.

40. The formula of a catalyst is written above the reaction arrow because a catalyst is neither a reactant nor a product of a reaction.

41. A catalyst increases the rate of reactions by providing an alternative reaction mechanism with a lower activation energy.

42. Statement **c** is true.

43. Gas molecules and oxygen molecules mix readily but do not have enough energy to react at room temperature. The flame raises the temperature and the energy of collisions, so the reaction rate is increased. The heat released by the reaction maintains the high temperature, and the reaction continues spontaneously.

44. In a reversible reaction, reactants are continuously forming products and products are continuously forming reactants.

45. The rate of formation of products from reactants and the rate of formation of reactants from products are equal.

46. The rates of the forward and reverse reactions are equal.

47. Le Châtelier's principle states that a system in dynamic equilibrium changes to relieve the stress applied to it. Carbonated drinks in closed containers have achieved a state of dynamic equilibrium between the carbon dioxide in the liquid and gas states. When the containers are opened, carbon dioxide gas escapes. Carbon dioxide from the liquid goes into the gas state in an attempt to re-establish equilibrium.

48. $K_{eq} = \dfrac{[NH_3]^2}{[H_2]^3 \times [N_2]}$

49. **a.** $K_{eq} = \dfrac{[H_2S]^2 \times [CH_4]}{[H_2]^4 \times [CS_2]}$

b. $K_{eq} = \dfrac{[PCl_3] \times [Cl_2]}{[PCl_5]}$

c. $K_{eq} = \dfrac{[NO_2]^2}{[NO]^2 \times [O_2]}$

d. $K_{eq} = \dfrac{[H_2] \times [CO_2]}{[CO] \times [H_2O]}$

50. **a.** highly favorable
b. slightly favorable

51. Free energy is the potential energy in a system that can become available to do work. A reaction is spontaneous if free energy is released.

52. A flame or ignition wire provides sufficient energy for activation. Once started, the spontaneous reaction can proceed rapidly.

53. An increase in order is an unfavorable entropy change.

54. *Entropy* is a measure of the disorder of a system.

55. **a.** completed jigsaw puzzle
b. 50 mL of ice
c. sodium chloride crystals

56. **a.** Entropy increases.
b. Entropy decreases.
c. Entropy increases.
d. Entropy decreases.

57. No; some endothermic processes are spontaneous because of their favorable change in entropy.

58. The favorable exothermic change of the condensation process offsets the unfavorable entropy change.

59. In combination, the change in heat content (enthalpy) and the change in entropy determine whether a process is spontaneous.

60. $\Delta G^0 = \Delta H^0 - T\Delta S^0$

$= \frac{178.5\ \cancel{kJ}}{mol} \times \frac{1000\ J}{1\ \cancel{kJ}} - 298\ \cancel{K} \times \frac{161.6\ J}{\cancel{K} \times mol}$

$= \frac{130\ 300\ J}{mol}$

$= 130.3$ kJ/mol; nonspontaneous

61. a. The specific rate constant is the proportionality constant relating the concentrations of the reactants to the reaction rate.
b. A first-order reaction has a reaction rate proportional to the concentration of one reactant.
c. The rate law is an equation relating the reaction rate to the concentrations of the reactants.

62. Rate $= k\,[NO][O_3]$

63. The reaction is 75% complete after 100 minutes.

64.

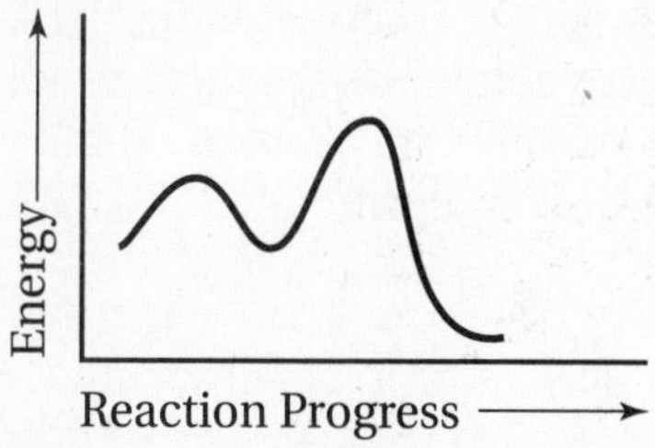

Reactants Products
$2NO + O_2 \rightarrow 2NO_2$

65. a. Rate $= \frac{6.08 \times 10^{-4}}{1\ s} \times \frac{0.200\ mol}{1\ L}$

$= 1.22 \times 10^{-4} \frac{mol}{L\ s}$

b. Rate $= \frac{6.08 \times 10^{-4}}{1\ s} \times \frac{0.319\ mol}{1\ L}$

$= 1.94 \times 10^{-4} \frac{mol}{L\ s}$

66. a. not sufficient
b. not sufficient
c. sufficient
Statements **a** and **b** together are sufficient.

67. The activation energy of the reverse reaction is 25 kJ.

68. The change from Figure **a** to Figure **b** is spontaneous, favored by an increase in entropy. The change from Figure **b** to Figure **c**, however, will not occur because it would result in a decrease in entropy, causing the process to be nonspontaneous.

69. a. Yes. More complex molecules are made, and less solid is present.
b. Yes. More gas is made even though molecules are simpler.
c. No. Less gas is made and molecules are only slightly more complex.
d. Yes. More gas is made and molecules are only slightly less complex.

70. a. increase in products
b. decrease in products
c. decrease in products

71. $K_{eq} = \frac{[CO][H_2O]}{[CO_2][H_2]}$

$= \frac{0.448\ mol\ CO \times 0.448\ mol\ H_2O}{0.552\ mol\ CO_2 \times 0.552\ mol\ H_2}$

$= 0.659$

72. a. $K_{eq} = \frac{[ICl]^2}{[I_2] \times [Cl_2]}$

b. $K_{eq} = \frac{[NO]^2 \times [O_2]}{[NO_2]^2}$

c. $K_{eq} = \frac{[SO_3]^2}{[SO_2]^2 \times [O_2]}$

d. $K_{eq} = \frac{[PCl_5]}{[Cl_2] \times [PCl_3]}$

73. Increasing pressure tends to reduce volume and increase density, so the system responds by favoring production of the liquid, which has the greater density.

74.

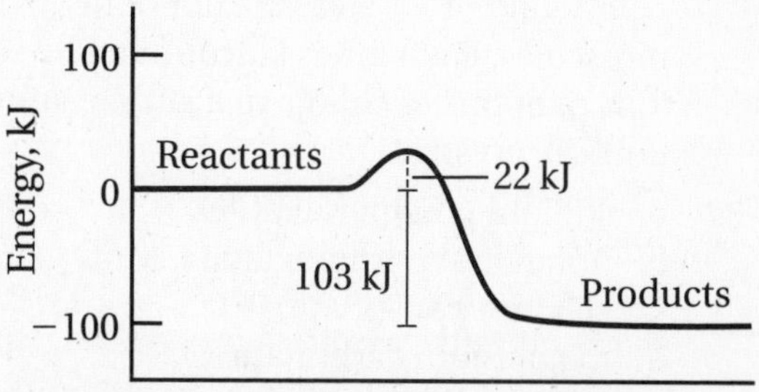

75. The reaction is slow because activation energy is high. Breaking strong bonds in diamond requires high activation energy. Also, the diamond particles are large. As a result, surface area is small, slowing the reaction rate.

76. A catalyst will help establish equilibrium more quickly, but it does not change the equilibrium position.

77. $\Delta S^0 = S^0 \text{ (products)} - S^0 \text{ (reactants)}$

$$= 2 \text{ mol} \times \frac{192.5 \text{ J}}{\text{K mol}} + \frac{5}{2} \text{ mol} \times \frac{205.0 \text{ J}}{\text{K mol}}$$

$$-2 \text{ mol} \times \frac{210.6 \text{ J}}{\text{K mol}} - 3 \text{ mol} \times \frac{188.7 \text{ J}}{\text{K mol}}$$

$$= -89.80 \text{ J}/(\text{K} \times \text{mol})$$

Critical Thinking

78. a. 3
    b. 1

79. A catalyst increases the efficiency of the collisions; a greater number of collisions results in the formation of the product.

80. Possible answers: using a blow dryer, flushing the toilet, mowing the lawn, cooking breakfast, driving a car, and simply breathing.

Cumulative Review

81. a. fluoride ion (anion)
    b. copper(II) ion (cation)
    c. phosphide ion (anion)
    d. hydrogen ion (cation)
    e. sodium ion (cation)
    f. iodide ion (anion)
    g. oxide ion (anion)
    h. magnesium ion (cation)

82. Crystalline substances have a regular, repeating pattern of atoms, ions, or molecules in three dimensions. Amorphous substances have an irregular arrangement of particles.

83. Solid potassium chloride is an ionic compound of K^+ and Cl^-, not of KCl molecules. Each ion is surrounded by six ions of opposite charge in a simple cubic unit cell crystal.

84. a. sodium perchlorate, ClO_4^-
    b. potassium permanganate, MnO_4^-
    c. calcium phosphate, PO_4^{3-}
    d. magnesium carbonate, CO_3^{2-}
    e. sodium sulfate, SO_4^{2-}
    f. potassium dichromate, $Cr_2O_7^{2-}$

85. Ionic compounds are crystalline solids, have high melting points, are insulators when solid and conductors in the molten state, are brittle, are not malleable or ductile, and dissolve in water.

86. a. $1s^2 2s^2 2p^6 3s^2 3p^6 3d^{10} 4s^2 4p^2$ ·G̈e·
    b. $1s^2 2s^2 2p^6 3s^2 3p^6 3d^{10} 4s^2$ ·Ca·
    c. $1s^2 2s^2 2p^4$:Ö·
    d. $1s^2 2s^2 2p^6 3s^2 3p^6$:Är:
    e. $1s^2 2s^2 2p^6 3s^2 3p^6 3d^{10} 4s^2 4p^5$:Br̈·
    f. $1s^2 2s^2 2p^6 3s^2 3p^3$ ·P̈·

87. a. Li^+ :B̈r:⁻
    b. :C̈l:⁻ Al^{3+} :C̈l:⁻
             :C̈l:⁻
    c. :F̈:⁻ Mg^{2+} :F̈:⁻
    d. Na^+ :S̈:²⁻ Na^+

88. a. $1s^2 2s^2 2p^6 3s^2 3p^6$:C̈a:²⁺
    b. $2s^2$ Li:⁺
    c. $1s^2 2s^2 2p^6 3s^2 3p^6 3d^{10} 4s^2 4p^6$:B̈r:⁻
    d. $1s^2 2s^2 2p^6 3s^2 3p^6$:S̈:²⁻

89. positive ions: **b., e., f., g., h.,** and **j.**; negative ions: **a., c., d.,** and **i.**

Concept Challenge

90. The additional H^+ reacts with the OH^-, shifting the reaction toward more products. As a result, more of the reactant, tooth enamel, is broken down.

91. a.

    b. For $t = 100$ s:

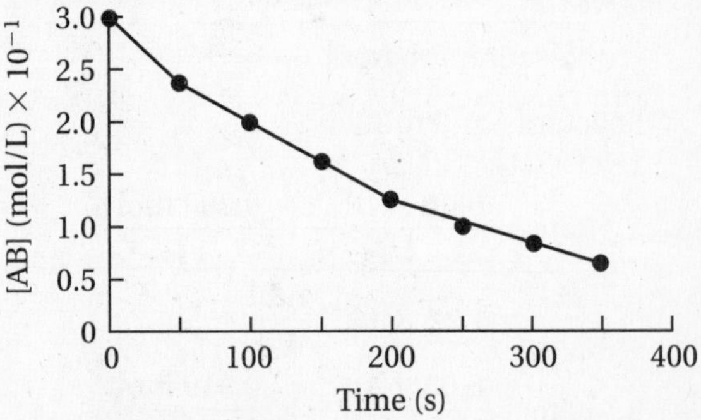

$$\text{rate} = \frac{\Delta [AB]}{\Delta t} = 8.01 \times 10^{-4} \text{ mol}/(\text{L} \times \text{s})$$

    For $t = 250$ s:

$$\text{rate} = \frac{\Delta [AB]}{\Delta t} = 4.41 \times 10^{-4} \text{ mol}/(\text{L} \times \text{s})$$

92. a. about $10 \text{ g} - 7 \text{ g} = 3 \text{ g}$
    b. about $2.5 \text{ g} - 1.25 \text{ g} = 1.2 \text{ g}$

Standardized Test Prep

1. (a)
   In an equilibrium constant expression, products appear in the numerator and reactants in the denominator.
2. (a)
   Gases are less ordered than solids.
3. (a)
   To relieve the stress of the added heat, which is a product of the reaction, the equilibrium will shift in favor of the reactants.
4. (a)
5. (a): −; (b): +; (c): −; (d): + or −
6. (1) and (2) at low temperatures; (3) at high temperatures
7. (c), (b), (a)
8. True, False
   The amount of energy released by a reaction is not affected by a catalyst.
9. False, True
   An exothermic reaction will not be spontaneous if there is a decrease in entropy large enough to offset the favorable heat change.
10. False, True
    Water vapor has less order than ice.
11. True, True
12. True, False
    The ratio of products to reactants is < 1 when reactants are favored at equilibrium.

20 ACIDS AND BASES

Concept Practice

34. **a.** $HNO_2(aq)$
b. $Al(OH)_3(aq)$
c. $H_2Se(aq)$
d. $Sr(OH)_2(aq)$
e. $H_3PO_4(aq)$
f. $CH_3COOH(aq)$

35. $H_2O(l) \rightleftharpoons H^+(aq) + OH^-(aq)$

36. The concentrations are $1.0 \times 10^{-7}M$ for both H^+ and OH^- at 25 °C.

37. The pH of a solution is the negative logarithm of the hydrogen ion concentration.

38. The hydrogen-ion concentration of pure water at 25 °C is $1.0 \times 10^{-7}M$. The negative logarithm, or pH, of this concentration is 7.00.

39. **a.** $pH = -\log[H^+]$
$= -\log(1 \times 10^{-2}M)$
$= 2$, acidic

b. $pH = -\log[H^+]$
$$= -\log\frac{K_w}{[OH^-]}$$
$$= -\log\frac{1.0 \times 10^{-14}M^2}{1 \times 10^{-2}M}$$
$= 12$, basic

c. $$pH = -\log\frac{1.0 \times 10^{-14}M^2}{1 \times 10^{-8}M}$$
$= 6$, acidic

d. $pH = -\log(1 \times 10^{-6}M)$
$= 6$, acidic

40. **a.** $$[OH^-] = \frac{K_w}{[H^+]}$$
$$= \frac{K_w}{\text{antilog}(-pH)\,M}$$
$$= \frac{1.0 \times 10^{-14}M^2}{\text{antilog}(-4.0)M}$$
$= 1.0 \times 10^{-10}M$

b. $$[OH^-] = \frac{1.0 \times 10^{-14}M^2}{\text{antilog}(-8.0)M} = 1.0 \times 10^{-6}M$$

c. $$[OH^-] = \frac{1.0 \times 10^{-14}M^2}{\text{antilog}(-12.0)M} = 1.0 \times 10^{-2}M$$

41. **a.** $pH = -\log[H^+]$
$= -\log(2.4 \times 10^{-6})$
$= -(\log 2.4 + \log 10^{-6})$
$= -(0.38 - 6)$
$= 5.62$

b. $pH = -\log(9.1 \times 10^{-9})$
$= -\log(9.1 \times 10^{-9})$
$= -(0.96 - 9)$
$= 8.04$

c. $\log[H^+] = -pH$
$= -13.2$
$= 0.80 - 14$
$[H^+] = 10(0.80 - 14)$
$[H^+] = 6.3 \times 10^{-14}M$

d. $\log[H^+] = -pH$
$= 0.30 - 7$
$[H^+] = 10(0.30 - 7)$
$[H^+] = 2.0 \times 10^{-7}M$

42. $\log[H^+] = -pH$
$= -3.80$
$[H^+] = 10^{(0.20 - 4)}$
$[H^+] = 1.6 \times 10^{-4}M$

43. **a.** $KOH(s) \xrightarrow{H_2O} K^+(aq) + OH^-(aq)$
b. $Mg(OH)_2(s) \xrightarrow{H_2O} Mg^{2+}(aq) + 2OH^-(aq)$

44. Acids ionize to give hydrogen ions in aqueous solution. Bases ionize to give hydroxide ions in aqueous solution.

45. **a.** base
b. acid
c. base
d. acid
e. acid
f. acid

46. monoprotic: **b.**, **d.**, and **e.**; diprotic: **f.**

47. **a.** $2Li(s) + 2H_2O(s) \rightarrow 2LiOH(aq) + H_2(g)$
b. $Ba(s) + 2H_2O(s) \rightarrow Ba(OH)_2(aq) + H_2(g)$

48. **a.** HNO_3, acid; H_2O, base
b. CH_3COOH, acid; H_2O, base
c. H_2O, acid; NH_3, base
d. H_2O, acid; CH_3COO^-, base

49. **a.** HNO_3 with NO_3^-, H_2O with H_3O^+
b. CH_3COOH with CH_3COO^-, H_2O with H_3O^+
c. H_2O with OH^-, NH_3 with NH_4^+
d. H_2O with OH^-, CH_3COO^- with CH_3COOH

50. An amphoteric substance can act as an acid or a base.

51. A Lewis acid accepts a pair of electrons to form a covalent bond. A Lewis base donates a pair of electrons to form a covalent bond. The Lewis theory includes as acids or bases many substances that do not donate or accept hydrogen ions.

52. **a.** strong base
b. strong acid
c. weak base
d. strong acid

53. A strong acid is completely dissociated. The K_a measures the ratio of dissociated acid to undissociated acid. Therefore K_a must be large for a strong acid.

54. The strength of a base depends on the ratio of dissociated to undissociated base. $Mg(OH)_2$ and $Ca(OH)_2$ have high K_b values even though their concentration in saturated solution is low because of their low solubility.

55. **a.** $K_a = \dfrac{[H^+][I^-]}{[HI]}$

b. $K_a = \dfrac{[H^+][HCO_3^-]}{[H_2CO_3]}$

56. $HCrO_4^- + H_2O \rightleftharpoons CrO_4^{2-} + H_3O^+$

$K_a = [H_3O^+] \times \dfrac{[CrO_4^{2-}]}{[HCrO_4^-]}$

pH = 3.50; $H^+ = 3.2 \times 10^{-4}M$

Concentrations	$[HCrO_4^-]$	$[H^+]$	$[CrO_4^{2-}]$
Initial	0.0250	0	0
Change	-3.2×10^{-4}	$+3.2 \times 10^{-4}$	$+3.2 \times 10^{-4}$
Equilibrium	0.0247	$+3.2 \times 10^{-4}$	$+3.2 \times 10^{-4}$

$K_a = \dfrac{3.2 \times 10^{-4} \times 3.2 \times 10^{-4}}{0.02468} = 4.1 \times 10^{-6}$

Concept Mastery

57. A concentrated substance has a large amount of solute dissolved in solvent. A weak acid is only slightly ionized. Acids such as acetic acid can be concentrated weak acids that dissolve well but ionize poorly.

58. $HPO_4^{2-} \rightleftharpoons H^+ + PO_4^{3-}$
$HPO_4^{2-} + H^+ \rightleftharpoons H_2PO_4^-$

59. $\log [H^+] = -pH$
$= -1.83$
$= 0.17 - 2$
$[H^+] = 1.5 \times 10^{-2}M$
$[NO_2^-] = 1.5 \times 10^{-2}M$
$[HNO_2] = 0.50M - 0.015M = 0.49M$
$K_a = \dfrac{[H^+]\,[NO_2^-]}{[HNO_2]}$
$= \dfrac{(1.5 \times 10^{-2}M)(1.5 \times 10^{-2}M)}{(0.49M)}$
$= 4.6 \times 10^{-4}M$

60. **a.** CO_3^{2-}, carbonate ion
b. I^-, iodide ion
c. NH_3, ammonia
d. HSO_3^-, hydrogen sulfite ion

61. **a.** $HClO_2$, chlorous acid
b. H_3PO_4, phosphoric acid
c. H_3O^+, hydronium ion
d. NH_4^+, ammonium ion

62. $[H^+] = \dfrac{1.40}{100} \times 0.080M = 0.0011M$
$[A^-] = 0.0011M$
$[HA] = 0.080M - 0.0011M = 0.079M$
$K_a = \dfrac{[H^+]\,[A^-]}{[HA]} = \dfrac{(0.0011M)(0.0011M)}{(0.079M)}$
$= 1.5 \times 10^{-5}M$

63. **a.** $\log [H^+] = -pH$
$= -4.60$
$= 0.40 - 5$
$[H^+] = 10(0.40 - 5)$
$[H^+] = 2.5 \times 10^{-5}M$
$[OH^-] = \dfrac{K_w}{[H^+]}$
$= \dfrac{1.0 \times 10^{-14}M^2}{2.5 \times 10^{-5}M}$
$= 4.0 \times 10^{-10}M$

b. $\log [H^+] = -9.30$
$= 0.70 - 10$
$[H^+] = 5.0 \times 10^{-10}M$
$[OH^-] = \dfrac{1.0 \times 10^{-14}M^2}{5.0 \times 10^{-10}M}$
$= 2.0 \times 10^{-5}M$

c. $[H^+] = \dfrac{K_w}{[OH^-]}$
$= \dfrac{1.0 \times 10^{-14}M^2}{1.8 \times 10^{-2}M}$
$= 5.6 \times 10^{-13}M$
$pH = -\log [H^+]$
$= -\log (5.6 \times 10^{-13})$
$= -(\log 5.6 + \log 10^{-13})$
$= -(0.75 - 13)$
$= 12.25$

d. $[H^+] = \dfrac{1 \times 10^{-14}M^2}{7.3 \times 10^{-9}}$
$= 1.4 \times 10^{-6}M$
$pH = -(\log 1.4 \times 10^{-6})$
$= -(\log 1.4 + 10^{-6})$
$= -(0.15 - 6)$
$= 5.85$

64. $H_3PO_4 \rightleftharpoons H^+ + H_2PO_4^-$
$H_2PO_4^- \rightleftharpoons H^+ + HPO_4^{2-}$
$HPO_4^{2-} \rightleftharpoons H^+ + PO_4^{3-}$

65. a. KOH is the base; HBr is the acid.
b. HCl is the acid; H_2O is the base.

Critical Thinking

66. a. 3
b. 2
c. 1

67. Answers will vary; students are likely to consider the Arrhenius theory the easiest to understand. All three theories provide definitions and describe accepted behavior of a certain group of compounds. Because it is more general, the Brønsted-Lowry theory includes a greater number of compounds than the Arrhenius theory. The Lewis theory includes the greatest number of compounds because it is the most general. Each theory has advantages in certain circumstances.

68. Because $\log(a \times b) = \log a + \log b$, and $K_w = [H^+] \times [OH^-] = 1.0 \times 10^{-14}$, taking the log of each concentration term gives:
$\log[H^+] + \log[OH^-] = -14$
$-\log[H^+] - \log[OH^-] = 14$
$pH + pOH = 14$

69. The *y*-axis might correspond to $[H^+]$ or pOH because HCl is a strong acid.

Cumulative Review

70. $400.0 \text{ mL} \times \frac{1 \text{ L}}{1000 \text{ mL}} \times \frac{0.680 \text{ mol KOH}}{1 \text{ L}}$
$= 0.272 \text{ mol KOH}$
$0.272 \text{ mol KOH} \times \frac{56.1 \text{ g KOH}}{1 \text{ mol KOH}} = 15.3 \text{ g KOH}$
Add 15.3 g KOH to distilled water and dissolve. Then bring the volume of the solution to 400.0 mL.

71. $M_1 \times V_1 = M_2 \times V_2$
$V_1 = \frac{M_2 \times V_2}{M_1}$
$V_1 = \frac{2.5M \times 1.50 \text{ L}}{8.0M}$
$= 0.47 \text{ L}$

72. a. Increasing the pressure will shift the equilibrium position to the right in favor of products.
b. no change
c. The reaction will shift in the direction of the formation of products, until equilibrium is reestablished.
d. Decreasing the temperature will cause the position of the equilibrium to shift to the right in favor of products.
e. Removing product will cause the reaction to shift to the right in the direction of products until equilibrium is reestablished.

73. a. $K_{eq} = \frac{[CO]^2[O_2]}{[CO_2]^2}$
b. $K_{eq} = \frac{[NH_3]^2}{[H_2]^3[N_2]}$

74. $Kb = \frac{[HCN][OH^-]}{[CN^-]}$
$2.1 \times 10^{-5} = \frac{x^2}{0.010M}$
$x = [OH^-] = 4.6 \times 10^{-4}M$
$[H^+] = \frac{K_W}{[OH^-]}$
$= \frac{1 \times 10^{-14}M^2}{4.6 \times 10^{-4}M}$
$= 2.2 \times 10^{-11}M$
$pH = -\log[H^+]$
$= -\log(2.2 \times 10^{-11})$
$= -(\log 2.2 + \log 10^{-11})$
$= -(.34 - 11)$
$= 10.66$

75. $K_w = K_aK_b = \frac{[H^+][A^-]}{[HA]} \times \frac{[HA][OH^-]}{[A^-]}$
$= [H^+][OH^-]$

76. a. 7.4721, 7.2675, 7.0835, 6.9165, 6.7675, 6.6310

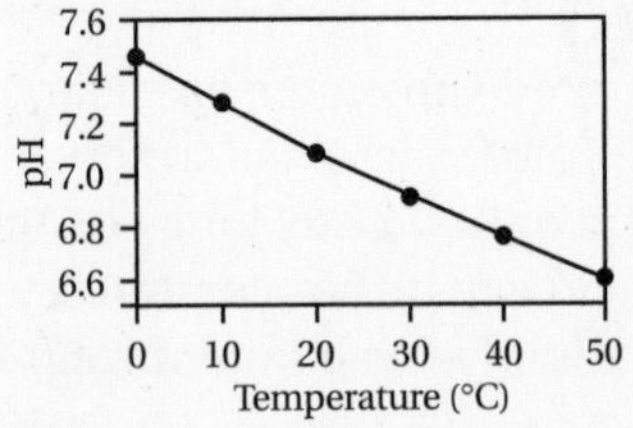

b. 7.36
c. 35 °C

77. 50.0 mL; The pH = 7 when $[H^+] = [OH^-]$. Because HCl is a strong acid that supplies one hydrogen ion per formula unit and NaOH is a strong base that supplies one hydroxide ion per formula unit, $[H^+] = [OH^-]$ when equal volumes of solutions of the same molarity are combined.

Standardized Test Prep

1. (b)
   Based on the K_a, the acid is weak with a pH between 5 and 6.
2. (b)
3. (c)
4. (c)
   The pH is 7.64.
5. $CH_3COOH(aq) + H_2O(l) \rightleftharpoons CH_3COO^-(aq) + H_3O^+(aq)$
6. 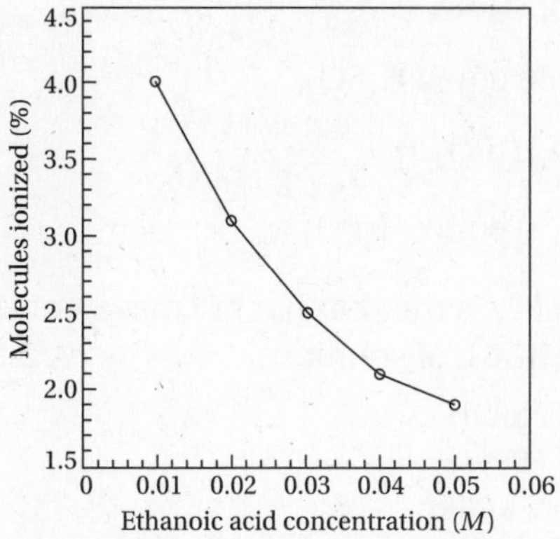

7. Yes; Increasing the water concentration puts a stress on the system, which is relieved by a shift to the right. As the concentration of ethanoic acid decreases, the percent of molecules ionized increases.
8. about 3.4%
9. (c), (a), (b)
10. one
    The acid in (b), which is completely dissociated, is the only strong acid.
11. (c)
    One acid particle has dissociated to form a conjugate base and a hydronium ion; nine acid particles have not dissociated.
12. Indicators give a quick approximation of the pH. For accurate and precise pH measurements, you need a pH meter.
13. Ammonia does not produce hydroxide ions in solution; thus, it does not qualify as a base according to Arrhenius.
14. *Weak* and *strong* refer to the degree of dissociation of an acid or base. *Dilute* and *concentrated* refer to the quantity of an acid or base dissolved in solution.

21 NEUTRALIZATION

Concept Practice

36. Acid + base → salt + water

37. a. $HNO_3(aq) + KOH(aq) \rightarrow KNO_3(aq) + H_2O(l)$

b. $2HCl(aq) + Ca(OH)_2(aq) \rightarrow CaCl_2(aq) + 2H_2O(l)$

c. $H_2SO_4(aq) + 2NaOH(aq) \rightarrow Na_2SO_4(aq) + 2H_2O(l)$

38. At the end point of a titration, neutralization occurs.

39. a. Find mol HCl needed for neutralization.

$$28.0\ \text{mL HCl} \times \frac{1\ \text{L HCl}}{1000\ \text{mL HCl}} \times \frac{1\ \text{mol HCl}}{1\ \text{L HCl}} = 0.0280\ \text{mol HCl}$$

Find mol NaOH neutralized.

$$0.0280\ \text{mol HCl} \times \frac{1\ \text{mol NaOH}}{1\ \text{mol HCl}} = 0.0280\ \text{mol NaOH}$$

$$M_{\text{NaOH}} = \frac{0.0280\ \text{mol NaOH}}{20.0\ \text{mL NaOH}} \times \frac{1000\ \text{mL NaOH}}{1\ \text{L NaOH}} = 1.40M\ \text{NaOH}$$

b. Find mol H_3PO_4 needed for neutralization.

$$17.4\ \text{mL}\ H_3PO_4 \times \frac{1\ \text{L}\ H_3PO_4}{1000\ \text{mL}\ H_3PO_4} \times \frac{1\ \text{mol}\ H_3PO_4}{1\ \text{L}\ H_3PO_4} = 0.0174\ \text{mol}\ H_3PO_4$$

Find mol NaOH neutralized.

$$0.0174\ \text{mol}\ H_3PO_4 \times \frac{3\ \text{mol NaOH}}{1\ \text{mol}\ H_3PO_4} = 0.0522\ \text{mol NaOH}$$

$$M_{\text{NaOH}} = \frac{0.0522\ \text{mol NaOH}}{20.0\ \text{mL NaOH}} \times \frac{1000\ \text{mL NaOH}}{1\ \text{L NaOH}} = 2.61M\ \text{NaOH}$$

40. a. molar mass of KOH = 56.1 g/mol
gram equivalent mass of KOH =

$$\frac{56.1\ \text{g/mol}}{1\ \text{equiv/mol}} = 56.1\ \text{g/equiv}$$

b. molar mass of HCl = 35.5 g/mol
gram equivalent mass of HCl =

$$\frac{35.5\ \text{g/mol}}{1\ \text{equiv/mol}} = 35.5\ \text{g/equiv}$$

c. molar mass of H_2SO_4 = 98.1 g/mol
gram equivalent mass of H_2SO_4 =

$$\frac{98.1\ \text{g/mol}}{2\ \text{equiv/mol}} = 49.1\ \text{g/equiv}$$

41. a. $3.7\ \text{g}\ Ca(OH)_2 \times \frac{1\ \text{equiv}\ Ca(OH)_2}{37.0\ \text{g}\ Ca(OH)_2} = 0.10\ \text{equiv}\ Ca(OH)_2$

b. $189\ \text{g}\ H_2SO_4 \times \frac{1\ \text{equiv}\ H_2SO_4}{49.0\ \text{g}\ H_2SO_4} = 3.86\ \text{equiv}\ H_2SO_4$

c. $9.8\ \text{g}\ H_3PO_4 \times \frac{1\ \text{equiv}\ H_3PO_4}{32.7\ \text{g}\ H_3PO_4} = 0.30\ \text{equiv}\ H_3PO_4$

42. Normality is the number of equivalents of solute in 1 L of solution.

43. a. $1N$ NaOH

b. $2N$ HNO_3

c. $0.2N$ KOH

d. $0.2\ N$ H_2SO_4

44. a. Find equiv NaOH.

$$10\ \text{g NaOH} \times \frac{1\ \text{mol NaOH}}{40.0\ \text{g NaOH}} \times \frac{1\ \text{equiv NaOH}}{1\ \text{mol NaOH}} = 0.25\ \text{equiv NaOH}$$

$$N_{\text{NaOH}} = \frac{0.25\ \text{equiv NaOH}}{250\ \text{mL NaOH}} \times \frac{1000\ \text{mL NaOH}}{1\ \text{L NaOH}} = 1.0N\ \text{NaOH}$$

b. Find equiv H_2SO_4.

$$4.9\ \text{g}\ H_2SO_4 \times \frac{1\ \text{mol}\ H_2SO_4}{98.1\ \text{g}\ H_2SO_4} \times \frac{2\ \text{equiv}\ H_2SO_4}{1\ \text{mol}\ H_2SO_4} = 0.10\ \text{equiv}\ H_2SO_4$$

$$N_{H_2SO_4} = \frac{0.10\ \text{equiv}\ H_2SO_4}{750\ \text{mL}\ H_2SO_4} \times \frac{1000\ \text{mL}\ H_2SO_4}{1\ \text{L}\ H_2SO_4} \times 0.13N\ H_2SO_4$$

c. Find equiv HCl.

$$0.74\ \text{g HCl} \times \frac{1\ \text{mol HCl}}{36.5\ \text{g HCl}} \times \frac{1\ \text{equiv HCl}}{1\ \text{mol HCl}} = 0.020\ \text{equiv HCl}$$

$$N_{\text{HCl}} = \frac{0.020\ \text{equiv HCl}}{270\ \text{mL HCl}} \times \frac{1000\ \text{mL HCl}}{1\ \text{L HCl}} = 0.074N\ \text{HCl}$$

d. Find equiv HNO_3.

$$18.6\ \text{g HNO}_3 \times \frac{1\ \text{mol HNO}_3}{63.0\ \text{g HNO}_3} \times \frac{1\ \text{equiv HNO}_3}{1\ \text{mol HNO}_3} = 0.295\ \text{equiv HNO}_3$$

$$N_{HNO_3} = \frac{0.295\ \text{equiv HNO}_3}{2.80\ \text{L}} = 0.105N\ \text{HNO}_3$$

e. Find equiv HCl.

$$7.3\ \text{g HCl} \times \frac{1\ \text{mol HCl}}{36.5\ \text{g HCl}} \times \frac{1\ \text{equiv HCl}}{1\ \text{mol HCl}} = 0.20\ \text{equiv HCl}$$

$$N_{HCl} = \frac{0.20\ \text{equiv HCl}}{250\ \text{mL HCl}} \times \frac{1000\ \text{mL HCl}}{1\ \text{L HCl}} = 0.80N\ \text{HCl}$$

f. Find equiv HNO_3.

$$18.4\ \text{g HNO}_3 \times \frac{1\ \text{mol HNO}_3}{63.0\ \text{g HNO}_3} 0 \times \frac{1\ \text{equiv HNO}_3}{1\ \text{mol HNO}_3} = 0.292\ \text{equiv HNO}_3$$

$$N_{HNO_3} = \frac{0.292\ \text{equiv HNO}_3}{1250\ \text{mL HNO}_3} \times \frac{1000\ \text{mL HNO}_3}{1\ \text{L HNO}_3} = 0.234N\ \text{HNO}_3$$

45. a. $N_A = \frac{N_B \times V_B}{V_A} = \frac{0.100N\ \text{NaOH} \times 15.0\ \text{mL}}{25.0\ \text{mL}} = 0.0600N\ H_2SO_4$

b $N_B = \frac{N_A \times V_A}{V_B} = \frac{0.200N\ \text{HCl} \times 20.0\ \text{mL}}{10.0\ \text{mL}} = 0.400N\ \text{NaOH}$

c. $N_B = \frac{N_A \times V_A}{V_B} = \frac{0.120N\ \text{HNO}_3 \times 25.0\ \text{mL}}{17.5\ \text{mL}} = 0.171N\ \text{NaOH}$

d. $N_A = \frac{N_B \times V_B}{V_A} = \frac{0.0950N\ \text{KOH} \times 39.6\ \text{mL}}{50.0\ \text{mL}} = 0.0752N\ CH_3COOH$

46. Hydrolyzing salts are usually composed of a cation from a weak base and an anion from a strong acid, or of a cation from a strong base and an anion from a weak acid.

47. $HCO_3^-(aq) + H_2O(l) \rightleftharpoons H_2CO_3(aq) + OH^-(aq)$

48. Weak-acid anions accept protons from water, increasing the pH of the solution. Weak-base cations donate protons to water, decreasing the pH.

49. **a.** basic **b.** acidic **c.** neutral **d.** basic **e.** neutral **f.** acidic

50. Eventually the buffer capacity of the buffer is exceeded and the pH will change significantly with further addition of strong acid or base.

51. A buffer is a solution of a weak acid and one of its salts. Because HCl is a strong acid, an HCl and NaCl solution would not be a good buffer.

52. a. $K_{sp} = [Ni^{2+}][S^{2-}]$

b. $K_{sp} = [Ba^{2+}][CO_3^{2-}]$

53. The solubility product constant K_{sp} is the product of the ion concentrations raised to the power of their coefficients given in the dissociation equation. It is an equilibrium constant that describes the solubility of an electrolyte.

54. **c., b., d., a.**

55. Adding a common ion to a solution lowers the solubility of another substance that dissociates in solution to give the same ion.

Concept Mastery

56. a. $NaOH + HCl \rightarrow NaCl + H_2O$

b. $N_{NaOH} = \frac{N_{HCl} \times V_{HCl}}{V_{NaOH}} = \frac{1.0N \times 18\ \text{mL}}{25\ \text{mL}} = 0.72N$

57. The product of the concentrations of the two ions is greater than the solubility product constant of the precipitate.

58. Number of equivalents = $V(\text{L}) \times N$

a. $5.8\ \text{L} \times 0.55\ \frac{\text{equiv}}{\text{L}} = 3.2\ \text{equivalents}$

b. $330\ \text{mL} \times \frac{1\ \text{L}}{10^3\ \text{mL}} \times 1.4\ \frac{\text{equiv}}{\text{L}} = 0.46\ \text{equivalents}$

c. $0.14\ \text{L} \times 0.22\ \frac{\text{equiv}}{\text{L}} = 0.031\ \text{equivalents}$

59. $H_2PO_4^- + OH^- \rightleftharpoons H_2O + HPO_4^{2-}$

$HPO_4^{2-} + H^+ \rightleftharpoons H_2PO_4^-$

Added OH^- is neutralized by $H_2PO_4^-$ and added acid is neutralized by HPO_4^{2-}.

60. a. $86.3 \text{ g Mg(OH)}_2 \times \frac{1 \text{ mol Mg(OH)}_2}{58.3 \text{ g Mg(OH)}_2}$

$\times \frac{2 \text{ equiv}}{1 \text{ mol}} = 2.96 \text{ equiv Mg(OH)}_2$

$N = \frac{2.96 \text{ equiv Mg(OH)}_2}{2.5 \text{ L}}$

$= 1.2N \text{ Mg(OH)}_2$

b. $5.6 \text{ g HBr} \times \frac{1 \text{ mol HBr}}{80.9 \text{ g HBr}}$

$\times \frac{1 \text{ equiv}}{1 \text{ mol}} = 0.069 \text{ equiv HBr}$

$450 \text{ mL} \times \frac{1 \text{ L}}{1000 \text{ mL}} = 0.450 \text{ L}$

$N = \frac{0.069 \text{ equiv HBr}}{0.450 \text{ L}} = 0.15N \text{ HBr}$

c. $49.4 \text{ g } H_2SO_3 \times \frac{1 \text{ mol } H_2SO_3}{82.1 \text{ g } H_2SO_3}$

$\times \frac{2 \text{ equiv}}{1 \text{ mol}} = 1.20 \text{ equiv } H_2SO_3$

$N = \frac{1.20 \text{ equiv } H_2SO_3}{1.5 \text{ L}} = 0.80N \, H_2SO_3$

61.

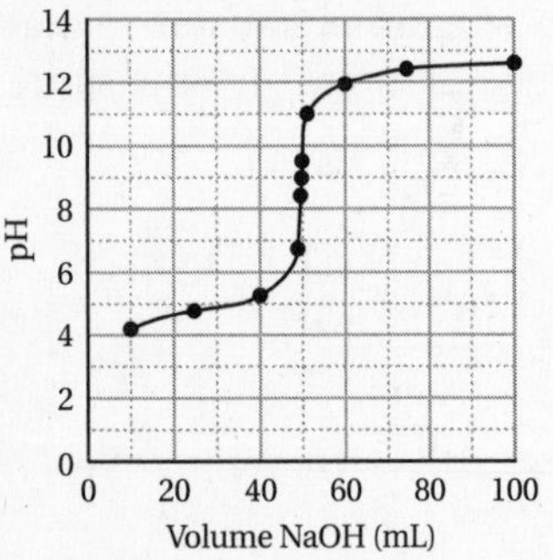

a. The pH of the end point is 8.73.

b. The best indicators would be phenolphthalein or thymol blue.

62. a. $2HCl + Mg(OH)_2 \rightarrow MgCl_2 + 2H_2O$

b. $2HCl + CaCO_3 \rightarrow H_2O + CO_2 + CaCl_2$

c. $Al(OH)_3 + 3HCl \rightarrow AlCl_3 + 3H_2O$

63. $N_1 \times V_1 = N_2 \times V_2$

$V_1 = \frac{N_2 \times V_2}{N_1}$

$V_1 = \frac{0.100N \times 250 \text{ mL}}{2.00N} = 12.5 \text{ mL}$

64. a. $K_{sp} = [Zn^{2+}] \times [OH^-]^2$

$= \frac{[OH^-]}{2} \times [OH^-]^2 = 3.0 \times 10^{-16}$

$[OH^-] = 8.4 \times 10^{-6}M$

b. $K_{sp} = [Ca^{2+}] \times [OH^-]^2$

$= \frac{[OH^-]}{2} \times [OH^-]^2 = 6.5 \times 10^{-6}$

$[OH^-] = 2.4 \times 10^{-2}M$

c. $K_{sp} = [Al^{3+}] \times [OH^-]^3 = \frac{[OH^-]}{3} \times [OH^-]^3$

$= 3.0 \times 10^{-34}$

$[OH^-] = 5.5 \times 10^{-9}M$

65. If hydroxide ion is consumed by the addition of a substance, the reaction will shift in the direction that produces more hydroxide ion. If hydroxide ion is produced by the addition of a substance, the reaction shifts in the direction that consumes hydroxide ion.

a. The reaction would shift to the left in favor of reactants because

$HSO_4^- + OH^- \rightarrow SO_4^{2-} + H_2O$

b. The equilibrium would shift to the right in favor of products because

$CO_3^{2-} + H_2O \rightleftharpoons HCO_3^- + OH^-$

66. $NaC_2H_3O_2 + H_2O \rightleftharpoons Na^+ + HC_2H_3O_2 + OH^-$

67. **b., c., d., a.**

68. Dissociation of $BaCO_3$ adds a negligible amount of CO_3^{2-} to the solution. The concentration of CO_3^{2-} comes from the 0.25 mol of K_2CO_3, and is equal to 0.25 *M*.

$K_{sp} = [Ba^{2+}] \times [CO_3^{2-}]$

$[Ba^{2+}] = \frac{K_{sp}}{[CO_3^{2-}]} = \frac{5.0 \times 10^{-9}}{0.25}$

$= 2.0 \times 10^{-8}M$

Critical Thinking

69. a. 2

b. 3

70. Hyperventilation speeds up the removal of CO_2 from the blood. The equilibrium shifts toward CO_2, which reduces the concentration of H_2CO_3 and H^+. The result is an increase in blood pH (alkalosis). Hypoventilation allows CO_2 concentration to build up in blood. In response, the equilibrium shifts toward H_2CO_3 and H^+, causing blood pH to decrease (acidosis).

71. The OH^- in alkaline seawater reacts with the H^+ formed, pulling the reaction in the direction of products. More CO_2 from the seawater and air becomes carbonate. Pure water, which lacks OH^-, does not reduce H^+ concentration. As a result, less CO_2 becomes carbonate. Therefore, pure water can have a higher concentration of CO_2.

Cumulative Review

72. **a.** Bromocresol green is blue at pH 6 and higher; phenolphthalein is colorless up to pH 8. Therefore, the pH of the solution is between 6 and 8.
b. The pH can be determined more accurately by using a pH meter.

73. **a.** $pH = -\log(4.6 \times 10^{-6}) = -(0.66 - 6) = 5.34$
b. $pH = -\log(5.0 \times 10^{-12}) = -(0.70 - 12) = 11.30$
c. $pH = -\log(3.0 \times 10^{-1}) = -(0.48 - 1) = 0.52$
d. $pH = -\log(9.8 \times 10^{-10}) = -(0.99 - 10) = 9.01$

74. $45.0\ \text{mL H}_2\text{O} \times \frac{1\ \text{g H}_2\text{O}}{1\ \text{mL H}_2\text{O}} \times \frac{5.0\ \text{g KCl}}{100\ \text{g H}_2\text{O}}$
$= 2.3\ \text{g KCl}$

75. **a.** HSO_4^-
b. CN^-
c. OH^-
d. NH_3

76. **a.** $NaCl(aq)$
b. $CO_2(g)$
c. $H_2O(l)$ at 60 °C

77. $NaOH + HCl \rightarrow NaCl + H_2O$

$$M_{NaCl} = 200\ \text{mL NaOH} \times \frac{1.00\ \text{mol NaOH}}{1000\ \text{mL NaOH}} \times \frac{1\ \text{mol NaCl}}{1\ \text{mol NaOH}} \times \frac{1}{400\ \text{mL}} \times \frac{1000\ \text{mL}}{1\ \text{L}} = 0.500M$$

Concept Challenge

78. One mole of H_2SO_4 reacts with one mole of Na_2CO_3.

$$0.424\ \text{g Na}_2\text{CO}_3 \times \frac{1\ \text{mol Na}_2\text{CO}_3}{106.0\ \text{g Na}_2\text{CO}_3} \times \frac{1\ \text{mol H}_2\text{SO}_4}{1\ \text{mol Na}_2\text{CO}_3} = 4.00 \times 10^{-3}\ \text{mol H}_2\text{SO}_4$$

$$\text{Equiv} = 4.00 \times 10^{-3}\ \text{mol H}_2\text{SO}_4 \times \frac{2\ \text{equiv}}{1\ \text{mol}} = 8.00 \times 10^{-3}\ \text{equiv H}_2\text{SO}_4$$

$$80.0\ \text{mL} \times \frac{1\ \text{L}}{1000\ \text{mL}} = 0.0800\ \text{L}$$

$$N = \frac{8.00 \times 10^{-3}\ \text{equiv H}_2\text{SO}_4}{0.0800\ \text{L}} = 1.00 \times 10^{-1} N\ \text{H}_2\text{SO}_4$$

79. $AgNO_3 + HCl \rightarrow AgCl + HNO_3$

$$0.213\ \text{g AgCl} \times \frac{1\ \text{mol AgCl}}{143.3\ \text{g AgCl}} \times \frac{1\ \text{mol AgNO}_3}{1\ \text{mol AgCl}} \times \frac{169.9\ \text{g AgNO}_3}{1\ \text{mol AgNO}_3} = 0.253\ \text{g AgNO}_3$$

$$\text{Percent} = \frac{0.253\ \text{g AgNO}_3}{0.340\ \text{g AgNO}_3} \times 100\% = 74.4\%\ \text{AgNO}_3$$

80. $HOCN + OH^- \rightleftharpoons H_2O + OCN^-$
$OCN^- + H^+ \rightleftharpoons HOCN$
Added base is neutralized by HOCN and added acid is neutralized by OCN^-. The original hydrogen ion concentration remains constant.

Standardized Test Prep

1. (d)

$$2.4\ \cancel{\text{mol } H_2SO_4} \times \frac{2\ \text{mol NaOH}}{1\ \cancel{\text{mol } H_2SO_4}}$$

$$= 4.8\ \text{mol NaOH}$$

2. (a)
3. (b)

$$\frac{15.5\ \cancel{\text{mL}}}{25.0\ \cancel{\text{mL}}} \times 0.800M = 0.496M$$

4. (c)
5. (c)
   A buffer contains a weak acid or base and one of its salts. H_2SO_4 is a strong acid.
6. (E)
7. (D)
8. (A)
9. (C)
10. (c)
    A weak base and a strong acid form an acidic solution at the equivalence point.
11. (b)
    A strong base and a strong acid form a neutral solution at the equivalence point.
12. (a)
    A strong base and a weak acid form a basic solution at the equivalence point.
13. (b)
    There are two fewer HA molecules in window (b).

22 OXIDATION-REDUCTION REACTIONS

Concept Practice

25. Reduction is always accompanied by oxidation.

26. a. $2Ba(s) + O_2(g) \rightarrow 2BaO(s)$
b. $3CaO(s) + 2Al(s) \rightarrow Al_2O_3(s) + 3Ca(s)$
c. $C_2H_5OH(l) + 3O_2(g) \rightarrow 2CO_2(g) + 3H_2O(l)$

27. a. $C_2H_4(g) + 3O_2(g) \rightarrow 2CO_2(g) + 2H_2O(l)$
b. $2KClO_3(s) \rightarrow 2KCl(s) + 3O_2(g)$
c. $CuO(s) + H_2(g) \rightarrow Cu(s) + H_2O(l)$
d. $2H_2(g) + O_2(g) \rightarrow 2H_2O(l)$

28. When an element is reduced it gains one or more electrons.

29. In any redox reaction, the number of electrons lost in oxidation must equal the number of electrons gained in reduction.

30. a. $2Al(s) + 3Cl_2(g) \rightarrow 2AlCl_3(s)$
b. $2KClO_3(s) \rightarrow 2KCl(s) + 3O_2(g)$
c. $3Cl_2(g) + 6KOH(aq) \rightarrow KClO_3(aq) + 5KCl(aq) + 3H_2O(l)$
d. $2HNO_3(aq) + 3H_2S(aq) \rightarrow 3S(s) + 2NO(g) + 4H_2O(l)$
e. $KIO_4(aq) + 7KI(aq) + 8HCl(aq) \rightarrow 8KCl(aq) + 4I_2(s) + 4H_2O(l)$

31. Many single-replacement, combustion, combination, and decomposition reactions are redox reactions.

32. a., b., c., d.

33. a., b., c.

34. a. Li is the reducing agent. H is the oxidizing agent.
b. Cr is the oxidizing agent. Cl is the reducing agent.
c. Al is the reducing agent. H is the oxidizing agent.
d. P is the reducing agent. S is the oxidizing agent.

35. a. Mn is the reducing agent. Pb is the oxidizing agent.
b. Cl is the oxidizing agent. Cl is also the reducing agent.
c. I is the oxidizing agent. C is the reducing agent.
d. not a redox reaction

Concept Mastery

36. a. $2Li + 2H_2O \rightarrow 2LiOH + H_2$ (by inspection)

b.
$1 \times (-3) = -3$
$\overset{+1}{K_2}\overset{+6}{Cr_2}\overset{-2}{O_7} + 14\overset{+1}{H}\overset{-1}{Cl} \rightarrow 2\overset{+1}{K}\overset{-1}{Cl} + 2\overset{+3}{Cr}\overset{-1}{Cl_3} + 7\overset{+1}{H_2}\overset{-2}{O} + 3\overset{0}{Cl_2}$
$3 \times (+1)\ 5\ +3$

c. $2Al + 6HCl \rightarrow 2AlCl_3 + 3H_2$ (by inspection)

d.
$16 \times (+5) = +80$
$4\overset{0}{P_4} + 5\overset{0}{S_8} \rightarrow 8\overset{+5}{P_2}\overset{-2}{S_5}$
$40 \times (-2) = -80$

37. a. $MnO + PbO_2 \rightarrow MnO_4^- + 5Pb^{2+}$
Reduction: $PbO_2 + 4H^+ + 2e^- \rightarrow Pb^{2+} + 2H_2O$
Oxidation: $MnO + 3H_2O \rightarrow MnO_4^- + 6H^+ + 5e^-$
Multiply the reduction equation by 5, and the oxidation equation by two.
Reduction:
$5PbO_2 + 20H^+ + 10e^- \rightarrow 5Pb^{2+} + 10H_2O$
Oxidation:
$2MnO + 6H_2O \rightarrow 2MnO_4^- + 12H^+ + 10e^-$
Add the half-reactions and simplify.
$5PbO_2 + 8H^+ + 2MnO \rightarrow 5Pb^{2+} + 4H_2O + 2MnO_4^-$
b. $Cl_2 + H_2O \rightarrow HCl + HClO$ (by inspection)
c.
$2 \times (-5) = -10$
$\overset{+5}{I_2}\overset{-2}{O_5} + 5\overset{+2}{C}\overset{-2}{O} \rightarrow \overset{0}{I_2} + 5\overset{+4}{C}\overset{-2}{O_2}$
$5 \times (+2) = +10$
d. $H_2O + SO_3 \rightarrow H_2SO_4$ (not a redox reaction)

38. a +4
b. +5
c. +5
d. +3
e. +5
f. +3

39. a. Carbon is oxidized.
b. Cl is the oxidizing agent.

40. a. Cl is oxidized. Mn is reduced. MnO_2 is the oxidizing agent. HCl is the reducing agent.
b. Cu is oxidized. N is reduced. HNO_3 is the oxidizing agent. Cu is the reducing agent.
c. P is oxidized. N is reduced. HNO_3 is the oxidizing agent. P is the reducing agent.
d. Sn is oxidized. Bi is reduced. $Bi(OH)_3$ is the oxidizing agent. Na_2SnO_2 is the reducing agent.

41 **a.** $MnO_2(s) + 4HCl(aq) \rightarrow MnCl_2(aq) + Cl_2(g) + 2H_2O(l)$
b. $Cu(s) + 4HNO_3(aq) \rightarrow Cu(NO_3)_2(aq) + 2NO_2(g) + 2H_2O(l)$
c. $3P(s) + 5HNO_3(aq) + 2H_2O(l) \rightarrow 5NO(g) + 3H_3PO_4(aq)$
d. $2Bi(OH)_3(s) + 3Na_2SnO_2(aq) \rightarrow 2Bi(s) + 3Na_2SnO_3(aq) + 3H_2O(l)$

Critical Thinking

42. **a.** 1
b. 2

43. Double-replacement reactions never involve the transfer of electrons; instead, they involve the exchange of positive ions in aqueous solution.

Cumulative Review

44. **a.** $pH = -\log [H^+]$
$= -\log (0.000010)$
$= -\log (10^{-5})$
$= 5.00$

b. $[H^+] = \dfrac{K_w}{[OH^-]}$
$= \dfrac{1.0 \times 10^{-14} M^2}{1 \times 10^{-4} M}$
$= 1.0 \times 10^{-10} M$
$pH = -\log [H^+]$
$= -\log (1.0 \times 10^{-10})$
$= 10.00$

c. $[H^+] = \dfrac{1.0 \times 10^{-14} M^2}{1 \times 10^{-1} M}$
$= 1.0 \times 10^{-13} M$
$pH = -\log (1.0 \times 10^{-13})$
$= 13.00$

d. $pH = -\log [H^+]$
$= -\log (3.0 \times 10^{-7})$
$= -(0.5 - 7)$
$= 6.52$

45. **a.** acidic **c.** basic
b. basic **d.** acidic

46. **a.** NH_4^+ and NH_3; H_2O and H_3O^+
b. H_2SO_3 and HSO_3^-; NH_2^- and NH_3
c. HNO_3 and NO_3^-; I^- and HI

47. $2KOH + H_2SO_4 \rightarrow K_2SO_4 + 2H_2O$

$$V_{KOH} = 45.0\ \text{mL} \times \frac{2.50\ \text{mol } H_2SO_4}{1000\ \text{mL}} \times \frac{2\ \text{mol KOH}}{1\ \text{mol } H_2SO_4} \times \frac{1000\ \text{mL}}{4.00\ \text{mol KOH}} = 56.3\ \text{mL}$$

48. **a.** $\log [H^+] = -pH = -2.00$
$[H^+] = 1.0 \times 10^{-2} M$
b. $\log [H^+] = -11.0$
$[H^+] = 1.0 \times 10^{-11} M$
c. $\log [H^+] = -8.8 = 0.2 - 9$
$[H^+] = 1.6 \times 10^{-9} M$

49. $$\text{Mol} = 46.4\ \text{g } H_3PO_4 \times \frac{1\ \text{mol } H_3PO_4}{98.0\ \text{g } H_3PO_4} \times \frac{3\ \text{equiv}}{1\ \text{mol}} = 1.42\ \text{equiv } H_3PO_4$$

$$N = \frac{1.42\ \text{equiv } H_3PO_4}{1.25\ \text{L}} = 1.14N\ H_3PO_4$$

50. $PbBr_2(s) \rightarrow Pb^{2+} + 2Br^-$
$K_{sp} = [Pb^{2+}][Br^-]^2 = 2.1 \times 10^{-6}$
Let $x = [PB^{2+}]$.
Then $2x = [Br^-]$.
$(x)(2x)^2 = 2.1 \times 10^{-6}$
$4x^3 = 2.1 \times 10^{-6}$
$x = [Pb^{2+}] = 8.1 \times 10^{-3}$
The solubility of $PbBr_2$ is 8.1×10^{-3} mol/L.

51. Test tube B has the NaCl added to it. Due to the common-ion effect, the addition of either sulfate ion or barium ion to a saturated solution of $BaSO_4$ will cause the solubility product of $BaSO_4$ to be exceeded, and barium sulfate will precipitate, as shown in test tubes A and C.

52. $$V_2 = \frac{M_1 \times V_1}{M_2} = \frac{1.5M\ \text{HCl} \times 440\ \text{mL HCl}}{6.0M\ \text{HCl}}$$
$= 110$ mL of $6.0M$ HCl
Dilute 110 mL of $6.0M$ HCl to 440 mL total volume.

53. **a.**

Alkane burned	O_2 (mol)	CO_2 produced (mol)	H_2O produced (mol)
CH_4	2	1	2
C_2H_6	3.5	2	3
C_3H_8	5	3	4
C_4H_{10}	6.5	4	5
C_5H_{12}	8	5	6
C_6H_{14}	9.5	6	7

b. $C_xH_y + \left(x + \dfrac{y}{4}\right) O_2 \rightarrow xCO_2 + \dfrac{y}{2} H_2O$

Concept Challenge

54. $Cu + 2AgNO_3 \rightarrow Cu(NO_3)_2 + 2Ag$

$$\frac{0.150 \text{ mol } AgNO_3}{1 \text{ L}} \times 85.0 \text{ mL} \times \frac{1 \text{ L}}{1000 \text{ mL}}$$
$$= 0.0128 \text{ mol } AgNO_3$$
$$\times \frac{1 \text{ mol Cu}}{2 \text{ mol } AgNO_3} = 6.38 \times 10^{-3} \text{mol Cu}$$
$$6.38 \times 10^{-3} \text{ mol Cu} \times \frac{63.5 \text{ g Cu}}{1 \text{ mol Cu}}$$
$$= 0.405 \text{ g Cu}$$

55. $2K_2Cr_2O_7 + 2H_2O + 3S \rightarrow$
$3SO_2 + 4KOH + 2Cr_2O_3$

$$1.40 \text{ g S} \times \frac{1 \text{ mol S}}{32.1 \text{ g S}}$$
$$\times \frac{2 \text{ mol } K_2Cr_2O_7}{3 \text{ mol S}} = 0.0291 \text{ mol } K_2Cr_2O_7$$
$$V_{K_2Cr_2O_7} = 0.0291 \text{ mol } K_2Cr_2O_7$$
$$\times \frac{1 \text{ L}}{0.280 \text{ mol } K_2Cr_2O_7} \times \frac{1000 \text{ mL}}{1 \text{ L}} = 104 \text{ mL}$$

56. a. $5CO + I_2O_5 \rightarrow I_2 + 5CO_2$

b. C is oxidized; I is reduced.

c. $$0.55 \text{ g } I_2O_5 \times \frac{1 \text{ mol } I_2O_5}{333.8 \text{ g } I_2O_5}$$
$$\times \frac{5 \text{ mol CO}}{1 \text{ mol } I_2O_5} = 0.0082 \text{ mol CO}$$
$$0.0082 \text{ mol CO} \times \frac{28.0 \text{ g CO}}{1 \text{ mol CO}} = 0.23 \text{ g CO}$$

Standardized Test Prep

1. (a)

2. (d)
The oxidation number of N is +2 in N_2H_4, −3 in NH_4^+, +5 in NO_3^-, +4 in N_2O_4, +1 in N_2O, and +3 in NO_2^-.

3. (b)
The oxidation number of H increases from 0 to +1; the oxidation number of Cl decreases from +1 to −1.

4. (b)
The oxidation number of Cr decreases from +6 to +3; the oxidation number of Mn decreases from +7 to +2.

5. (b)
In a double replacement reaction, the charges on the ions do not change.

6. (a)
The reducing agent must be oxidized. The oxidation number of S increases from +4 in SO_2 to +6 in SO_4^{2-}.

7. arrow 1

8. group 3

9. group 5

10. nickel

11. magnesium

12. Based on the relative sizes of the atom and ion, the atom is a metal, which loses electrons—one definition of oxidation. The neutral atom has an oxidation number of 0; the ion has an oxidation number greater than or equal to +1.

13. The sulfide ion (184 pm) should be larger than the sulfur atom (103 pm) because electrons are gained—one definition of reduction.

23 ELECTROCHEMISTRY

Concept Practice

20. A half-reaction is an equation showing either the reduction or the oxidation of a species in an oxidation-reduction reaction.
oxidation: $Al(s) \rightarrow Al^{3+}(aq) + 3e^-$,
reduction: $Cu^{2+}(aq) + 2e^- \rightarrow Cu(s)$

21. No reaction occurs. If you look at the activity series of metals in Table 23.1, you will see that magnesium is higher on the list than lead. Thus, lead is not oxidized by magnesium ions.

22. **a.** Cu **d.** Sn
b. Ca **e.** Zn
c. Mg **f.** Al

23. Reduction occurs at the cathode.

24. The salt bridge allows ions to pass from one half-cell to the other, but prevents the solutions from mixing.

25. The anode is zinc. The cathode is carbon (graphite).

26. Water is produced by the redox reaction as sulfuric acid is used up. Water has a lower density than sulfuric acid.

27. $Pb(s) \mid H_2SO_4(aq) \parallel PbO_2(s) \mid H_2SO_4(aq)$

28. Fuel cells cannot generate electricity as economically as more conventional forms of electrical generation can.

29. A fuel cell does not have to be recharged and does not produce toxic wastes if the fuel is hydrogen gas.

30. The standard reduction potential of the hydrogen electrode is arbitrarily assigned a value of 0.00 V.

31. The electrical potential is the ability of a voltaic cell to produce a current.

32. The relative order is the same because both tables rank the elements according to their tendency to undergo oxidation/reduction.

33. The aluminum half-cell is connected to a standard hydrogen half-cell and a voltmeter is used. The aluminum half-cell has the indicated voltage because the voltage of the standard hydrogen half-cell is 0.00 V.

34. **a.** $E^0_{cell} = E^0_{red} - E^0_{oxid}$
$= E^0_{Cu^{2+}} - E^0_{H^+}$
$= -0.34\,V - 0.00\,V$
$= -0.34\,V$
The reaction is nonspontaneous.

b. $E^0_{cell} = E^0_{red} - E^0_{oxid}$
$= E^0_{Ag^+} - E^0_{Fe^{2+}}$
$= -0.80\,V - (-0.44\,V)$
$= -1.24\,V$
The reaction is nonspontaneous.

35. **a.** $E^0_{cell} = E^0_{red} - E^0_{oxid}$
$= 1.36\,V - (-0.25\,V)$
$= 1.61\,V$

b. $E^0_{cell} = 0.80\,V - (-0.14\,V)$
$= 0.94\,V$

36. An *alternating* current deposits and then removes plated metal as the flow of electrons reverses; a direct current flows in one direction only.

37. The teaspoon is the cathode in an electrolytic cell with silver cyanide as the electrolyte. When the DC current flows, the silver ions deposit on the teaspoon.

Concept Mastery

38. Voltaic cells convert chemical energy into electrical energy. Electrolytic cells use electrical energy to cause a chemical reaction.

39. Two half-cells are needed because oxidation or reduction cannot occur in isolation. One half-cell gains electrons and one loses them, producing an electric current.

40. In a fully discharged lead storage battery, the anode and cathode grids are both packed with $PbSO_4$. The electrolyte is very dilute sulfuric acid.

41. Some of the iron dissolves and the nail becomes coated with copper.
$Fe(s) + CuSO_4(aq) \rightarrow FeSO_4(aq) + Cu(s)$
Oxidation: $Fe \rightarrow Fe^{2+} + 2e^-$
Reduction: $Cu^{2+} + 2e^- \rightarrow Cu$

42. **a.** $Sn(s) + Pb^{2+}(aq) \rightarrow Sn^{2+}(aq) + Pb(s)$
$E^0_{cell} = E^0_{red} - E^0_{oxid}$
$= E^0_{Pb^{2+}} - E^0_{Sn^{2+}}$
$= -0.13\,V - (-0.14\,V)$
$= +0.01\,V$

b. $H_2(g) + Br_2(l) \rightarrow 2H^+(aq) + 2Br^-(aq)$

$$E^0_{cell} = E^0_{Br^-} - E^0_{H^+}$$
$$= +1.07\,V - 0.00\,V$$
$$= +1.07\,V$$

43. Lead(II) sulfate and lead dioxide are very insoluble in sulfuric acid. Since there are no ions involved in the half-cell reactions, no salt bridge is needed.

44. Write the equation for the electrolysis of water.

$$2H_2O \xrightarrow{\text{electricity}} 2H_2 + O_2$$

	H_2O used	H_2 formed	O_2 formed
a.	2.0 mol	2.0 mol	1.0 mol
b.	18.0 g	2.0 g	16.0 g
c.	90 mL	10.0 g	80 g
d.	44.4 g	4.9 g	39.5 g
e.	7.07 g	8.80 L (STP)	4.40 L (STP)
f.	66.0 mL	7.3 g	41.1 L (STP)

a. $2.0\text{ mol }H_2O \rightarrow 2.0\text{ mol }H_2 + 1.0\text{ mol }O_2$ (by inspection)

b. $$16.0\,\cancel{g\,O_2} \times \frac{1\text{ mol }O_2}{32.0\,\cancel{g\,O_2}} \doteq 0.500\text{ mol }O_2$$

$$1.00\,\cancel{mol\,H_2} \times \frac{2.0\text{ g }H_2}{1\,\cancel{mol\,H_2}} = 2.0\text{ g }H_2$$

c. $$10.0\,\cancel{g\,H_2} \times \frac{1\text{ mol }H_2}{2.0\,\cancel{g\,H_2}} = 5.0\text{ mol }H_2$$

$$5.0\,\cancel{mol\,H_2O} \times \frac{18.0\text{ g }H_2O}{1\,\cancel{mol\,H_2O}}$$
$$= 90\text{ g }H_2O$$

Assume the density of water is 1 g/cm^3 or 1 g/mL.

$$V = \frac{90\,\cancel{g\,H_2O}}{1\,\frac{\cancel{g\,H_2O}}{mL\,H_2O}} = 90\text{ mL }H_2O$$

$$2.5\,\cancel{mol\,O_2} \times \frac{32.0\text{ g }O_2}{1\,\cancel{mol\,O_2}} = 80\text{ g }O_2$$

d. $$44.4\,\cancel{g\,H_2O} \times \frac{1\text{ mol }H_2O}{18.0\,\cancel{g\,H_2O}} = 2.47\text{ mol }H_2O$$

$$2.47\,\cancel{mol\,H_2} \times \frac{2.0\text{ g }H_2}{1\,\cancel{mol\,H_2}} = 4.9\text{ g }H_2$$

$$1.235\,\cancel{mol\,O_2} \times \frac{32.0\text{ g }O_2}{1\,\cancel{mol\,O_2}} = 39.5\text{ g }O_2$$

e. $$8.80\,\cancel{L\,H_2} \times \frac{1\text{ mol }H_2}{22.4\,\cancel{L\,H_2}} = 0.393\text{ mol }H_2$$

$$0.393\,\cancel{mol\,H_2O} \times \frac{18.0\text{ g }H_2O}{1\,\cancel{mol\,H_2O}}$$
$$= 7.07\text{ g }H_2O$$

$$0.1965\,\cancel{mol\,O_2} \times \frac{22.4\text{ L }O_2}{1\,\cancel{mol\,O_2}} = 4.40\text{ L }O_2$$

f. Assume the density of H_2O is 1 g/cm^3 or 1 g/mL.

$$66.0\,\cancel{mL}\,H_2O \times \frac{1\text{ g}}{\cancel{mL}} = 66.0\text{ g }H_2O$$

$$66.0\,\cancel{g\,H_2O} \times \frac{1\text{ mol }H_2O}{18.0\,\cancel{g\,H_2O}} = 3.67\text{ mol }H_2O$$

$$3.67\,\cancel{mol}\,H_2 \times \frac{2.0\text{ g }H_2}{1\,\cancel{mol}\,H_2} = 7.3\text{ g }H_2$$

$$1.835\,\cancel{mol}\,O_2 \times \frac{22.4\text{ L }O_2}{1\,\cancel{mol}\,O_2} = 41.1\text{ L }O_2$$

Critical Thinking

45. Gold belongs near the bottom, below silver, because it is one of the least active metals.

46. The paste in a dry cell allows for the easy movement of electrons but not ions.

47. The chemists' definition focuses on the electrons that are produced by oxidation at the anode of a voltaic cell; the dictionary definition is probably based on an electrolytic cell, whose electrodes are defined by the battery terminals to which they are attached.

48. **a.** 2; **b.** 1; **c.** 4

49. The figure shows an electrolytic cell. Copper metal is oxidized at the anode and reduced at the cathode. As a result the baby shoe becomes plated with copper.

50. d; The voltage of a dry cell falls steadily during use.

Cumulative Review

51. $V_2 = \dfrac{V_1 \times T_2}{T_1}$

$= \dfrac{425 \text{ mL } O_2 \times (60 + 273) \cancel{K}}{(30 + 273) \cancel{K}} = 467 \text{ mL } O_2$

52. **a.** $3H_2S(g) + 2HNO_3(aq) \rightarrow$
$3S(s) + 2NO(g) + 4H_2O(l)$

b. $2AgNO_3(aq) + Pb(s) \rightarrow$
$Pb(NO_3)_2(aq) + 2Ag(s)$

c. $3Cl_2(g) + 6NaOH(aq) \rightarrow$
$5NaCl(aq) + NaClO_3(aq) + 3H_2O(l)$

53. $V_2 = \dfrac{M_2 \times V_2}{M_1}$

$= \dfrac{\dfrac{1.0 \cancel{\text{mol HNO}_3}}{1 \cancel{L}} \times \dfrac{1 \cancel{L}}{1000 \cancel{\text{mL}}} \times 500 \text{ mL}}{\dfrac{16 \cancel{\text{mol HNO}_3}}{1 \cancel{L}} \times \dfrac{1 \cancel{L}}{1000 \cancel{\text{mL}}}}$

$= 31$ mL

Dilute 31 mL of 16*M* acid to 500 mL total volume.

54. **a.** $\overset{+1}{K_2}\overset{+6}{Cr_2}\overset{-2}{O_7}$ **c.** $\overset{+7}{Mn}\overset{-2}{O_4}{}^{-}$

b. $\overset{+1}{K}\overset{+5}{I}\overset{-2}{O_3}$ **d.** $\overset{+3}{Fe}\overset{-1}{Cl_3}$

55. **a.** $2AgCl + Ni \rightarrow 2Ag + NiCl_2$

$E^0_{cell} = E^0_{red} - E^0_{oxid}$
$= E^0_{AgCl} - E^0_{Ni^+}$
$= +0.22\text{ V} - (-0.25\text{ V})$
$= +0.47\text{ V}$

b. $3Cl_2 + 2Al \rightarrow 2AlCl_3$

$E^0_{cell} = E^0_{red} - E^0_{oxid}$
$= E^0_{Cl^-} - E^0_{Al^{3+}}$
$= +1.36\text{ V} - (-1.66\text{ V})$
$= +3.02\text{ V}$

56.

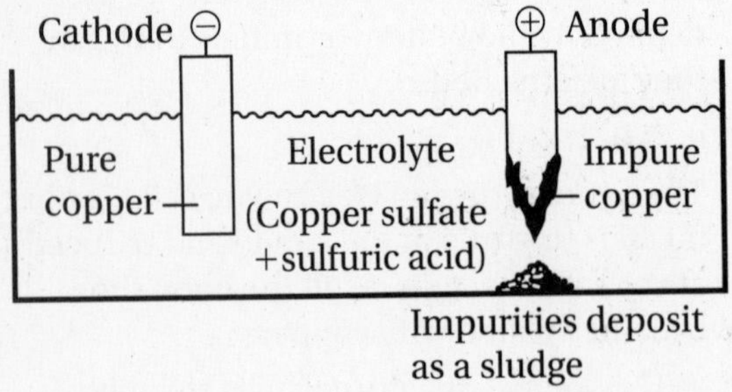

Impure copper is used as the anode in an electrolytic cell that contains a solution of copper sulfate and sulfuric acid as the electrolyte. The cathode is initially a thin sheet of very pure copper. When the cell operates, copper dissolves at the anode and deposits at the cathode. The reactions are:

Oxidation: $2Cu \text{ (impure)} + 2H_2SO_4 \rightarrow$
$2Cu^{2+} + 2H_2 + 2SO_4{}^{2-}$

Reduction: $2Cu^{2+} + 2SO_4{}^{2-} + 2H_2O \rightarrow$
$2Cu \text{ (pure)} + 2H_2SO_4 + O_2$

Net cell reaction: $2Cu \text{ (impure)} + 2H_2O \rightarrow$
$2Cu \text{ (pure)} + 2H_2 + O_2$

57.

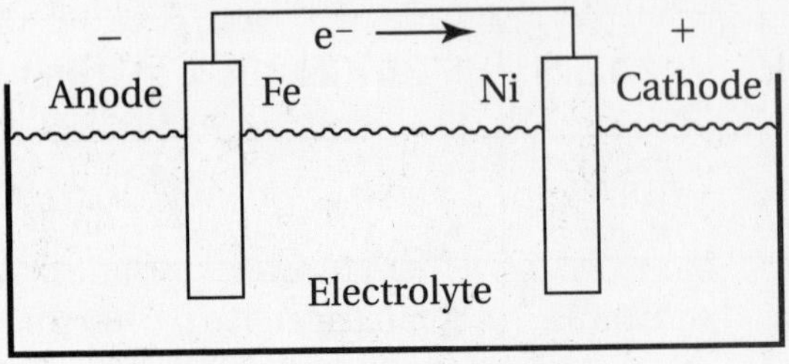

a. The iron electrode is the anode; the nickel electrode is the cathode.

b. The anode is negative; the cathode is positive.

c. anode: $Fe(s) \rightarrow Fe^{2+}(aq) + 2e^-$
cathode: $Ni^{2+}(aq) + 2e^- \rightarrow Ni(s)$

d. $E^0_{cell} = E^o_{red} - E^0_{oxid}$
$= -0.25\text{ V} - (-0.44\text{ V}) = +0.19\text{ V}$

Standardized Test Prep

1. (d)
2. (a)
3. (d)
4. (a)
5. (a)
6. potassium
7. aluminum
8. The more active the metal, the more easily it is oxidized.
9. Aluminum would be oxidized and copper ions would be reduced. Copper would plate out on the aluminum.
10. No. Because zinc is more easily oxidized than copper, copper cannot reduce the zinc ions in solution.
11. Zinc is more easily oxidized than iron. If iron atoms lose electrons through oxidation, zinc can act as a reducing agent to replace those lost electrons.
12. $Al^{3+}(aq) + 3e^- \rightarrow Al(s)$
13. $2H_2O(l) \rightarrow O_2(g) + 2H_2(g)$
14. electrode A
15. The spheres representing the molecules of H_2 and Cl_2 will be in a 1 : 1 ratio.
16. In both cells, electrons flow from the anode to the cathode through an external circuit. Reduction occurs at the anode; oxidation occurs at the cathode. In a voltaic cell, the flow of electrons is spontaneous; an outside source of power is needed to drive the reaction in an electrolytic cell. The negative electrode is the anode in a voltaic cell; it is the cathode in an electrolytic cell.

24 THE CHEMISTRY OF METALS AND NONMETALS

Concept Practice

28. $2\ Na(s) + O_2(g) \rightarrow Na_2O_2(s)$
$2\ Na(s) + 2H_2O(l) \rightarrow 2NaOH(aq) + H_2(g)$

29. The group 1A elements are the alkali metals. The group 2A elements are the alkaline earth metals.

30. Lime is calcium oxide, CaO. It is made from limestone, $CaCO_3$, in a kiln at 900 °C.

31. Their atomic diameters are smaller.

32. $Ca(s) + 2H_2O(l) \rightarrow Ca(OH)_2(s) + H_2(g)$;
$CaO(s) + H_2O(l) \rightarrow Ca(OH)_2(s)$

33. Bauxite is a mineral rich in aluminum oxide (Al_2O_3).

34. Aluminum has strength and ductility, low density, high electrical conductivity, and high corrosion resistance.

35. Three allotropes of carbon are diamond, graphite, and buckminsterfullerene.

36. Ammonia (NH_3) is a colorless gas that has a strong odor, a relatively high boiling and melting point (compared to other molecules of similar mass), a high heat of vaporization, and a high solubility in water.

37. Nitric acid is used in dye and fertilizer manufacture, etching, and the production of explosives.

38. Phosphorus occurs in white and red forms; the white form is more reactive with oxygen.

39. Plants cannot directly incorporate atmospheric nitrogen (N_2) into their tissues. Nitrogen-fixing bacteria must first transform it into nitrogen compounds.

40. Ammonia is used to manufacture products such as fertilizers, cleaning products, and nitric acid. It is also used as a refrigerant.

41. The three conditions are a temperature of 500 °C, a pressure of 10^5 kPa, and an iron oxide catalyst.

42. Ammonia (NH_3), ammonium sulfate [$(NH_4)_2SO_4$], and ammonium nitrate (NH_4NO_3) are used as fertilizers.

43. **a.** The major commercial use of oxygen is for the manufacture of steel.
b. Sulfur is used for the production of sulfuric acid (H_2SO_4).
c. Selenium is used to produce photoelectric cells and other light-sensitive instruments.

44. **a.** Oxygen is a colorless, odorless gas at room temperature and 1 atm of pressure.
b. Ozone is a pale-blue, odorous gas at room temperature and 1 atm of pressure.
c. Sulfur is a pale-yellow, odorless, water-insoluble solid at room temperature and 1 atm of pressure.

45. Hydrogen peroxide is used as a bleach and an antiseptic.

46. Oxygen is found on Earth as an atmospheric gas, in water molecules, and in compounds found in rocks and soils, such as quartz, limestone, marble, gypsum, and clay.

47. The volume percent of oxygen gas in the atmosphere is 21%. Air also contains nitrogen gas, water vapor, carbon dioxide, and small amounts of other gases.

48. Paramagnetism is the magnetic attraction caused by unpaired electrons. Molecules of liquid oxygen appear to have two unpaired electrons, one on each oxygen atom, and are weakly attracted to a magnet.

49. The major commercial use of oxygen is the manufacture of steel by the basic oxygen process.

50. Ozone is produced naturally by ultraviolet light in Earth's upper atmosphere.

51. **a.** $2Mg(s) + O_2(g) \rightarrow 2MgO(s)$
b. $2H_2(g) + O_2(g) \rightarrow 2H_2O(l)$
c. $S(s) + O_2(g) \rightarrow SO_2(g)$

52. Stable rhombic crystals contain S_8 rings.

53. Sulfur is used for the production of sulfuric acid, which is used extensively in manufacturing fertilizers, in the steel industry, in petroleum refining, and in many other industries. Sulfur is also used in the vulcanization of rubber, the manufacture of paper from wood pulp, and the preparation of matches, paints, plastics, drugs and dyes.

54. fluorine (F_2); chlorine (Cl_2); bromine (Br_2); iodine (I_2); astatine (At_2)

55. Chlorine in solution is a strong oxidizing agent that kills disease-causing bacteria.

56. Chlorine is produced by the electrolysis of aqueous or molten sodium chloride.

57. Iodine is obtained by reacting sodium iodate with sodium hydrogen sulfite solution to precipitate iodine crystals.

58. Fluorine is obtained by the electrolysis of an ice-cold solution of potassium fluoride dissolved in hydrogen fluoride.

59. Chlorine is a yellow-green gas with a sharp odor. Bromine is a dark red liquid with a strong smell. Iodine is a shiny purple-blue crystal with no odor.

60. The common oxides of iron are Fe_2O_3 (hematite) and Fe_2O_4 (magnetite).

61. Nickel is used to electroplate iron and steel and to catalyze industrial reactions. *Monel* metal is a strong, corrosion-resistant alloy of nickel and copper.

62. Copper, silver, and gold occur in the free state and were collected by people in ancient times.

63. Reduction converts positively charged metal ions in a compound to the free metal.

64. The noble gases are used in lighter-than-air balloons, artificial and inert atmospheres, and gas discharge tubes.

65. Superheated water and compressed air are sent down two tubes into the sulfur beds. A third tube brings sulfur froth to the surface. Sulfur is not mined because it is found under quicksand.

66. In hydrogenation, oil is treated with hydrogen gas at a high temperature and pressure in the presence of a catalyst. This process converts liquid oils into solid fats. Hydrogenated vegetable oils are found in many foods.

Concept Mastery

67. $1 \text{ mol Al} \times \dfrac{27.0 \text{ g Al}}{1 \text{ mol Al}} = 27.0 \text{ g Al}$

gram formula mass of Na_3AlF_6 = 210.0 g

$\% \text{ Al} = \dfrac{27.0 \text{ g}}{210.0 \text{ g}} \times 100\% = 12.9\% \text{ Al}$

68. When free metal is formed from its ion by electrolysis, reduction occurs at the cathode.

69. a.

Mass of Fe_2O_3 (kg)	Amount of Fe_2O_3 (mol)	Mass of C (kg)	Amount of C (mol)
8.65×10^4	5.42×10^5	1.95×10^4	1.63×10^6
1.26×10^5	7.89×10^5	2.84×10^4	2.37×10^6
2.01×10^5	1.26×10^6	4.54×10^4	3.78×10^6
6.56×10^5	4.11×10^6	1.48×10^5	1.23×10^7
9.61×10^5	6.02×10^6	2.17×10^5	1.81×10^7

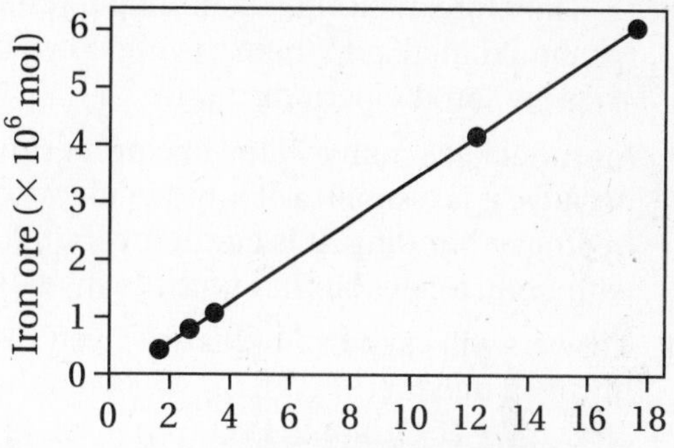

b.

c. $\text{Slope} = \dfrac{\Delta \text{ Iron ore } (\times 10^6 \text{ mol})}{\Delta \text{ Coke } (\times 10^6 \text{ mol})}$

$= \dfrac{3 \text{ mol } Fe_2O_3}{9 \text{ mol C}} = \dfrac{1 \text{ mol } Fe_2O_3}{3 \text{ mol C}}$

70. $\%\text{Ti} = \dfrac{47.9 \text{ g Ti}}{55.9 \text{ g} + 47.9 \text{ g} + (3 \times 16 \text{ g})} \times 100\%$

$= 31.6\% \text{ Ti}$

71. $\text{Percent} = \dfrac{58.9 \text{ g Co}}{58.9 \text{ g} + 74.9 \text{ g} + 32.1 \text{ g}} \times 100\%$

= 35.5% Co in CoAsS

In the ore: % Co = (35.5%) (0.726) = 25.8%

In 1000 kg of ore: $1000 \text{ kg ore} \times \dfrac{25.8 \text{ kg Co}}{100 \text{ kg ore}}$

= 258 kg Co

72. Aluminum is refined by electrolysis of a solution of Al_2O_3 in cryolite, Na_3AlF_6.

73. The two allotropic forms of oxygen are oxygen gas and ozone. Oxygen gas is obtained from liquid air by fractional distillation. Ozone is made by passing an electrical discharge through oxygen gas.

74. Oxygen (O_2) is stable, odorless, and colorless. Ozone (O_3) is unstable, has a sharp odor, and is pale blue.

75. a. $3H_2(g) + N_2(g) \rightarrow 2NH_3(g)$

b. $H_2(g) + Cl_2(g) \rightarrow 2HCl(g)$

c. $H_2(g) + Ca(s) \rightarrow CaH_2(s)$

76. The order of increasing electronegativity of halogens is I, Br, Cl, and F.

77. Sulfuric acid is used to prepare fertilizers and to pickle iron and steel. It is also used in petroleum refining and in many other industries.

78. a. Both melting points and boiling points increase with increasing atomic mass.
b. The larger number of electrons in larger atoms results in stronger molecular interactions between molecules. Therefore, melting and boiling points should increase when moving down any group on the periodic table.

79. Ammonia has many water-like properties because it is a small, polar molecule with hydrogen bonding. It is covalently bonded with bond angles similar to those in water.

80. Answers will vary. Examples are given below.
nitrogen dioxide:
$3NO_2(g) + H_2O(l) \rightarrow 2HNO_3(aq) + NO(g)$
calcium oxide:
$CaO(s) + H_2O(l) \rightarrow Ca(OH)_2(s)$

Critical Thinking

81. a. 3
b. 4

82. Earth is not massive enough to hold these lightweight elements, except as compounds in the case of hydrogen. The stars, however, are made up mostly of hydrogen and helium and can hold on to them because of their much larger mass and strong gravitational pull.

83. All the processes require an input of energy, either electricity or heat. Steam reforming produces poisonous carbon monoxide and requires the use of a nonrenewable resource, natural gas. The method using steam and white-hot coke produces carbon dioxide, which contributes to global warming.

84. The production of aluminum from its minerals requires enormous amounts of electrical energy. Recycling aluminum metal would probably be less expensive. The environmental pollution caused by generating electricity would be reduced.

85. Bronze is an alloy of mostly copper and tin. These metals can be separated from their ores relatively easily. The separation of iron from its ore, however, requires much greater heat and more advanced technology. Because the technology for producing copper and tin was developed more easily, it occurred first.

86. a. $25.5\ \text{g Cl} \times \dfrac{1\ \text{mol Cl}}{35.4\ \text{g Cl}} = 0.720\ \text{mol Cl}$

$74.5\ \text{g Pb} \times \dfrac{1\ \text{mol Pb}}{207.2\ \text{g Pb}} = 0.360\ \text{mol Pb}$

$\dfrac{0.720\ \text{mol Cl}}{0.360\ \text{mol Pb}} = \dfrac{2\ \text{mol Cl}}{1\ \text{mol Pb}}$

The chemical formula is $PbCl_2$.
b. Using the same method as shown in Part a., the chemical formula is $CuCl_2$.
c. Using the same method as shown in Part a., the chemical formula is $CoCl_2$.
d. Using the same method as shown in Part a., the chemical formula is $NiCl_2$.
e. Using the same method as shown in Part a., the chemical formula is $MnCl_2$.
f. Using the same method as shown in Part a., the chemical formula is $CaCl_2$.
g. Using the same method as shown in Part a., the chemical formula is $FeCl_3$.

Cumulative Review

87. a. CaO
b. HgO
c. CO
d. Al_2O_3
e. SO_2
f. Na_2O_2

88. a. $\dfrac{(3 \times 55.8)\ \text{g Fe}}{(3 \times 55.8)\ \text{g Fe} + (4 \times 16.0)\text{g O}} \times 100\% = 72.3\%\ \text{Fe}$

b. $\dfrac{2 \times 55.8\ \text{g Fe}}{(2 \times 55.8)\ \text{g Fe} + (3 \times 16.0)\text{g O}} \times 100\ \% = 69.9\%\ \text{Fe}$

89. a. $1s^22s^22p^63s^23p^63d^64s^2$
b. $1s^22s^22p^63s^23p^63d^34s^2$
c. $1s^22s^22p^63s^23p^63d^{10}4s^24p^64d^{10}5s^1$
d. $1s^22s^22p^63s^23p^63d^5$
e. $1s^22s^22p^63s^23p^63d^{10}4s^1$
f. $1s^22s^22p^63s^23p^63d^8$
g. $1s^22s^22p^63s^23p^63d^{10}4s^2$
h. $1s^22s^22p^63s^23p^63d^{10}4s^24p^64d^{10}$

90. **a.** $46\ \cancel{mg}\ Mg^{2+} \times \frac{1\ \cancel{g}}{1000\ \cancel{mg}} \times \frac{1\ mol}{24.3\ \cancel{g}}$
$= 0.0019\ mol\ Mg^{2+}$
$M = \frac{mol}{L} = \frac{0.0019\ mol\ Mg^{2+}}{1\ L}$
$= 0.0019M\ Mg^{2+}$

b. $V = \frac{mol}{M} = \frac{1.00\ \cancel{mol\ Mg^{2+}}}{\frac{0.0019\ \cancel{mol\ Mg^{2+}}}{1L}} = 526\ L$

91. **a.** Li^+, Br^- **b.** Ca^{2+}, OH^- **c.** K^+, I^- **d.** Cd^{2+}, Br^-

92. **a.** nonelectrolyte
b. nonelectrolyte
c. weak electrolyte
d. strong electrolyte
e. strong electrolyte
f. strong electrolyte

93. **a.** 0; **b.** +5; **c.** +4; **d.** +1; **e.** +3

94. The oxidizing agent is I_2O_5. The reducing agent is CO.

95. $CaCO_3(s) + 2HCl(aq) \rightarrow CaCl_2(aq) + H_2O(l) + CO_2(g)$

Concept Challenge

96. $Cu_2S + \frac{3}{2}O_2 \rightarrow Cu_2O + SO_2$

$Ag_2S + \frac{3}{2}O_2 \rightarrow Ag_2O + SO_2$

Find the kg of Cu_2S and Ag_2S in 1000 kg ore.

$1000\ kg\ ore \times \frac{7.2\ kg\ Cu_2S}{100\ kg\ ore} = 72\ kg\ Cu_2S$

$1000\ kg\ ore \times \frac{0.6\ kg\ Ag_2S}{100\ kg\ ore} = 6\ kg\ Ag_2S$

Find the moles of SO_2 produced by the Cu_2S and Ag_2S.

$72\ \cancel{kg}\ \cancel{Cu_2S} \times \frac{1\ \cancel{mol}}{159.2\ \cancel{g}} \times \frac{1\ mol\ SO_2}{1\ \cancel{mol}\ \cancel{Cu_2S}} \times \frac{1000\ \cancel{g}}{1\ \cancel{kg}}$
$= 452\ mol\ SO_2$

$6\ \cancel{kg}\ \cancel{Ag_2S} \times \frac{1\ \cancel{mol}}{247.8\ \cancel{g}} \times \frac{1\ mol\ SO_2}{1\ \cancel{mol}\ \cancel{Ag_2S}} \times \frac{1000\ \cancel{g}}{1\ \cancel{kg}}$
$= 24\ mol\ SO_2$

Finally, calculate the mass of SO_2.

$(452 + 24)\ \cancel{mol}\ SO_2 \times \frac{64.1\ \cancel{g}}{1\ \cancel{mol}} \times \frac{1\ kg}{1000\ \cancel{g}}$
$= 31\ kg\ SO_2$

97. $2Na + Cl_2 \rightarrow 2NaCl$
First, calculate the number of moles of Cl_2.

$0.50\ \cancel{g\ Na} \times \frac{1\ \cancel{mol\ Na}}{23.0\ \cancel{g\ Na}} \times \frac{1\ mol\ Cl_2}{2\ \cancel{mol\ Na}}$
$= 0.011\ mol\ Cl_2$

Then find the volume of Cl_2.

$V = \frac{n \times R \times T}{P} =$

$$\frac{0.011\ \cancel{mol}\ Cl_2 \times \frac{62.4\ \cancel{mm\ Hg}\ L}{\cancel{mol}\ \cancel{K}} \times (20 + 273)\ \cancel{K}}{740\ \cancel{mm\ Hg}}$$

$= 0.27\ L\ Cl_2$

98. Find the number of moles of each substance.

$55.3\ \cancel{g}\ Cu \times \frac{1\ mol}{63.5\ \cancel{g}} = 0.871\ mol\ Cu$

$6.97\ \cancel{g}\ C \times \frac{1\ mol}{12.0\ \cancel{g}} = 0.581\ mol\ C$

$37.1\ \cancel{g}\ O \times \frac{1\ mol}{16.0\ \cancel{g}} = 2.32\ mol\ O$

$0.585\ \cancel{g}\ H \times \frac{1\ mol}{1.0\ \cancel{g}} = 0.585\ mol\ H$

Determine the ratio of moles of each substance relative to mol C.

$\frac{0.871\ mol\ Cu}{0.581\ mol\ C} = 1.5{:}1$

$\frac{0.581\ mol\ C}{0.581\ mol\ C} = 1{:}1$

$\frac{2.32\ mol\ O}{0.581\ mol\ C} = 4{:}1$

$\frac{0.585\ mol\ H}{0.581\ mol\ C} = 1{:}1$

The simplest formula is $Cu_3C_2O_8H_2$.

99. **a.** $3.20\ \cancel{g\ Mg(OH)_2} \times \frac{1\ \cancel{mol\ Mg(OH)_2}}{58.3\ \cancel{g\ Mg(OH)_2}}$
$\times \frac{2\ mol\ HCl}{1\ \cancel{mol\ Mg(OH)_2}} = 0.110\ mol\ HCl$

0.110 mol of HCl = 0.110 mol of H^+ is needed to completely neutralize 3.20 g of $Mg(OH)_2$.

b. $\frac{0.110\ \cancel{mol}\ HCl}{3.00\ (\cancel{mol}/L)\ HCl} = 0.0367\ L\ HCl$

36.7 mL of $3.00M$ HCl are needed to completely neutralize 3.20 g of $Mg(OH)_2$.

100. $20.0\ \text{g BaO}_2 \times \frac{1\ \text{mol BaO}_2}{169.3\ \text{g BaO}_2} \times \frac{1\ \text{mol O}_2}{2\ \text{mol BaO}_2}$

$= 0.0591\ \text{mol O}_2$

$P = \frac{nRT}{V} =$

$$= \frac{0.0591\ \text{mol O}_2 \times 8.31\ \frac{\text{L} \times \text{kPa}}{\text{K} \times \text{mol}} \times 298\ \text{K}}{1\ \text{L}}$$

$= 1.46 \times 10^2\ \text{kPa O}_2$

101. Mass = density × volume

$= \frac{6.5 \times 10^{-2}\ \text{g Br}^-}{1\ \text{L}} \times \frac{1\ \text{kg}}{1000\ \text{g}} \times 1\ \text{mile}^3$

$\times \frac{(1.62 \times 10^3\ \text{m})^3}{1\ \text{mile}^3} \times \frac{1000\ \text{L}}{1\ \text{m}^3}$

$= 2.8 \times 10^8\ \text{kg Br}^-$

102. $S + O_2 \rightarrow SO_2$

$200\ \text{g S} \times \frac{1\ \text{mol S}}{32.1\ \text{g S}} \times \frac{1\ \text{mol SO}_2}{1\ \text{mol S}}$

$= 6.23\ \text{mol SO}_2$

$\text{Mass} = 6.23\ \text{mol SO}_2 \times \frac{64.1\ \text{g SO}_2}{1\ \text{mol SO}_2}$

$= 400\ \text{L SO}_2$

103. $\text{Volume} = \frac{3.00\ \text{L H}_2\text{O}_2}{100\ \text{L}} \times 1\ \text{L}$

$= 0.0300\ \text{L H}_2\text{O}_2$

Mass = density × volume

$= \frac{1.44\ \text{g}}{1\ \text{cm}^3} \times \frac{1000\ \text{cm}^3}{1\ \text{L}} \times 0.0300\ \text{L H}_2\text{O}_2$

$= 43.2\ \text{g H}_2\text{O}_2$

$43.2\ \text{g H}_2\text{O}_2 \times \frac{1\ \text{mol}}{34.0\ \text{g}} = 1.27\ \text{mol H}_2\text{O}_2$

$\text{Volume} = 1.27\ \text{mol H}_2\text{O}_2 \times \frac{1\ \text{mol O}_2}{2\ \text{mol H}_2\text{O}_2}$

$\times \frac{22.4\ \text{L O}_2}{1\ \text{mol O}_2} = 14.2\ \text{L O}_2$

104. a. The three types of plants emitting the greatest amount of SO_2 are the following: greater than 600 MW and less than 15 years old; less than 300 MW and 16-30 years old; less than 300 MW and greater than 30 years.

b. The emissions of these three kinds of plants are approximately 3.0, 2.7, and 2.4 million tons, respectively. Find the percent of 13 million tons that this represents.

$3.0 + 2.7 + 2.4 = 9.1$ million tons

$\frac{9.1\ \text{million tons}}{13\ \text{millions tons}} \times 100\% = 70\%$

Standardized Test Prep

1. (b)
2. (c)
3. (d)
4. (b)
5. (c)
6. (a)
7. sulfur
8. silver
9. silicon
10. (E)
11. (C)
12. (B)
13. (D)
14. (b)
    Nitrogen is the limiting reagent. Three molecules of nitrogen react with nine molecules of hydrogen, producing six molecules of ammonia and two excess molecules of hydrogen.
15. $CH_4(g) + H_2O(g) \rightarrow CO(g) + 3H_2(g)$
16. The window would contain two carbon monoxide molecules, six hydrogen molecules, and one water molecule.

Concept Practice

28. $CH_3CH_2CH_2CH_2CH_3$ pentane
$CH_3CH_2CH_2CH_2CH_2CH_3$ hexane

29. a. propane
b. octane
c. pentane

30.

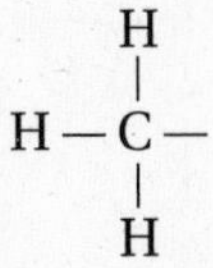

$$H-\overset{\overset{\displaystyle H}{|}}{\underset{\underset{\displaystyle H}{|}}{C}}- \quad \text{methyl}$$

$$H-\overset{\overset{\displaystyle H}{|}}{\underset{\underset{\displaystyle H}{|}}{C}}-\overset{\overset{\displaystyle H}{|}}{\underset{\underset{\displaystyle H}{|}}{C}}- \quad \text{ethyl}$$

$$H-\overset{\overset{\displaystyle H}{|}}{\underset{\underset{\displaystyle H}{|}}{C}}-\overset{\overset{\displaystyle H}{|}}{\underset{\underset{\displaystyle H}{|}}{C}}-\overset{\overset{\displaystyle H}{|}}{\underset{\underset{\displaystyle H}{|}}{C}}- \quad \text{propyl}$$

31. a. 2,2-dimethylpentane; The prefix *di-* means two methyl groups are bonded to the parent chain. Locations of both groups must be identified by a number.
b. pentane; The longest carbon chain is misidentified.
c. 2-methylbutane; Lowest numbering for substituent is not followed.
d. 3-methylpentane; The longest carbon chain is misidentified.

32. a. 2-methylbutane
b. 2,3-dimethylbutane
c. 3-methylhexane

33. The bonds between carbons are nonpolar and carbon-hydrogen bonds are very weakly polar; thus alkanes are nonpolar.

34. The prefix *meth-* implies a single carbon atom and the suffix *-ene* implies the presence of a double bond. Alkenes have a double bond between two carbon atoms.

35. a. propene (or 1-propene)
b. *trans*-2-pentene
c. 4-methyl-1-pentene
d. 3-ethyl-2-methyl-2-pentene
e. 1-hexene

36. $CH_2=CHCH_2CH_2CH_3$
  1-pentene

$CH_3CH=CHCH_2CH_3$
  2-pentene

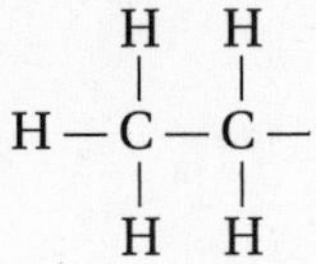

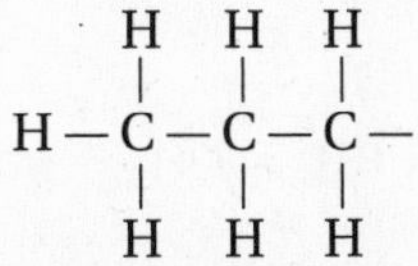

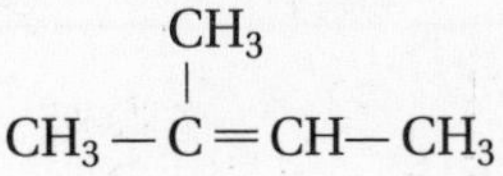

$$CH_3-\overset{\overset{\displaystyle CH_3}{|}}{C}=CH-CH_3$$
  2-methyl-2-butene

37. Five structural isomers of molecular formula C_6H_{14} exist.

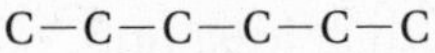

$$C-C-C-C-C-C$$
hexane

$$C-\overset{\overset{\displaystyle C}{|}}{\underset{\underset{\displaystyle C}{|}}{C}}-C-C$$
2, 2-dimethylbutane

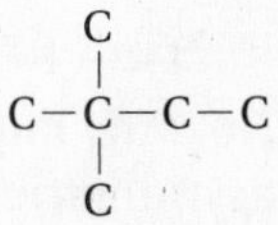

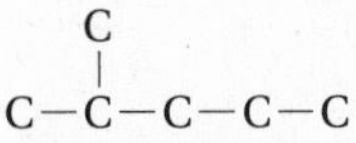

$$C-\overset{\overset{\displaystyle C}{|}}{C}-C-C-C$$
2-methylpentane

$$C-\overset{\overset{\displaystyle C}{|}}{C}-\overset{\overset{\displaystyle C}{|}}{C}-C$$
2, 3-dimethylbutane

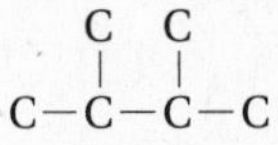

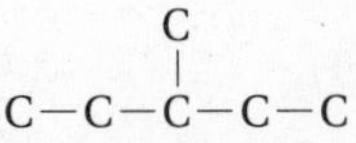

$$C-C-\overset{\overset{\displaystyle C}{|}}{C}-C-C$$
3-methylpentane

38. a. Accept any isomer with 5 carbons and 12 hydrogens.
b. Accept any isomer with 7 carbons and 16 hydrogens.
c. Accept any isomer with 11 carbons and 24 hydrogens.

39. a.

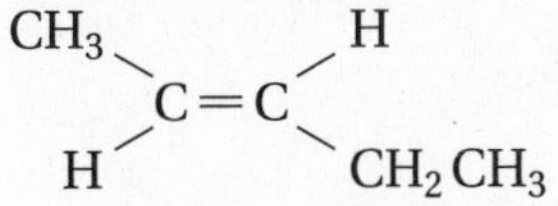

$$\begin{array}{ccc} CH_3 & & H \\ & C=C & \\ H & & CH_2CH_3 \end{array}$$

trans-2-pentene

$$\begin{array}{ccc} CH_3 & & CH_2CH_3 \\ & C=C & \\ H & & H \end{array}$$

cis-2-pentene

b.

$$\begin{array}{ccc} CH_3 & & CH_2CH \\ & C=C & \\ H & & CH_3 \end{array}$$

cis-3-methyl-2-pentene

c.

$$\begin{array}{ccc} CH_3 & & CH_2CH_3 \\ & C=C & \\ H & & CH_2CH_3 \end{array}$$

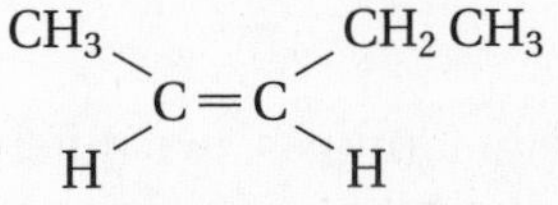

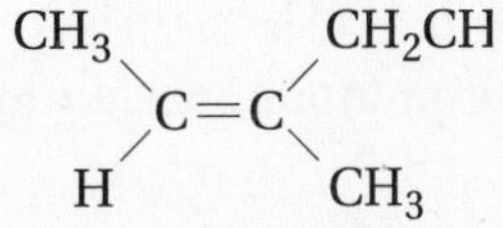

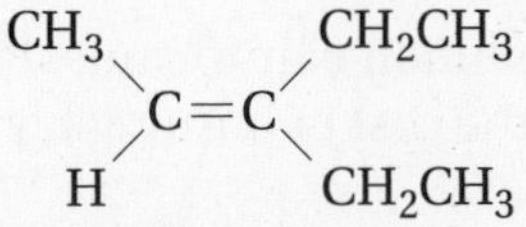

3-ethyl-2-pentene

40. Because no rotation can occur around the double bond, these two structures cannot be superimposed on each other and are geometric isomers.

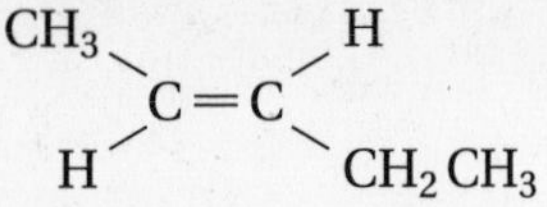

trans-2-pentene

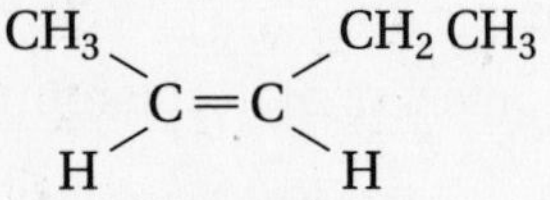

cis-2-pentene

41. No; only molecules with at least one asymmetric carbon have stereoisomers.

42. No arrangement results in any carbon atom attached to four different groups.

43. **a.**

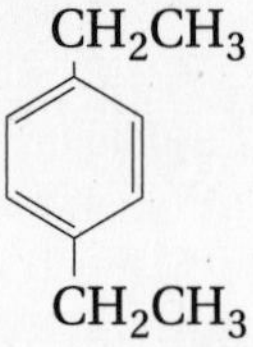

b.

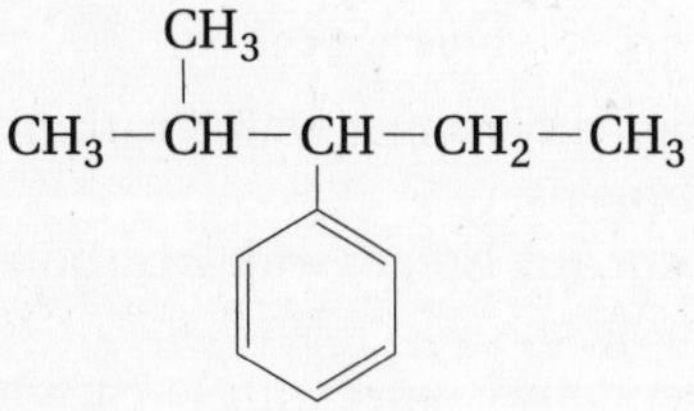

c.

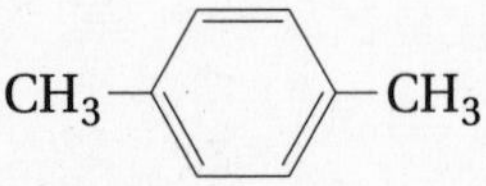

d.

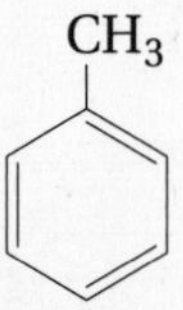

44. Using structural formulas, two different forms of 1,2-diethylbenzene are possible. This compound exhibits resonance.

45. $2C_8H_{18} + 25O_2 \rightarrow 16CO_2 + 18H_2O$

46. peat, lignite, bituminous coal, anthracite coal

47. Coal consists largely of aromatic compounds of high molar mass.

48. The cost of pollution control must be factored into the cost of burning high-sulfur-containing coal.

Concept Mastery

49. **a.** single bonds and double bond; ethene (ethylene)
b. single bonds; propane
c. single bonding within substituents and between substituents and ring; aromatic bonding (alternating single and double bonds) within the ring; methylbenzene

50. **a.** $CH{\equiv}C{-}CH_3$

b.

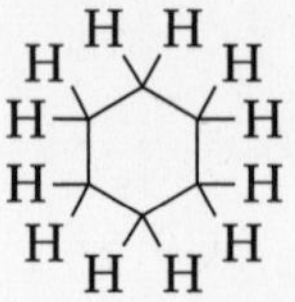

c.

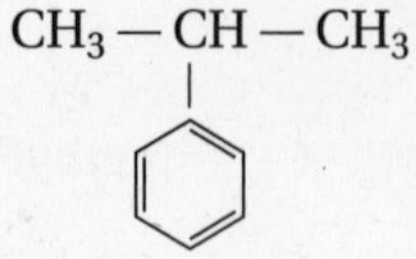

d.

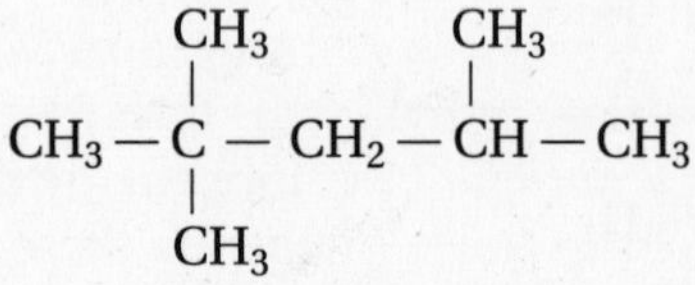

e.

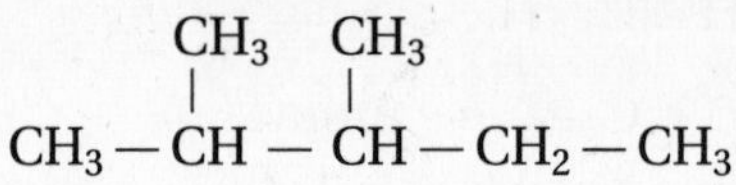

f.

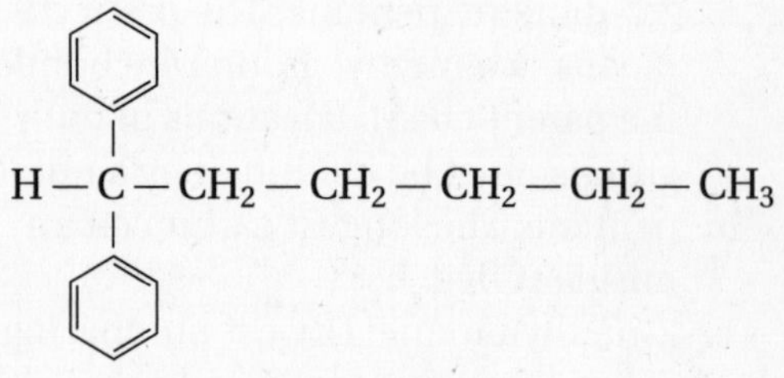

51. propane, butane, pentane

52. **a.**

b.

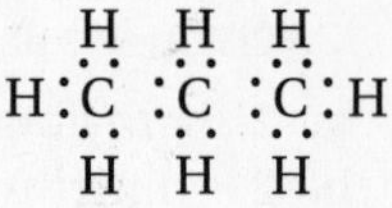

c. H:C:::C:H

d.

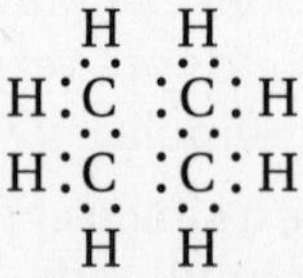

53. The middle structure is the most stable due to resonance within its benzene ring. The double bonds of the other structures are reactive.

54. **a.** Benzene and ethyl benzene are the two aromatic compounds on the list:
$(5.3 \times 10^9) + (4.3 \times 10^9) = 9.6 \times 10^9$ kg

b. The total amount of aliphatic compounds produced (ethylene, propylene, urea, ethylene dichloride, and vinyl chloride) is 41.1×10^9 kg. The total amount for all seven compounds is 50.7×10^9 kg.

$$\frac{41.1 \times 10^9 \text{ kg}}{50.7 \times 10^9 \text{ kg}} \times 100\% = 81\%$$

55. No; The structures are identical; one has been flipped over. Each is *cis*-2-butene.

Critical Thinking

56. a. 1
b. 4
c. 2

57. Cyclic hydrocarbons are more structurally rigid, so their van der Waals forces are stronger. Thus, it takes more energy (a higher temperature) to liberate these molecules from the liquid state.

Cumulative Review

58. a. $[H^+] = \frac{K_w}{[OH^-]}$

$= \frac{1.0 \times 10^{-14} M^2}{1.00 \times 10^{-4} M}$

$= 1.0 \times 10^{-10} M$

$pH = -\log [H^+]$

$= -\log (1.0 \times 10^{-10})$

$= 10.00$

b. $[H^+] = \frac{1.0 \times 10^{14} M^2}{3.9 \times 10^{7} M}$

$= 2.6 \times 10^{-8} M$

$pH = -\log (2.6 \times 10^{-8} M)$

$= 7.59$

c. $[H^+] = \frac{1.0 \times 10^{-14} M^2}{0.010 M}$

$= 1 \times 10^{-12} M$

$pH = -\log(1 \times 10^{-12})$

$= 12.00$

d. $[H^+] = \frac{1.0 \times 10^{-14} M^2}{0.0050 M}$

$= 2 \times 10^{-12}$

$pH = -\log (2\times 10^{-12})$

$= 11.70$

59. a. Ca, +2; C, +4; O, −2
b. Cl, 0
c. Li +1; I, +5; O, −2
d. Na, +1; S, +4; O, −2

60. a. H : P̈ : H pyramidal
H

b. :C ⋮⋮ O: linear

c. :S̈ :: C :: S̈: linear

d.
 :F̈:
:F̈ : C : F̈:
 :F̈:

61. a. $K_{eq} = \frac{[ICl]^2}{[I_2][Cl_2]}$

b. $K_{eq} = \frac{[H_2][Br_2]}{[HBr]^2}$

c. $K_{eq} = \frac{[HCl]^4[S]^3[SO_2]}{[S_2Cl_2]^2[H_2O]^2}$

d. $K_{eq} = \frac{[NH_3]^2}{[N_2][H_2]^3}$

62. Parts **d.** (CaS) and **f.** ($Ba(OH)_2$) are incorrect.

63. a. Bromthymol blue has a pH range of 6.0 to 7.6. Phenolphthalein has a range of 8.3 to 10. Therefore pH is approximately 8.
b. The pH can be determined more accurately by using a pH meter.

Concept Challenge

64. The boiling point of undecane is 196 °C.

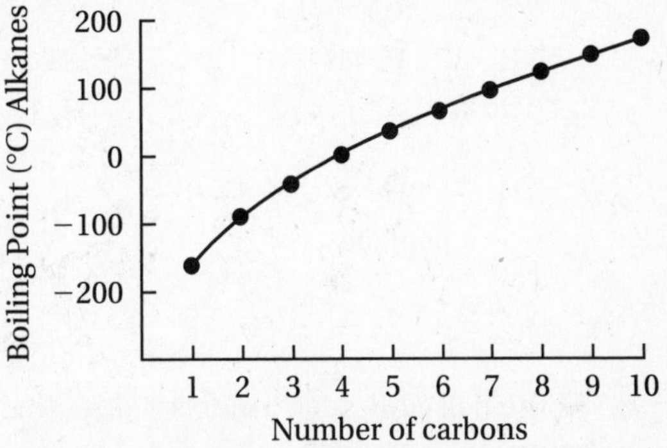

65. Answers will vary.

66. a. $C_6 = 5$, $C_7 = 9$, $C_8 = 18$, $C_9 = 35$, $C_{10} = 75$
b. As the size of the alkane molecule gets larger, the number of different ways that the carbon atoms can be bonded together (structural isomers) increases dramatically.

Standardized Test Prep

1. (c)
2. (a)
3. (b)
   There are eight carbon atoms in the octane chain and two in each ethyl group.
4. (a)
   The rigid double bond in 2-pentene allows for the possibility of *cis-trans* isomers.
5. (b)
   Methylbenzene also has seven carbon atoms, but it has fewer hydrogen atoms.
6. (c)
9. (D)
10. (C)
11. (B)
12. (A)
13. (d)
14. (d)
15. (c)
16. (a)
17. (3)
18. (1)
19. (5)
20. (4)
21. (2)

7.

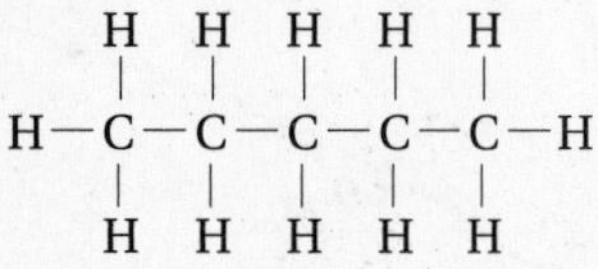

pentane

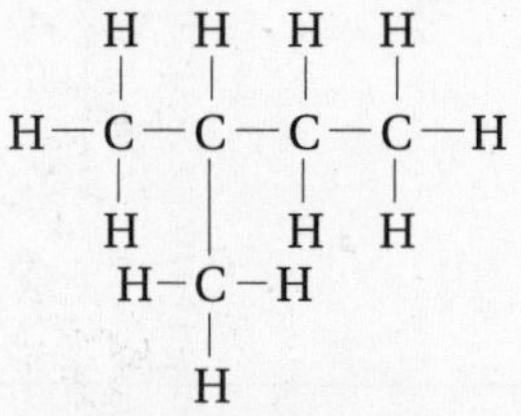

2-methylbutane

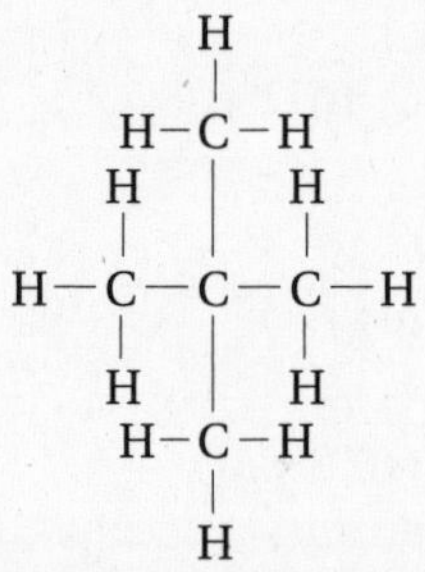

2,2-dimethylpropane

8. In the ball-and-stick models below, the black spheres represent carbon and the white spheres represent hydrogen.

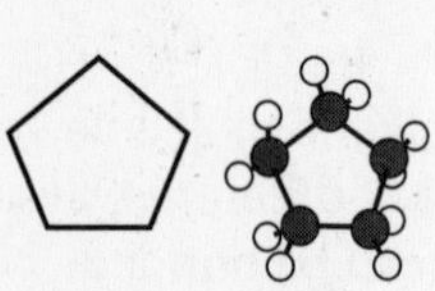

cyclopentane

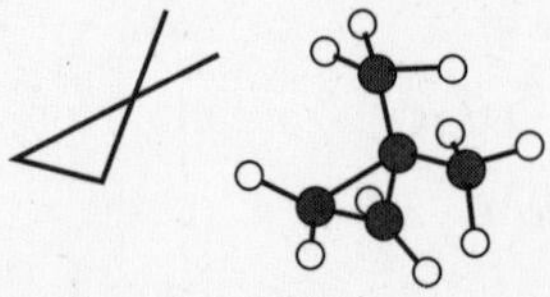

1,1-dimethylcyclopropane

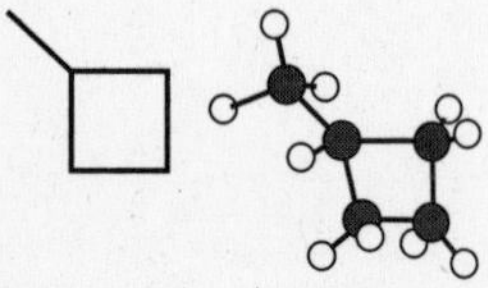

methylcyclobutane

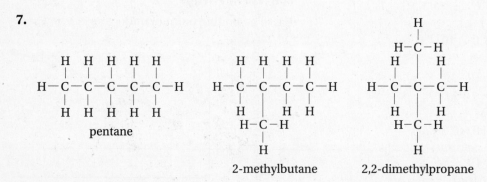

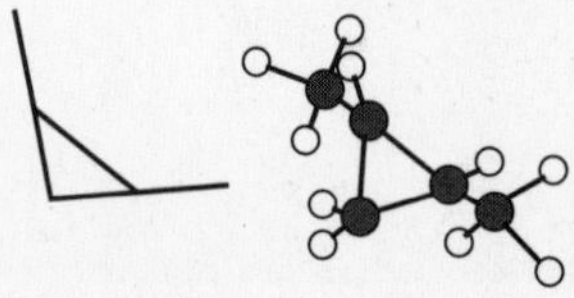

1,2-dimethylcyclopropane

Concept Practice

20. R represents a carbon chain or ring attached to the functional group.

21. a.

$$ClCH_2\overset{\displaystyle Cl}{\underset{\displaystyle Cl}{C}}CH_2CH_3$$

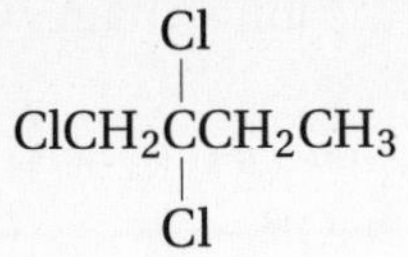

b.

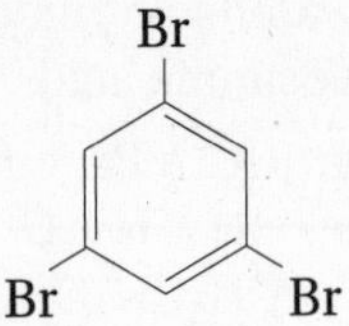

c.

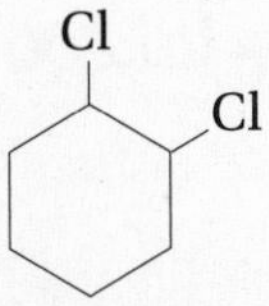

22. a. 3-chloropropene
b. 1,2-dichloro-4-methylpentane
c. 1,3-dibromobenzene

23. a.

$$\overset{\displaystyle Cl}{\underset{\displaystyle Cl}{CH}}-CH_2-CH_3$$

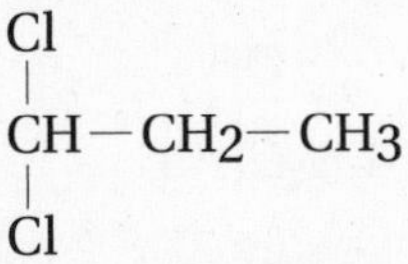

1,1-dichloropropane

$$\overset{\displaystyle Cl}{CH_2}-\overset{\displaystyle Cl}{CH}-CH_3$$

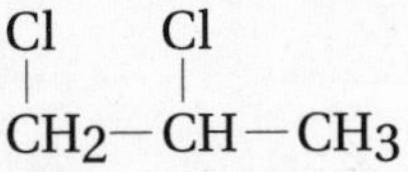

1,2-dichloropropane

$$\overset{\displaystyle Cl}{CH_2}-CH_2-\overset{\displaystyle Cl}{CH_2}$$

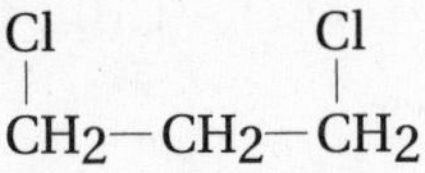

1,3-dichloropropane

$$CH_3-\overset{\displaystyle Cl}{\underset{\displaystyle Cl}{C}}-CH_3$$

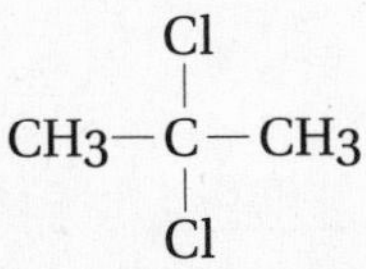

2,2-dichloropropane

b.

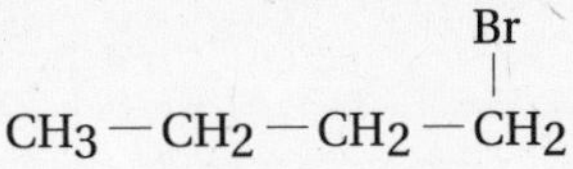

$$CH_3-CH_2-CH_2-\overset{\displaystyle Br}{CH_2}$$

1-bromobutane

$$CH_3-CH_2-\overset{\displaystyle Br}{CH}-CH_3$$

2-bromobutane

$$CH_3-\overset{\displaystyle CH_3}{CH}-\overset{\displaystyle Br}{CH_2}$$

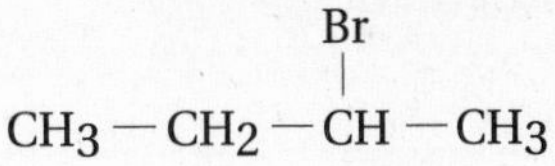

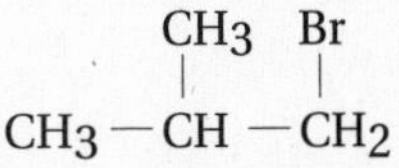

1-bromo-2-methylpropane

$$CH_3-\overset{\displaystyle CH_3}{\underset{\displaystyle Br}{C}}-CH_3$$

2-bromo-2-methylpropane

24. a. —OH   **b.** —OH

c. $CH_3-\overset{\displaystyle CH_3}{CH}-OH$ **d.** —Br

25. a. $\overset{\displaystyle Br\ \ Br}{CH_2CHCH_2CH_3}$ **b.** $\overset{\displaystyle I\ \ \ I}{CH_3CHCHCH_3}$

c. $\overset{\displaystyle H\ H}{CH_3CHCHCH_3}$ **d.**

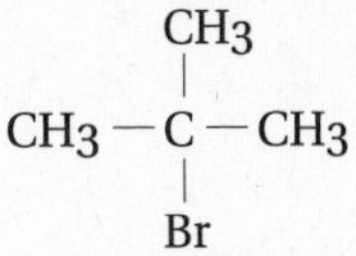

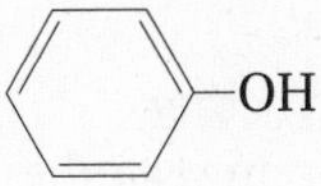

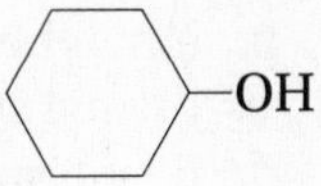

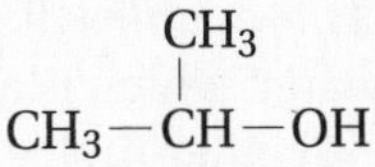

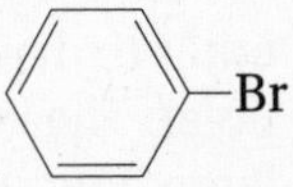

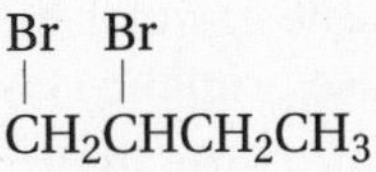

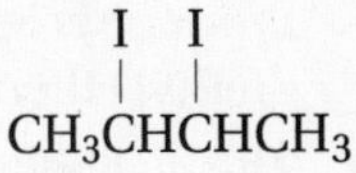

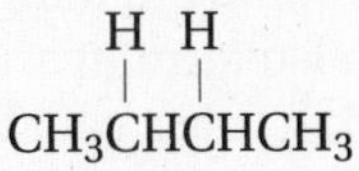

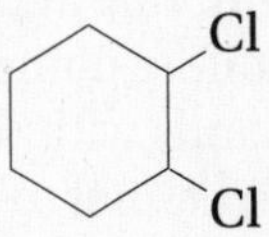

a.

$$\overset{\displaystyle H}{\underset{\displaystyle}{\,}}\quad\overset{\displaystyle Br}{\underset{\displaystyle}{\,}}$$
$$\underset{\displaystyle}{CH_2}-\underset{\displaystyle}{CH_2}$$

bromoethane

b.

$$\overset{\displaystyle Cl}{\,}\quad\overset{\displaystyle Cl}{\,}$$
$$CH_2-CH_2$$

1, 2-dichloroethane

c.

$$\overset{\displaystyle H}{\,}\quad\overset{\displaystyle OH}{\,}$$
$$CH_2-CH_2$$

ethanol

d.

$$\overset{\displaystyle H}{\,}\quad\overset{\displaystyle H}{\,}$$
$$CH_2-CH_2$$

ethane

e.

$$\overset{\displaystyle H}{\,}\quad\overset{\displaystyle Cl}{\,}$$
$$CH_2-CH_2$$

chloroethane

27.
a. ethylmethyl ether
b. ethylphenyl ether
c. divinyl ether or vinyl ether
d. diisopropyl ether or propyl ether

28. The oxygen atom in diethyl ether polarizes the small molecule. This enables diethyl ether to dissolve in water, which is also polar. The large dihexyl ether molecule has large nonpolar parts and does not dissolve. Propane is less soluble in water than is diethyl ether because propane is nonpolar.

29. The alcohol molecules form hydrogen bonds with one another, resulting in a higher boiling point. They also form hydrogen bonds with water molecules, causing 1-butanol to be more soluble than diethyl ether. (Although diethyl ether is polar, 1-butanol has greater polarity.)

30.
a. propanone or acetone
b. 3-methylbutanal
c. 2-phenylethanal
d. diphenylmethanone or diphenyl ketone or benzophenone
e. ethanal or acetaldehyde
f. 3-hexanone or ethylpropyl ketone

31. Boiling point increases with the strengths of the intermolecular forces. In order of increasing boiling point: propane, propanal, and propanol.

32. Acetaldehyde is polarized by its carbonyl oxygen, forming stronger intermolecular attractions. Nonpolar propane has weak intermolecular attractions. Thus propane molecules are more easily liberated from the liquid state.

33. The short-chain ethanoic acid has a higher water solubility than the long-chain decanoic acid.

34.
a. $HCOOH + KOH \rightarrow HCOO^-K^+ + H_2O$
b. $CH_3CH_2COOH + NaOH \rightarrow$ $CH_3CH_2COO^-Na^+ + H_2O$
c. $CH_3COOH + NaOH \rightarrow CH_3COO^-Na^+ + H_2O$

35.
a. formic acid
b. acetic acid
c. propionic acid
d. stearic acid

36.
a. 1-propanol, $CH_3CH_2CH_2OH$

b. 2-butanol, $CH_3CH_2\overset{\displaystyle OH}{\underset{\displaystyle}{C}}HCH_3$

c. 2-methyl-1-butanol, $CH_3CH_2\overset{\displaystyle CH_3}{\underset{\displaystyle}{C}}HCH_2OH$

37.
a. $CH_3CH_2OH \xrightarrow{K_2Cr_2O_7} CH_3-\overset{\displaystyle}{\underset{\displaystyle \|}{C}}-H$ with O double bonded

b. $CH_3CH_2CHO \xrightarrow{K_2Cr_2O_7} CH_3-CH_2-\overset{O}{\overset{\|}{C}}-OH$

c. $CH_3CH_2\overset{\displaystyle}{\underset{\displaystyle CH_3}{C}}HOH \xrightarrow{K_2Cr_2O_7} CH_3-CH_2-\overset{O}{\overset{\|}{C}}-CH_3$

d. $\bigcirc - CH_2CHO \xrightarrow{K_2Cr_2O_7}$

$\bigcirc - CH_2 - \overset{O}{\overset{\|}{C}} - OH$

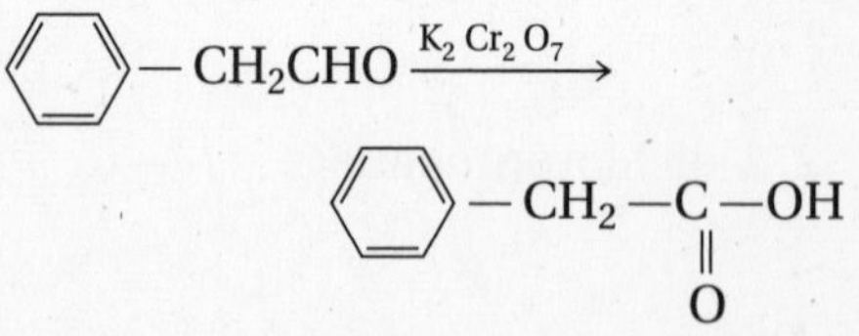

e. No reaction takes place because it is a ketone.

38. **a.** CH_3OH methanol

b. $CH_3-CH(OH)-CH_3$ 2-propanol

c. $CH_3-CH(CH_3)-C(H)(H)-OH$

2-methyl-1-propanol

d. 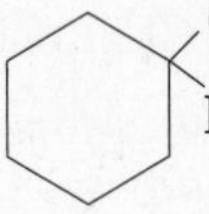 OH, H cyclohexanol

39. **a.** $CH_3CH_2COO^-Na^+$, CH_3CH_2OH

b. $CH_3COO^-K^+$, 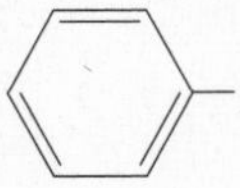 OH

c. CH_3CH_2COOH, $CH_3CH(CH_3)CH_2OH$

40.

a. $CH_3COOCH_3 + H_2O \xrightarrow{HCl} CH_3-C(=O)-OH + CH_3OH$

methyl ethanoate (methyl acetate), water → ethanoic acid (acetic acid), methanol

b. $CH_3CH_2CH_2COOCH_2CH_2CH_3 + H_2O \xrightarrow{NaOH}$

propyl butanoate (propyl butyrate), water

$CH_3CH_2CH_2-C(=O)-O^-Na + CH_3CH_2CH_2OH$

sodium butanoate (sodium butyrate), 1-propanol

c. $HCOOCH_2CH_3 + H_2O \xrightarrow{KOH}$

ethyl methanoate (ethyl formate), water

$H-C(=O)-O^-K + CH_3CH_2OH$

potassium methanoate (potassium formate), ethanol

41. **a.** $H-C(=O)-O-CH_3$

methyl methanoate
(methyl formate)

b. $CH_3CH_2CH_2-C(=O)-O-CH_2CH_3$

ethyl butanoate
(ethyl butyrate)

c. $CH_3-C(=O)-O-CH_2CH_2CH_3$

propyl ethanoate
(propyl acetate)

42. The properties of polyethylene vary with the length of the polymer chains.

43. $-CH_2-CH(CH_2CH_3)-$ $-CH(Cl)-CH(Cl)-$

Concept Mastery

44. **a.** $R-X$

b. $R-C(=O)-R$

c. $R-C(=O)-O-R$

d. $R-C(=O)-N(H)-R$

45. **b.** CH_3CH_2OH (46) has the highest boiling point.

46. **a.** $CH_3-C(=O)-OCH_3 + H_2O$

methyl ethanoate (methyl acetate), water

b. $CH_3CH_2CH_2-C(=O)-O^-Na^+ + CH_3CH_2OH$

sodium butanoate (sodium butyrate), ethanol

c. $CH_3-C(=O)-H$

ethanal (acetaldehyde)

47. Both atoms in a carbon-carbon double bond have the same electronegativity, so the bond is nonpolar. Because oxygen is more electronegative than carbon, a carbon-oxygen double bond is very polar.

48. a. phenol
   b. ether
   c. alcohol
   d. phenol
   e. alcohol

49. a.

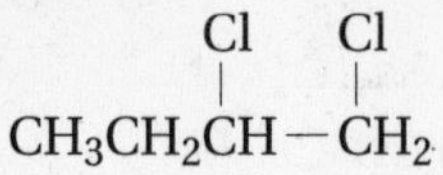

$$\underset{\underset{Cl}{|}}{CH_3CH_2CH} - \underset{\underset{Cl}{|}}{CH_2}$$

b.

$$\underset{\underset{Br}{|}}{CH_3CH_2CH} - \underset{\underset{Br}{|}}{CH_2}$$

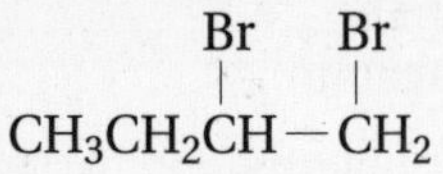

c.

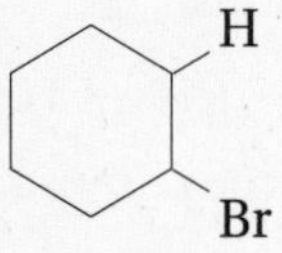

50. a. carboxylic acid, ethanoic acid (acetic acid)
   b. ether, diethyl ether
   c. ketone, propanone (acetone)
   d. alcohol, ethanol (ethyl alcohol)

Critical Thinking

51. The chemical properties (and toxicity) of organic compounds are determined by the compound as a whole. As a substituent in a molecule, a phenyl group ring does not have the same properties as benzene.

Cumulative Review

52. $M_2 = \dfrac{M_1 \times V_1}{V_2}$

$= \dfrac{0.210M\ Ca(NO_3)_2 \times 250\ mL}{450\ mL}$

$= 0.117M\ Ca(NO_3)_2$

53. In a saturated solution containing undissolved solute, an exchange occurs between undissolved and dissolved solute. Some solute molecules dissolve in water, while others precipitate. At any given moment, the rate of dissolving equals the rate of precipitation. As a result, the solution concentration remains constant.

54. The maximum number of orbitals in the p sublevel is 3 (**b**).

55. $:\!\overset{..}{F}\!: + e^- \longrightarrow :\!\overset{..}{\underset{..}{F}}\!:^-$

$H\!\cdot + :\!\overset{..}{O}\!: + e^- \longrightarrow \left(:\!\overset{..}{O}\!:H\right)^-$

56.

$$1\ \cancel{L}\ SO_2 \times \frac{1\ \cancel{mol\ SO_2}}{22.4\ \cancel{L}} \times \frac{64.1\ g\ SO_2}{1\ \cancel{mol\ SO_2}} = 3\ g\ SO_2$$

Concept Challenge

57. Cholesterol is an alcohol with a hydroxyl group on a cycloalkane. It has four nonaromatic rings. It has a double bond on one of its rings, as well as a large alkyl group, making it nonpolar.

58. $CH_2CH_2(g) + Br_2(l) \xrightarrow{\text{catalyst}} CH_2BrCH_2Br(l)$

$CH_2BrCH_2Br(l) + 2NaOH(aq) \xrightarrow[100\ °C]{H_2O}$
$CH_2OHCH_2OH(l) + 2NaBr(aq)$

Standardized Test Prep

1. (c)
2. (c)
3. (a)
4. (b)
5. (C)
6. (D)
7. (A)
8. (B)

In the ball-and-stick models for answers 9 and 10, black spheres represent carbon, gray spheres represent oxygen, and white spheres represent hydrogen.

9. a. 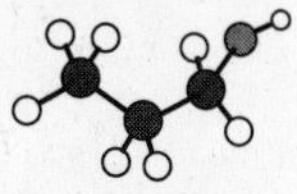

1-propanol

b. 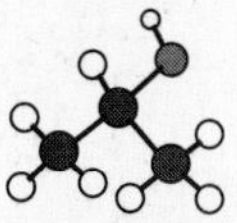

2-propanol

c. 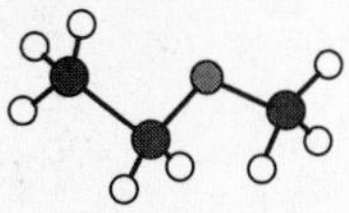

ethylmethyl ether

10. 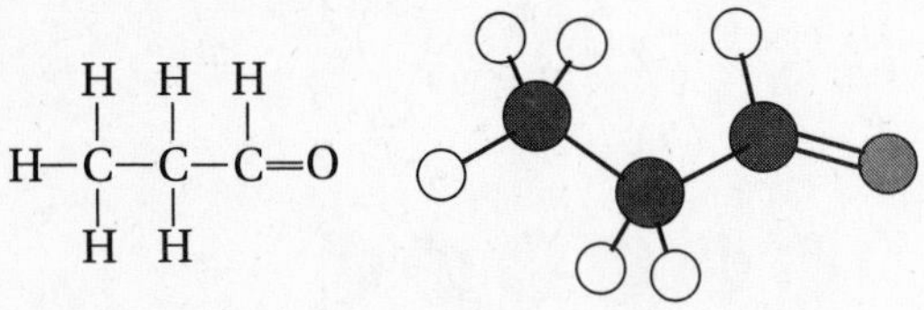

propanal

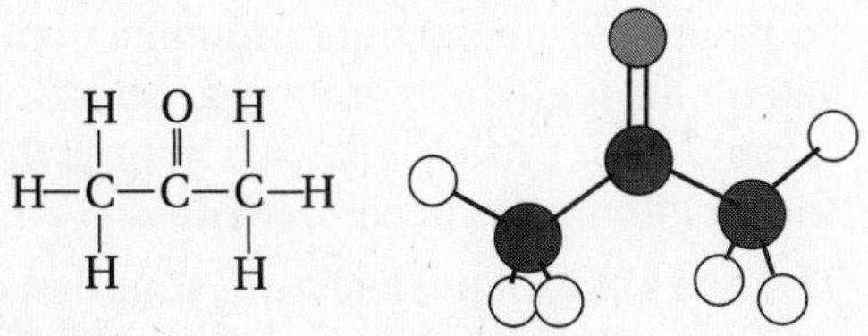

propanone

11. oxidation
12. addition
13. esterification
14. polymerization
15. substitution
16. True, True, correct explanation
17. True, False
Primary alcohols are oxidized to aldehydes, which are oxidized to carboxylic acids.
18. False, True
Ethanol is miscible with water.
19. False, True
Benzene resists hydrogenation because the hybrid bonds in benzene make it more stable than ethene.

Concept Practice

22. Photosynthetic organisms capture and use energy from sunlight to synthesize glucose.

23. The glucose produced during photosynthesis is used by both plants and animals to fuel the synthesis of more complex biomolecules.

24. $C_6H_{12}O_6 + 6O_2 \rightarrow 6CO_2 + 6H_2O + energy$

25. glucose and fructose

26. Glucose is found in blood, corn, and grapes. Fructose is found in honey and many fruits.

27. Glucose contains an aldehyde group. Fructose contains a ketone group.

28. glucose and fructose

29. a. glucose; **b.** glucose

30. The bond between two amino acids is called a peptide bond.

31. two

32. Enzymes are proteins that catalyze (speed up) biological reactions.

33. Peptide chains can fold into spiral helixes or into sheets in which peptide chains lie side by side.

34. Ala = alanine; Ser = serine; Gly = glycine
Although both tripeptides contain the same amino acids, their sequences are in reverse order relative to one another. Therefore, the tripeptides are not the same. In *a*, the free amino group is on the alanine and the free carboxyl group is on the glycine. In *b*, the free amino group is on the glycine and the free carboxyl group is on the alanine.

35. Fats are solid at room temperature; oils are liquid. Most fats are animal products; most oils are plant products.

36. A triglyceride is a triester of glycerol and long-chain carboxylic acids.

37. A soap is the alkali metal salt of a fatty acid.

38.

$$
\begin{array}{c}
CH_2-O-\overset{\displaystyle O}{\overset{\|}{C}}-(CH_2)_{16}CH_3 \\
| \\
CH_2-O-\overset{\displaystyle O}{\overset{\|}{C}}-(CH_2)_{16}CH_3 \quad + \quad 3NaOH \longrightarrow \\
| \\
CH_2-O-\overset{\displaystyle O}{\overset{\|}{C}}-(CH_2)_{16}CH_3
\end{array}
$$

Tristearin

$$
\begin{array}{c}
CH_2OH \\
| \\
CHOH \quad + \quad 3CH_3(CH_2)_{16}-\overset{\displaystyle O}{\overset{\|}{C}}-O^-\,Na^+ \\
| \\
CH_2OH
\end{array}
$$

Glycerol   Sodium stearate

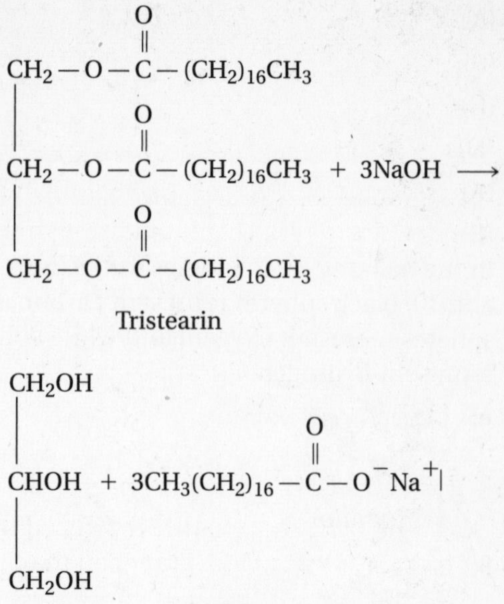

39.

40. Some membrane proteins act as channels for the transport of ions and molecules. Some are enzymes. Other proteins, that extend through the membrane, act as receptors for extracellular substances that trigger alterations in cell activities.

41. The two kinds of nucleic acids found in cells are deoxyribonucleic acid (DNA) and ribonucleic acid (RNA).

42. Nucleotides consist of a phosphate group, a 5-carbon sugar unit, and a nitrogen base.

43. The sugar in RNA (ribose) has one more oxygen than deoxyribose, the DNA sugar.

44. hydrogen bonding

45. No; there are termination codes that signal the end of a peptide chain.

46. b. A—T; **c.** C—G

47. Gene mutations are caused by the addition, deletion, or substitution of one or more DNA bases.

48. $8400\ \text{kJ} \times \dfrac{1\ \text{mol ATP}}{30.5\ \text{kJ}} = 280\ \text{mol ATP}$

49. They come from foods or from existing body tissues.

50. $\text{ATP} + H_2O \rightarrow \text{ADP} + P_i$

51. In catabolism, large biomolecules are broken down and energy is captured through the production of ATP. In anabolism, the products and energy from catabolism are used to make biomolecules.

52. The catabolism of one mol glucose yields 2.82×10^3 kJ of energy.

Concept Mastery

53. Glycogen, a polysaccharide produced by animals, is more highly branched than are plant starches.

54. Cellulose is a polymer of glucose. It is an important structural component of plant cell walls.

55. Sucrose gives glucose and fructose when hydrolyzed. The structures are

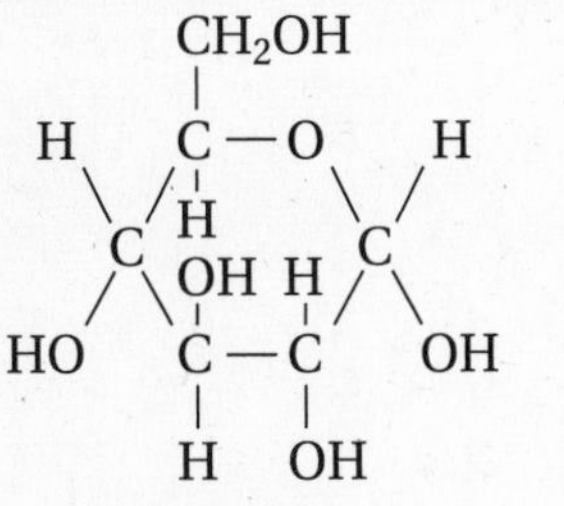

Glucose

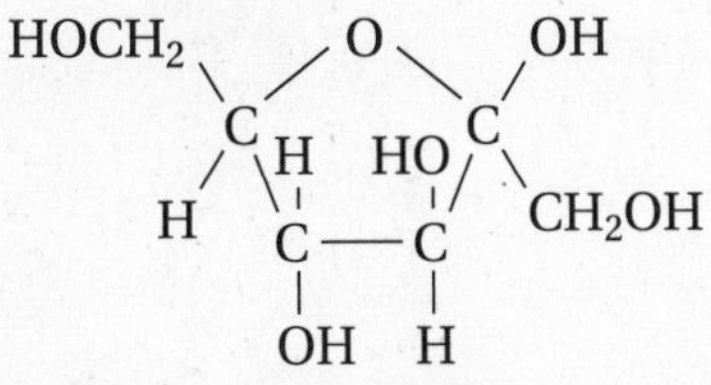

Fructose

56. An enzyme-substrate complex is a complex produced when a substrate molecule bonds to the active site of an enzyme.

57. The active site is the location on an enzyme where the substrate binds and is converted to products.

58. Some catalysts require coenzymes, which are often relatively small organic molecules or metal ions, to function properly. Coenzymes may help bind the substrate to the active site or assist in the conversion of substrate to product.

59. $CH_3(CH_2)_{14}{-}C({=}O){-}O^- Na^+$

60. Waxes are esters. Upon hydrolysis they yield long-chain alcohols and long-chain carboxylic acids.

61. **a.** Arg—Gly—Cys—Asn
b. Arg—Gly—Cys—Asn

62. C—G—A—C—C—A—A—G—A
Other combinations are possible because Ala, Gly, and Ser have multiple codes.

63. Met—Arg—Val—Tyr

64. G—C—T—A—G—G—T

65. Molecular diseases result from faulty genes. Sickle cell anemia and methemoglobinemia are molecular diseases.

66. Recombinant DNA research can lead to the production of new medicines, the treatment and control of molecular diseases, or to the development of disease- and pest-resistant plants.

67. Gene therapy can be used to transplant a normal gene into an individual with a faulty gene to cure a molecular disease.

68. **a.** Fe(II) **b.** Fe(III)

69. An error in a DNA sequence, a mutation, may be beneficial, harmful, or neutral to individuals and species.

70. Brain cells use only ATP produced from the catabolism of glucose; other cells have multiple energy sources.

71. More oxygen is needed for energy-producing processes.

72. At maximum efficiency, a cell may produce 38 mol of ATP for each mol of glucose oxidized.

$$38\ \text{mol ATP} \times \frac{30.5\ \text{kJ}}{1\ \text{mol ATP}} = 1.2 \times 10^3\ \text{kJ}$$

The combustion of 1 mol of glucose yields 2.82×10^3 kJ.

$$\frac{1.2 \times 10^3\ \text{kJ}}{2.82 \times 10^3\ \text{kJ}} \times 100\% = 43\%$$

Critical Thinking

73. a. 1; **b.** 4

74. Carbon dioxide is completely oxidized; it cannot produce energy through oxidation. Glucose can be oxidized to produce energy and carbon dioxide.

75. Base pairs are inside the helix. Before the genetic code can be read by the cell's protein synthesizing machinery, the DNA strands must unwind.

Cumulative Review

76. a. $C_3H_6O_2$
b. C_7H_{16}
c. C_7H_{14}
d. C_4H_8O

77. At the end-point, the equivalents of acid and base must be equal.

78. $2.00 \text{ mol } CH_3CH_2OH \times \dfrac{2 \text{ mol C}}{1 \text{ mol } CH_3CH_2OH}$

$\times \dfrac{6.02 \times 10^{23} \text{ atoms}}{1 \text{ mol C}}$

$= 2.41 \times 10^{24} \text{ atoms}$

79. 1-chlorobutane, 2-chlorobutane, 1-chloro-2-methylpropane, 2-chloro-2-methylpropane

80. a. 23   **c.** 36
b. 18   **d.** 18

81. a. fluorine
b. oxygen
c. chlorine

82. a. $pH = -\log[H^+] = -\log(7.0 \times 10^{-5}M)$
$= 4.15$

b. $[H^+] = \dfrac{K_w}{[OH^-]} = \dfrac{1.0 \times 10^{-14}}{1.8 \times 10^{-9}}$
$= 5.6 \times 10^{-6}M$
$pH = -\log(H^+] = -\log(5.6 \times 10^{-6}M)$
$= 5.25$

c. $[H^+] = \dfrac{K_w}{[OH^-]} = \dfrac{1.0 \times 10^{-14}}{6.1 \times 10^{-2}}$
$= 1.6 \times 10^{-13}M$
$pH = -\log[H^+] = -\log(1.6 \times 10^{-13}M)$
$= 12.80$

d. $pH = -\log[H^+] = -\log(4.4 \times 10^{-11}M)$
$= 10.36$

83. The molecule must have at least one asymmetric carbon.

Concept Challenge

84. Nutrients supply carbon compounds, ions, and energy needed for growth.

85.

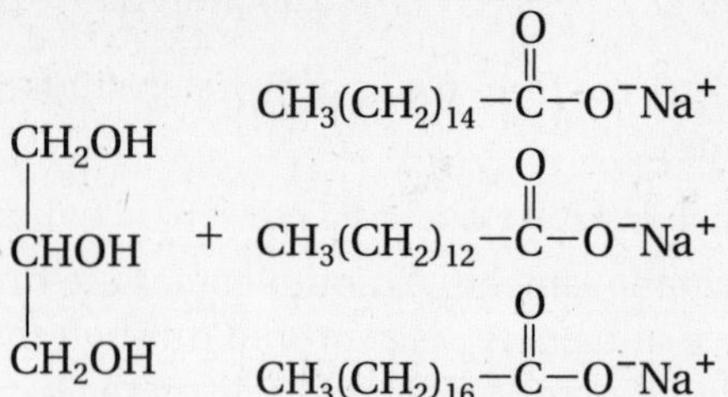

CH_2OH
$|$
$CHOH$
$|$
CH_2OH
Glycerol

$+$

$CH_3(CH_2)_{14}-\overset{\overset{O}{\|}}{C}-O^-Na^+$

$CH_3(CH_2)_{12}-\overset{\overset{O}{\|}}{C}-O^-Na^+$

$CH_3(CH_2)_{16}-\overset{\overset{O}{\|}}{C}-O^-Na^+$

Sodium salts of three fatty acid molecules

86. Phospholipid molecules have hydrophobic tails that aggregate to exclude water. Their polar heads are attracted to water, where they can be solvated.

Standardized Test Prep

1. (c)
2. (a)
3. (c)
4. $H_2NCH_2COOH(aq) + H_2O(l) \rightarrow H_2NCH_2COO^-(aq) + H_3O^+(aq)$
5. $H_2NCH_2COOH(aq) + H_2O(l) \rightarrow H_3N^+CH_2COOH(aq) + OH^-(aq)$
6. The carboxylic acid group can donate a proton to the amino group to form $H_3N^+CH_2COO^-$.
7. suspect S1
8. amino acids
9. nucleotides
10. fatty acids
11. monosaccharides
12. In the drawing, black spheres represent carbon, gray spheres represent oxygen, and white spheres represent hydrogen.

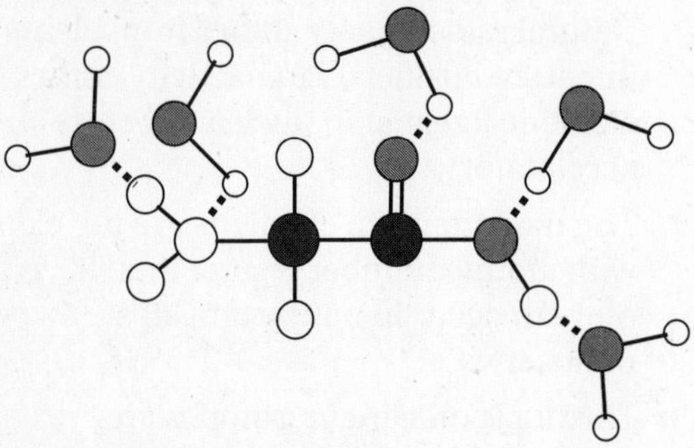

13. True, True, correct explanation
14. False, True
    Most organisms cannot digest cellulose.
15. True, True, correct explanation
16. True, False
    Triplets code for specific amino acids.

28 NUCLEAR CHEMISTRY

Concept Practice

22. Each isotope of an element has the same atomic number but a different atomic mass. A radioisotope is an isotope that is radioactive.

23. $^{226}_{88}\text{Ra} \rightarrow {}^{222}_{86}\text{Rn} + {}^{4}_{2}\text{He}$

24. $^{210}_{82}\text{Pb} \rightarrow {}^{210}_{83}\text{Bi} + {}^{0}_{-1}\text{e}$

25. **a.** α has a charge of $+2$
b. β has a charge of -1
c. γ has a charge of 0.

26. **a.** $^{238}_{92}\text{U} \rightarrow {}^{234}_{90}\text{Th} + {}^{4}_{2}\text{He}$
Thorium-234 is produced.
b. $^{230}_{90}\text{Th} \rightarrow {}^{226}_{88}\text{Ra} + {}^{4}_{2}\text{He}$
Radium-226 is produced.
c. $^{235}_{92}\text{U} \rightarrow {}^{231}_{90}\text{Th} + {}^{4}_{2}\text{He}$
Thorium-231 is produced.
d. $^{222}_{86}\text{Rn} \rightarrow {}^{218}_{84}\text{Po} + {}^{4}_{2}\text{He}$
Polonium-218 is produced

27. **a.** $^{14}_{6}\text{C} \rightarrow {}^{14}_{7}\text{N} + {}^{0}_{-1}\text{e}$
b. $^{90}_{38}\text{Sr} \rightarrow {}^{90}_{39}\text{Y} + {}^{0}_{-1}\text{e}$
c. $^{40}_{19}\text{K} \rightarrow {}^{40}_{20}\text{Ca} + {}^{0}_{-1}\text{e}$
d. $^{13}_{7}\text{N} \rightarrow {}^{13}_{8}\text{O} + {}^{0}_{-1}\text{e}$

28. **a.** In the emission of a beta particle, the atomic number increases by 1. The mass number remains the same.
b. In the emission of an alpha particle, the atomic number decreases by two, and the mass number decreases by 4.
c. In the emission of a gamma ray, the atomic number and mass number are unchanged.

29. **a.** $^{234}_{92}\text{U}$
b. $^{206}_{81}\text{Tl}$
c. $^{206}_{82}\text{Pb}$
d. $^{226}_{88}\text{Ra}$

30. It undergoes spontaneous radioactive decay.

31. $^{17}_{9}\text{F} \rightarrow {}^{17}_{8}\text{O} + {}^{0}_{+1}\text{e}$

32. **a.** $^{13}_{6}\text{C}$
b. $^{1}_{1}\text{H}$
c. $^{16}_{8}\text{O}$
d. $^{14}_{7}\text{N}$

33. **a.** platinum
b. thorium
c. francium
d. technetium
e. xenon
f. californium
g. vanadium
h. palladium
Francium (c), technetium (d), and californium (f) have no stable isotopes.

34. A short half-life means that the patient is exposed to radioactivity for a shorter period of time.

35. One half-life is the time required for one-half of the atoms of a radioisotope to emit radiation and decay.

36. Use the formula $A = A_0 \times (\frac{1}{2})^{t/T}$.
$A = 20 \text{ mg} \times (\frac{1}{2})^{40/8}$
$= 20 \text{ mg} \times 0.03125$
$= 0.625 \text{ mg}$
After 40 days, 0.625 mg of iodine-131 will remain.

37. Natural radioactivity comes from elements in nature. Artificial radioactivity comes from elements created in nuclear reactors and accelerators.

38. The transuranium elements are the elements with atomic number greater than 92. None of them occur in nature and all are radioactive.

39. The nuclei of certain isotopes are bombarded with neutrons. The nuclei break into two fragments and release more neutrons. The released neutrons hit other nuclei to start a chain reaction that releases large amounts of energy.

40. A power plant cannot maintain a constant output of electricity with spent fuel rods, which contain depleted fissionable isotopes and fission products. The rods are stored in pools.

41. Fusion requires a temperature of at least 4×10^7 °C. At that temperature, the fuel is a plasma of ions and electrons that destroys any container. No method has yet been successful for confining the fuel.

42. Ionizing radiation, such as x-rays and gamma radiation, has sufficient energy to remove electrons from the atoms it hits.

43. The film badge measures radiation exposure; an exposed film badge indicates how much radiation a worker has received.

44. In diagnosis, the amount of iodine uptake in the thyroid is measured; in treatment, the radioactive iodine-131 is concentrated in and by the thyroid.

Concept Mastery

45. **a.** $^{30}_{15}P \rightarrow ^{30}_{14}Si + ^{0}_{+1}e$
b. $^{13}_{6}C + ^{1}_{0}n \rightarrow ^{14}_{6}C$
c. $^{131}_{53}I \rightarrow ^{131}_{54}Xe + ^{0}_{-1}e$

46. Nuclear fusion takes place in the sun. A nuclear reactor utilizes nuclear fission.

47. **a.** $^{32}_{15}P \rightarrow ^{32}_{16}S + ^{0}_{-1}e$
b. $^{14}_{6}C \rightarrow ^{14}_{7}N + ^{0}_{-1}e$
c. $^{238}_{92}U \rightarrow ^{234}_{90}Th + ^{4}_{2}He$
d. $^{141}_{56}Ba \rightarrow ^{141}_{57}La + ^{0}_{-1}e$
e. $^{185}_{79}Au \rightarrow ^{181}_{77}Ir + ^{4}_{2}He$

48. **a.** $^{90}_{38}Sr \rightarrow ^{90}_{39}Y + ^{0}_{-1}e$
b. $^{14}_{6}C \rightarrow ^{14}_{7}N + ^{0}_{-1}e$
c. $^{137}_{55}Cs \rightarrow ^{137}_{56}Ba + ^{0}_{-1}e$
d. $^{239}_{93}Np \rightarrow ^{239}_{94}Pu + ^{0}_{-1}e$
e. $^{50}_{22}Ti \rightarrow ^{50}_{23}V + ^{0}_{-1}e$

49. **a.** about 20%
b. about 85 g
c. about 83 days
d. about 25 days

50. **a.** $^{222}_{86}Rn \rightarrow ^{218}_{84}Po + ^{4}_{2}He$
b. $^{234}_{90}Th \rightarrow ^{230}_{88}Ra + ^{4}_{2}He$
c. $^{210}_{84}Po \rightarrow ^{206}_{82}Pb + ^{4}_{2}He$

51. **a.** Marie Curie named radioactivity and discovered several radioactive elements.
b. Antoine Henri Becquerel discovered natural radioactivity from uranium ores.
c. James Chadwick discovered the neutron.
d. Ernest Rutherford performed the first artificial transmutation reaction, changing nitrogen into fluorine.

Critical Thinking

52. **a.** 4
b. 1
c. 3

53. In every round of the tournament, one-half the teams are eliminated; in every half-life, one-half of the substance decays. In the tournament a single team eventually emerges as the winner and the tournament stops, but radioactive decay continues (almost) indefinitely.

54. An alpha particle is much more likely than other kinds of radiation to collide with another particle and be stopped. At the atomic level, the larger the size of a particle, the greater is the chance of its striking another particle. The greater the magnitude of a particle's charge, the more strongly it will be attracted to particles of opposite charge.

55. Radioactive isotopes of these elements can be incorporated into the body tissues of organisms. When the isotopes decay, they can damage tissue very easily.

Cumulative Review

56. The Pauli exclusion principle states that no more than two electrons can occupy the same atomic orbital. Hund's rule states that when electrons occupy orbitals of equal energy, one electron enters each orbital until all orbitals contain one electron with their spins parallel.

57. **a.** $Ca(OH)_2 + 2HCl \rightarrow CaCl_2 + 2H_2O$
b. $Fe_2O_3 + 3H_2 \rightarrow 2Fe + 3H_2O$
c. $2NaHCO_3 + H_2SO_4 \rightarrow Na_2SO_4 + 2CO_2 + 2H_2O$
d. $2C_2H_6 + 7O_2 \rightarrow 4CO_2 + 6H_2O$

58. $\text{Volume} = \dfrac{\text{moles}}{\text{molarity}}$

$$= \frac{0.0020\ \cancel{\text{mol}\ Na_2SO_4}}{\dfrac{0.30\ \cancel{\text{mol}\ Na_2SO_4}}{1\cancel{L}} \times \dfrac{1\ \cancel{L}}{1000\ \text{mL}}}$$

$= 6.7$ mL

59. **a.** Iron-59 has 26 protons, 26 electrons, and 33 neutrons.
b. Uranium-235 has 92 protons, 92 electrons, and 143 neutrons.
c. Chromium-52 has 24 protons, 24 electrons, and 28 neutrons.

60. **a.** covalent
b. ionic
c. covalent
d. ionic

61. $Mg(s) + H_2SO_4(aq) \rightarrow MgSO_4(aq) + H_2(g)$

$$\text{Volume}_{H_2} = 10.00\ \text{g Mg} \times \frac{1\ \text{mol Mg}}{24.3\ \text{g Mg}} \times \frac{1\ \text{mol H}_2}{1\ \text{mol Mg}} \times \frac{22.4\ \text{L H}_2}{1\ \text{mol H}_2} \times \frac{1000\ \text{cm}^3\ \text{H}_2}{1\ \text{L H}_2} = 9220\ \text{cm}^3\ \text{H}_2$$

$$10.00\ \text{g Mg} \times \frac{1\ \text{mol Mg}}{24.3\ \text{g Mg}} \times \frac{1\ \text{mol H}_2}{1\ \text{mol Mg}} = 0.412\ \text{mol H}_2$$

Concept Challenge

62. A decay rate of 17 cpm is 1/32 of 544 cpm. This is 5 half-lives: $(0.5)^5 = 1/32$. Because the half-life is 30 years, this occurs $5 \times 30 = 150$ years later, or in the year 2135.

63. This graph shows the radioactive decay of carbon-14, along with the increase of the nitrogen product.

64. $^{211}_{83}\text{Bi} \rightarrow {}^{207}_{81}\text{Tl} + {}^{4}_{2}\text{He}$
Thallium-207 is produced.
$^{207}_{81}\text{Tl} \rightarrow {}^{207}_{82}\text{Pb} + {}^{0}_{-1}\text{e}$
Lead-207 is produced.

65. $^{234}_{90}\text{Th} \rightarrow {}^{214}_{83}\text{Bi} + 5\,{}^{4}_{2}\text{He} + 3\,{}^{0}_{-1}\text{e}$
Bismuth-214 remains.

66. The reasoning is not sound. Cells others than cancer cells may be fast-growing and therefore killed by radiation as well. Other tissues and cells affected by radiation include hair cells, bone marrow, and reproductive tissues.

Standardized Test Prep

1. (a)
2. (c)
15.2 days is 4 half-lives. The 20.0-g sample will be divided in half 4 times.
3. (b)
4. (d)
5. β emission
6. α emission
7. neutron capture
8. positron emission
9. Zirconium-90 and neon-21 nuclei are stable because their neutron-to-proton ratios are 1.25 (50/40) and 1.2 (11/10), respectively; neodymium-130 nuclei are unstable with a neutron-to-proton ratio of 2.2 (130/60).
10. 71%
11. 42%
12. 7.5%
13. (a) is carbon 14, ^{14}C; (b) is nitrogen-14, ^{14}N.
14. Carbon-14 is radioactive.
15. (C)
16. (E)
17. (A)
18. (B)
19. (D)